1K4

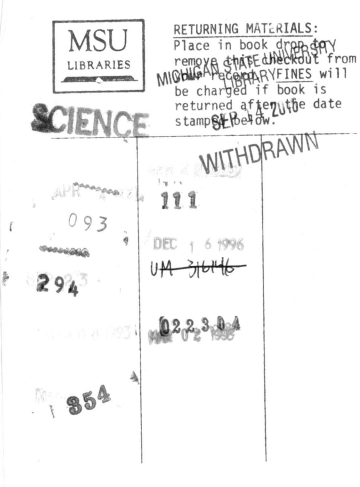

PATHWAYS TO HEALTH

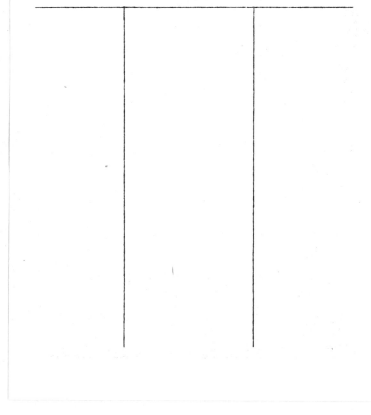

MSU
LIBRARIES

<u>RETURNING MATERIALS:</u>
Place in book drop to
remove this checkout from
your record. <u>FINES</u> will
be charged if book is
returned after the date
stamped below.

Pathways to Health

THE ROLE OF SOCIAL FACTORS

Edited by

JOHN P. BUNKER

DEANNA S. GOMBY

BARBARA H. KEHRER

THE HENRY J. KAISER FAMILY FOUNDATION
MENLO PARK, CALIFORNIA
1989

Copyright 1989 by The Henry J. Kaiser Family Foundation,
all rights reserved.

ISBN 0-944525-06-7

Library of Congress Catalogue Card Number: 89-83663

Design: Peter Rutledge Koch with assistance of Eric Johnson
Composition: Wilsted & Taylor
Printed in the United States of America

Acknowledgments

The editors extend special thanks for their assistance in the organization of the conference to the staff of the Kaiser Family Foundation, to Pamela M. Davis of Stanford, and to Gale Holm of Events Unlimited in Menlo Park; and to Ms. Davis for her skill and dedication in preparation of the manuscripts for publication. We also record our thanks to Sylvia Williams for her attentive copyreading and proofreading; to Kelly Roll for confirming all reference citations in extensive library searches; and to Barbara Battino of the Kaiser Family Foundation for her expert supervision of the production of this volume.

CONTENTS

Foreword

THIS VOLUME BRINGS together two themes that have been important to the development of the Kaiser Family Foundation's current philanthropic program: health promotion and improving the health and quality of life of persons of low socioeconomic status.

Since 1986, health promotion and disease prevention have been the major foci of the Kaiser Family Foundation's philanthropic program. Central to this program is the recognition that significant proportions of disease, disability, and untimely death are preventable. In particular, much of the ill health experienced by Americans can be attributed to individual behaviors, such as smoking, dietary habits, sedentary lifestyles, and self-destructive behaviors (such as violence), and therefore are potentially preventable.

An additional feature of the Foundation's program is its emphasis on the roles of social or environmental influences in the causal mechanisms that result in preventable morbidity and premature mortality. These influences include social norms of behavior, legislation, regulation, advertising, media content, and the quality of the physical environment. They cause disease, disability, and untimely death both directly, by exposing individuals to such health hazards as pollution, occupational hazards, unsafe housing and neighborhoods, and stress; and indirectly, by influencing individual behavior (as advertising influences people to smoke and the 55-mile-per-hour speed limit influences people to drive more slowly).

These considerations suggest that patterns of health behaviors and exposure to health hazards, as well as the diseases or health problems for which the behaviors and hazards are precursors, would vary among different societies and within a society among different subgroupings of the population. Thus differences are observed among nations and also within nations, between men and women, among ethnic groups, and, of particular interest to this volume, among different socioeconomic status groups.

"Socioeconomic status" (SES) generally refers to three characteristics of individuals or groups of individuals: educational attainment, income, and occupation. Further, relative position is often viewed as another, independent aspect of SES. That is, in addition to the absolute levels of education, income, and occupation, an individual's relative position in the SES hierarchy—being at the top, or the bottom, or in-between—seems to have an independent influence on health status.

In fashioning the Foundation's health promotion program, we have been sensitive to the fact that groups with low SES exhibit poorer health status than groups with high SES, and we have sought particularly to find creative approaches to advance the state of health of lower SES communities. To do so most effectively requires a greater depth of understanding of the relationship between SES and health than is yet available.

That low SES groups (e.g., the poor) would, on the average, exhibit poorer health status than higher SES groups (e.g., the nonpoor) probably accords with most people's commonsense perceptions, since low SES groups experience greater material deprivation of goods and services—such as medical care, quality of housing, and nutrition—that might be expected to contribute to better health. Yet, a remarkable body of evidence has accumulated over the past 15 years demonstrating not only the expected differences between low and higher SES groups, but also a positive association between SES and health status, in which health status improves over the entire *gradient* of socioeconomic classes, from very low to very high.

A satisfactory explanation of the relationship either between socioeconomic status as a whole and health or among the individual components of SES and health has not been demonstrated. Simple theories that relate improved health status to greater access to material goods and services cannot serve to explain the relationship between SES and health across the whole gradient of SES. One of the problems that arises is how to explain the observed differences in health between the highest SES group and the next highest SES group, since the next highest group cannot be said to be materially deprived in any meaningful way. The existence of the gradient points to the importance of individual behaviors and the social and environmental influences on health, which are more likely to exhibit a relationship with socioeconomic status over the whole range of SES classes.

To assist the Foundation to better understand the nature of the linkages between SES and health in order to develop more effective programs in health promotion, as well as to contribute to the state of the art and understanding of the field, we asked John P. Bunker, M.D., of Stanford University to convene a multidisciplinary conference of experts on SES and health. Dr. Bunker was assisted in this endeavor by his associate Deanna Gomby, Ph.D., and by a planning committee consisting of S. Leonard Syme, Ph.D., of the School of Public Health, University of California, Berkeley; Victor R. Fuchs, Ph.D., of the National Bureau of Economic Research and Stanford University; and, for the Foundation, Sarah E. Samuels, Dr.P.H., and Barbara H. Kehrer, Ph.D.

Twenty-four scientists from the United States and Great Britain attended the invitational conference, which was held at the Foundation's offices in Menlo Park, on March 25–27, 1987. At the opening session, we presented the participants with this challenge: "As consultants to the Foundation, we request that you apply your most imaginative and creative capacities to the conceptualization of practical applications—interventions for the public good. That is your principal charge. To get there, you may have to devote up to half of your time together on research topics: what do we know, how do we know what we know, and what do we not know yet. But your thinking must result in the outlines of effective interventions for the Foundation's programs if we are to count your consultation successful. A focus on interventions is a requirement of this conference. You will have to wander into even more uncertain territory than you would ordinarily choose. Let's try, together."

ALVIN R. TARLOV, M.D., *President*
BARBARA H. KEHRER, PH.D., *Vice President*
The Henry J. Kaiser Family Foundation

CONFERENCE PARTICIPANTS

MARK R. CULLEN, M.D., *Occupational Medicine Program, Yale University School of Medicine, New Haven, Connecticut*

DIANA B. DUTTON, PH.D., *Department of Medicine, Stanford University, Stanford, California*

ARNOLD EPSTEIN, M.D., M.A., *Institute for Health Research, Harvard School of Public Health, Boston, Massachusetts*

VICTOR FUCHS, PH.D., *Departments of Economics and of Family, Community and Preventive Medicine, Stanford University, National Bureau of Economic Research, Stanford, California*

ALAN GARBER, M.D., PH.D., *Departments of Economics and Medicine, Stanford University, Stanford, California*

STEVEN L. GORTMAKER, PH.D., *Department of Behavioral Sciences, Harvard School of Public Health, Boston, Massachusetts*

MICHAEL GROSSMAN, PH.D., *National Bureau of Economic Research, New York, New York*

MARY N. HAAN, DR.P.H., *Department of Health Services, Berkeley, California*

JEFFREY HARRIS, M.D., PH.D., *Department of Economics, Massachusetts Institute of Technology, Cambridge, Massachusetts*

ALBERT H. HASTORF, PH.D., *Department of Psychology, Stanford University, Stanford, California*

HOWARD H. HIATT, M.D., *Department of Medicine, Brigham & Women's Hospital, Boston, Massachusetts*

NEIL A. HOLTZMAN, M.D., M.P.H., *Office of Technology Assessment, Washington, D.C.*

BRIAN JARMAN, M.D., *Lisson Grove Health Center, London, England*

GEORGE A. KAPLAN, PH.D., *Human Population Laboratory, Department of Health Services, Berkeley, California*

SOL LEVINE, PH.D., *University Professor Program, Boston University, Boston, Massachusetts*

MICHAEL MARMOT, PH.D., *Department of Community Medicine, University College London and Middlesex Hospital Medical School, London, England*

DAVID MECHANIC, PH.D., *Institute for Health, Health Care Policy, and Aging Research, Rutgers University, New Brunswick, New Jersey*

JOAN E. MORGENTHAU, M.D., *Smith College, Northampton, Massachusetts*

LINCOLN MOSES, PH.D., *Department of Statistics, Stanford University, Stanford, California*

HERBERT W. NICKENS, M.D., *Office of Minority Health, Office of the Assistant Secretary for Health, DHHS, Washington, D.C.*

BARBARA STARFIELD, M.D., *Johns Hopkins School of Hygiene and Public Health, Baltimore, Maryland*

S. LEONARD SYME, PH.D., *Department of Epidemiology, School of Public Health, University of California, Berkeley, California*

HERMAN A. TYROLER, M.D., *Department of Epidemiology, School of Public Health, University of North Carolina, Chapel Hill, North Carolina*

FERNANDO E. VITERI, M.D., SC.D., *Department of Nutritional Sciences, University of California, Berkeley, California*

PARTICIPANTS FROM THE KAISER FAMILY FOUNDATION

ALVIN R. TARLOV, M.D., *President*

BARBARA H. KEHRER, PH.D., *Vice President*

JANICE ELDRED, *Director, San Francisco Bay Area Community Grants Program*

MICHAEL R. J. FELIX, *Program Officer*

JANE A. ROSS, *Program Officer/Grants Manager*

SARAH SAMUELS, DR.P.H., *Program Officer*

HARRISON J. ALTER, *Assistant to the President*

ELMER SANDY, *Controller*

BARBARA F. BATTINO, *Editor*

GEORGE BONHAM, *Consultant*

CONFERENCE STAFF
DEPARTMENT OF HEALTH RESEARCH AND POLICY
STANFORD UNIVERSITY

JOHN P. BUNKER, M.D.
DEANNA S. GOMBY, PH.D.

Preface

PLAN FOR THE CONFERENCE AND ITS REPORT

The Conference on Socioeconomic Status (SES) and Health was held March 25–27, 1987, at the Henry J. Kaiser Family Foundation's new Quadrus Conference Center in Menlo Park, California. Background papers were commissioned from Drs. Sol Levine and Diana Dutton; Michael Grossman and Theodore Joyce; Leonard Syme, Mary Haan, and George Kaplan; and Jeffrey Harris. These were distributed in advance of the conference to participants, who were then asked to comment briefly in writing; their responses were in turn distributed to all participants prior to the conference.

The conference itself consisted of a keynote address by Dr. David Mechanic and one and one-half days of discussion based largely on the prepared papers and responses. Dr. Alan Garber served as critic and philosopher and prepared an overview paper in the months immediately following the conference. This book consists of the several documents listed above, an annotated bibliography, and the following summary of the discussion and conclusions reached during the conference.

CONFERENCE SUMMARY

General Observations

The conference opened with a review of the database from which an association between socioeconomic status and health is imputed.

THE PHENOMENON: THE SES GRADIENT AND HEALTH

Researchers have observed a strong negative association between income and all-cause mortality and between education
and mortality in societies for which relevant data are available.
This remarkably robust negative association is observed with
few exceptions at all levels of SES; it is not simply limited to the
indigent or to those living under conditions of deprivation. In
Great Britain, thus, individuals in upper management and their
families enjoy a greater life expectancy than do those individuals
in middle management. The same gradient effect has been observed for morbidity and mortality due to many specific conditions, including cardiovascular and cerebrovascular disease and
many forms of cancer. The papers by Dutton and Levine (chapter 3) and Haan, Kaplan, and Syme (chapter 4) in this volume detail the state of the literature that documents this relationship.

EXCEPTIONS TO THE LOW SES–POOR HEALTH RULE

The relationship between SES and health is strong, and most
studies detail its existence over many measures of health status.
Nevertheless, exceptions exist, and conference participants mentioned a number of such exceptions, including the following:

- While the positive association between income and health is
  a strong one *within* given societies, it does not hold for all
  health measures *across* societies. For example, life expectancy in Great Britain is as great as life expectancy in the
  United States, despite the fact that per capita income in
  Great Britain is only half that of the United States.
- Within the United States, per capita income varies considerably among states, but does not predict life expectancy
  differences among the states. Indeed, for some states, the effect is reversed.
- Conditions such as myopia, acne, allergies, and obesity are
  all more frequent in children from higher SES families than
  from lower. Similarly, higher SES children are more likely
  to die in motor vehicle collisions than lower SES children.
- Some specific illnesses follow contrary patterns. Prior to
  the availability of immunization, for example, paralytic poliomyelitis was more common among the wealthy than the

poor, presumably because the poor were exposed and developed immunity at an early age at which paralysis is less common. Today, malignant melanoma of the skin occurs more frequently in those of upper SES than lower, perhaps due to episodic suntanning during leisure time, as discussed by Harris in chapter 6.

Other examples were noted in which ethnic and cultural differences in health status persist even after controlling for SES. That is, while SES alone is a powerful determinant of health status, it can hardly be considered the only determinant of health status. The fact that blacks suffer from higher blood pressure levels than do whites of similar SES level, for example, suggests that something beyond SES determines high blood pressure levels. Similarly, while low SES mothers tend to have more low birthweight babies than upper SES mothers, low SES blacks have more low birthweight babies than do Mexican Americans of comparable SES levels, even after controlling for risk factors such as prenatal care, alcoholism, obesity, and smoking.

EXPLANATIONS OF THE SES GRADIENT

The causal factors that account for the negative association of SES and mortality and morbidity, or the factors that account for the exceptions to the rule, are not yet completely understood. Indeed, even the direction of causality is unclear. Poverty may lead to ill health or ill health, on the other hand, may lead to poverty. Occupation and environment contribute to the negative association between SES factors and mortality but are not sufficient explanations of the relationship. People are not randomly distributed in occupation or environment; to a very great extent, they choose their occupations, and individuals who choose dangerous occupations may differ in important ways from those who select more sedate pursuits.

Thus, while researchers agree that occupation and environment contribute to the negative association between SES and mortality, they have not reached a similar consensus to explain the large remaining effects of SES on health status. Possible explanations discussed in the literature and at the conference include the following:

- The poor have fewer resources, both financial and psychological, with which to respond to life events.
- Parental nurture plays an important mediating role in creating health and good health behaviors, and families with higher incomes and/or educational levels may be better than poorer families to provide the nurturance that leads to good health behavior.
- The greater access to medical care that upper SES individuals might be expected to enjoy may help to promote health and prevent disease.
- Low SES individuals may have poor self-esteem, a low sense of self-efficacy, or they may be unwilling to defer personal gratification to the same extent as higher SES individuals (cf. Fuchs's comments in chapter 7 and the paper by Grossman and Joyce regarding the potential role of differential time preference in chapter 5). These psychological differences may lead to differences between high and low SES individuals in the types of health behaviors in which they engage.
- Finally, as implied by the foregoing point, low SES individuals may practice different, and less healthful health behaviors than high SES individuals. They may display differences in smoking, drinking, exercise, or diet.

THE INFLUENCE OF HEALTH BEHAVIOR ON THE SES–HEALTH STATUS RELATIONSHIP

Conference participants discussed the last point at some length and noted that it is difficult to map changes in health behaviors onto changes in health status. For example, the relationship between coronary heart disease and SES has not always been as strong as it is currently, nor has it always been in the same direction. If health behaviors such as dietary intake influence coronary heart disease, then we would expect that changes in health-related behaviors should be observed differentially in different SES groups coincident with observed trends in health status across those groups.

However, existing data do not uniformly display such trends.

For example, changes in total fat intake do not vary with observed changes in coronary heart disease rates for different social classes, whereas changes in fatty acid intake do coincide with United States trends in SES and coronary heart disease.

ACCESS TO MEDICAL CARE

Discussion turned to the role of medical care in contributing to the negative association between SES and mortality and morbidity. While medical care may have some important effects on specific illnesses, it appears not to be an important factor in explaining the overall association between SES and mortality. In Great Britain, it was anticipated that the National Health Service, initiated in 1948, would lead to a narrowing of the discrepancy in mortality across social classes. The recently published report by a committee chaired by Sir Douglas Black, known as the *Black Report*, found to the contrary that mortality differences have actually increased.

Examination of mortality due to cancer provides further evidence against a role for access to medical care in ameliorating the SES gradient. If poor access to medical care were to contribute to the greater mortality from malignant disease in the lower social classes, the effect should be greater for those cancers that are most amenable to treatment. Available data show either no effect, or, in fact, a greater discrepancy across social classes for those malignancies least amenable to treatment.

In contrast, the report by Stamler et al. (1987) in which control of blood pressure eliminated all of the SES/mortality effect suggests that with respect to mortality due to one specific illness, medical care, broadly defined, is an important contributor to the relationship between SES and mortality. In that study of antihypertensive drugs, begun in 1970, 150,000 people were screened for high blood pressure, then randomly assigned to either usual care or intensive step-care groups. In the step-care, experimental group, in which individuals had access to special programs, a twofold difference in all-cause mortality across educational strata was eliminated following control of blood pressure.

WHY THE RELATIONSHIP IS HARD TO EXPLAIN

Shortcomings of available data are a major obstacle in the search for an explanation of the association between SES and health. Garber discusses the problems of heterogeneity, simultaneity, and measurement error in his paper (chapter 8), and Grossman and Joyce discuss difficulties posed by third variables in their paper (chapter 5).

In addition, authors Dutton and Levine, Grossman and Joyce, and Garber discuss how best to analyze the data that are collected.

Interventions

Participants discussed both the general principles that should guide all interventions and the specific interventions that should be sponsored.

GENERAL APPROACHES

Participants suggested general approaches that were community based, some recommending that particular groups or illnesses be targeted.

Community-based Interventions. Conferees strongly endorsed community-based interventions. Interventions should be initiated only with community participation and/or control in organization and implementation. Community control leads to a sense of empowerment that in turn may indirectly promote health.

Physicians and county and state level public and private agencies all should join in the effort. It may even be necessary to reorganize some agencies to streamline the provision of services.

The chance of success in such an ambitious undertaking will be bolstered if a community sees the project as addressing a problem that has been imposed upon it by others. For example, workers are much more likely to take action when they can blame an external threat such as asbestos for their health problems than when they must attribute their problems to self-caused habits, such as smoking or alcohol abuse.

Target Groups. Some participants recommended that future interventions target poor or minority communities or populations because that is where the need is greatest.

Target Specific Illnesses. Although interventions need not focus on just one illness, if they do, they should target diseases that both are prevalent and vary by socioeconomic status.

Interest. The interventions must have broad initial appeal, sustain the initial interest elicited, and encourage internalization of the values they seek to teach. Interventions must also be simple and easy to implement.

Dissemination of Efforts. To increase the chances of success of the initial projects and to help ensure that successful interventions are adopted elsewhere, pressure should be brought to bear on national professional bodies to become aware of the key issues addressed by the interventions. Public interest law suits might also be employed to force widespread change.

SPECIFIC APPROACHES

Participants suggested several specific interventions that could be used to address the health problems among the poor. Some conferees suggested targeting particular age groups, while others suggested particular tactics or topics for their interventions.

Previous Interventions. Previous interventions should be catalogued. Why interventions succeeded or failed and if they were successfully adopted in other sites should be included in the catalogue. The Head Start Program, the Mound Bayou project in Mississippi (described in the Dutton and Levine paper, chapter 3), and the ABCDarian project were all cited as examples of interventions that were remarkably successful at improving the physical and mental health and academic achievements of their participants, and it may be useful to analyze exactly what contributed to the success of those programs.

Children. The best intervention point may be early in life. Children could benefit greatly from some carefully conceived child care projects, either work-related day care facilities or perhaps infant and toddler day care programs.

Elderly. At the other end of the spectrum, some participants advocated interventions to promote health among the elderly. Projects were cited that helped organize the elderly to obtain food, housing, appropriate medical care, and cooking facilities (Senior Health Project in San Francisco's Tenderloin area); or reduce institutionalization and remove household dangers (Visiting Nurse Project in Minneapolis).

Parents. Several conferees urged that efforts be made to target parents or parents-to-be with classes to help them learn parenting skills. Interventions to provide prenatal care to expectant mothers were also suggested.

Nutrition. Suggestions to improve nutrition among the poor ranged from programs to provide school lunches to low SES children to enhancing the role of women in the society, because it is they who primarily control the food that winds up on the family table.

Medical Education. The education that doctors receive should be changed to include an introduction to the special health needs of the poor. Efforts should be made to recruit and train minority physicians because they will be best able to empathize with minority patients.

Alter External Factors. Interventions could be devised to alter the external factors that act to encourage or discourage health-related behaviors. For example, company cafeterias could be urged to carry fewer fatty or high calorie foods or to price such food higher than more healthful alternatives. Smoking could be discouraged by increasing the tax on cigarettes or by restricting the areas in which smoking is permitted.

Future Research

Just as participants suggested both specific and general approaches for future interventions, so too did they propose specific and general approaches for future research.

SPECIFIC APPROACHES

Participants posed a wealth of specific research ideas, ranging from studies to determine why and how education has the impact it does on health status to explorations of some of the psychological mechanisms that may determine health behaviors (e.g., self-efficacy, self-esteem, time preference, Type A personalities). Other suggested research questions included exploring the following:

- Why risk factors such as smoking or high blood pressure cluster on social class
- What characteristics of diet (e.g., fatty acids or cholesterol) are most problematical
- The influence of occupation on the gradient of health status by social class
- The characteristics that make up a successful child care program
- What accounts for the observed patterns of low birthweight babies across poor and nonpoor, and among different racial groups.

A final group of suggestions had in common the use of "natural experiments" to study the changes engendered by social programs such as Head Start or by societal trends such as the typical improvements in SES as migrants to the United States acculturate.

GENERAL APPROACHES

Participants recommended that when possible research and interventions be coordinated with or "piggybacked" on studies of a community that has already been targeted for some intervention. A longitudinal community-wide study would require large commitments of time and financial resources, but might be one of the best ways to understand the many forces at work in creating the observed SES and health relationships.

It was also noted that the exceptions to the low SES–poor health rule provide useful opportunities for investigation. Each of those exceptions could be the topic of an independent study. For example, researchers could explore why the relationship between coronary heart disease and SES has changed direction or become weaker than it has been in the past. Another series of investigations could target low income communities that enjoy better health outcomes than might be expected. What differentiates such communities from their less fortunate neighbors?

Participants urged that researchers of the SES-health relationship not fall prey to excessive caution. While study design and
data analysis of the relationship pose strong challenges, several
studies together can provide converging evidence as to the validity of some hypotheses, even if no one of the studies is perfect in
itself. Researchers should consider a study as one in a body of
work that together may lead to a greater understanding of causes
as a basis for future intervention.

JOHN P. BUNKER
DEANNA S. GOMBY

REFERENCES

Stamler, R., Hardy, R. J., Payne, G. H., et al. 1987. Educational
    level and five-year all-cause mortality in the hypertension de-
    tection and follow-up program. *Hypertension* 9:641–646.
Townsend, P., Davidson, N., eds. 1982. *Inequalities in health: the
    Black Report*. Harmondsworth, England: Penguin Books.

Part I
Introduction

1. Socioeconomic Status and Health: The Problem[1]

David Mechanic

THE ISSUES POSED by this Conference on Socioeconomic Status (SES) and Health are extraordinarily broad. The conference report, this book, includes an array of excellent papers that convey the complexity of this area of interest and the richness of questions and data that pertain to our charge. My paper, which follows, suggests some appropriate strategies. But here I go beyond the paper and respond more speculatively to Alvin Tarlov's challenge to identify possible points of leverage for constructive intervention.

In agreeing to speculate beyond what the evidence shows, and to use Tarlov's phrase of "taking our scientific hats off," I should emphasize the importance of having better scientific understanding of causal processes so that we can target our efforts most intelligently. How we explain major research findings— such as the conclusions from the RAND Health Insurance Experiment that cost-sharing did not result in appropriately selective decisions about when to seek care and that poor children were particularly at risk—leads to different strategies of intervention. If we view these findings as a product of inadequate health information, we would go in one direction; if we interpret them in terms of different willingness among educational groups to invest in children, as Grossman's theory might suggest, we would proceed very differently. When we intervene in social processes we are likely to do better with a rifle than a shotgun, but targeting our shots properly requires understanding of causal pathways.

It's abundantly clear from the papers that macro social forces account for many of the hazards to health. It is also apparent that within any socioeconomic stratum or social group there is large variation not explained by poverty or lack of social equity. Since the papers focus substantially on macro issues, I will particularly dwell on some of the family, peer, and sociocultural differences that may serve as a basis for useful intervention.

As I note in my paper, parental education is associated with the health behavior of adolescents. Less parental education, in turn, is related to the magnitude of stressful life events, distress, disagreements with children, and children's perceptions of less parental interest. Higher SES children also do better in school, participate in more religious activities, and seem less vulnerable to peer pressures. Parental culture, which in general is more oriented to health concerns than is adolescent peer culture regardless of social class, appears to have more authority in higher SES families. Adolescent peer culture, in contrast, commonly encourages experimentation with drugs, alcohol, and smoking, and seems to be more forceful among lower SES youth who live in families less likely to exercise strong parental authority over "moral sentiments."

Class is not the issue, however. The target area is the emotional and cognitive climate of the family and the degree to which youngsters can draw on the internal environment of the family for their security, sense of self, and future expectations and aspirations. For a variety of reasons, children in poor families are more likely to become alienated from the family context, and the family is less likely to set the high expectations necessary for successful adaptation.

Some years ago, Lee Robins carried out some important studies of mental health outcomes among black and white youth in St. Louis.[2] As one might anticipate, she found more pathology among lower status and black children as they grew up; the more important point, however, was that when favorable conditions operated in the lives of poor and black children, they did as well as others. Class and race are important in that they affect the probabilities that conditions necessary for an appropriate environment for socialization will be present.

It is essential to recognize that the causal links between SES and important outcomes involve contingencies. SES may be linked only loosely to particular life trajectories with complex transition probabilities. Put more simply, choices and decisions at a particular point in the life cycle, involving marriage, pregnancy, schooling, or job, may affect the probabilities of subsequent life pathways. Young people feeling oppressed by family life may choose to escape by entering premature relationships that are highly destructive. For example, choices about limiting schooling and early pregnancy have reverberations throughout life. These choices are not irreversible; but once the course is set, disengagement is extremely difficult. These are tough issues, but they are an important part of the story we have to understand. In many of our interventions, we are attempting to influence these trajectories, to change their timing and course. We need a clear concept of what we are trying to do.

Among the members of our research team at Rutgers, we've come to joke about what we call the "good kid" syndrome. We repeatedly find that some youth, more commonly from higher SES families, seem to be "good kids" regardless of the indicators we examine. They do well in school, they're cheerful and optimistic, they don't smoke or use drugs, and they get along with their parents and peers. And it seems to us that this is the product of a particular family environment and family process. The key, I would guess, is how the environment affects the way kids come to think about themselves and allows them to acquire coping strategies and interpersonal skills. But such environments also require expectations of competence and mastery, communicated in a constructive and supportive way.

In my paper I discuss the important work of Kohn and Schooler on the effects of complexity of task, nonroutineness of demands, and freedom from close supervision on intellectual flexibility, self-direction and well-being. To extrapolate, we can think of families as creating environments that have varying potentialities for the development of children. Such environments can either enhance or retard the development of a child's coping skills, sense of personal efficacy, and types of attitudes that are constructive and helpful. In this regard, I find useful Spaeth's interesting, although oversimplified, conception of parental schooling as a proxy for the complexity of the child's cognitive environment a useful frame of reference.

We know from a variety of studies that parental SES is associated with a wide variety of characteristics of the family environment, including talking to and playing with the child, talking to the child during meals, instructing the child, and providing feedback. We can't do a great deal about changing parental SES, but many of these more specific behaviors and relational patterns may be more amenable to intervention.

In reviewing the area in this rather general way, the issues become much oversimplified; recognizing the complexity keeps our hubris in check. How parents behave is not fully under their control; such behavior is conditioned by external events, by psychological state, by values, and by many other factors. Thus we should not think of programming parental behavior as a simple or direct intervention.

I find it interesting that in two different studies we have found that parental admonitions about health behavior are less influential on children's behavior than are children's perceptions of parental interest. How you try to communicate things to kids, and how they come to understand them, is a complicated process. A key issue is the success of families in developing self-direction in their children, and in helping them build self-esteem through the exercise of competence. I would guess that when adolescents have little self-esteem, they find it more difficult to resist peer pressures and are more amenable to unconstructive influences. Our data suggest that youngsters in families with strong ties are less intensively dependent on peers and probably are less susceptible to their influence.

Global concepts help us communicate, but efforts to intervene constructively require clear differentiation among the subgroups that may be our targets. We talk about the poor in a general way, but poverty is a heterogeneous category of persons lacking resources for varying reasons. It is particularly important to differentiate between the transient poor, who are the majority of this category, and those whose poverty is persistent, perhaps even across generations. Whether it is our intent to target all the poor, or only selected segments, we should be clear about our goals and our strategies as they might affect varying subgroups. As we consider strategies, some explanations are more helpful than others. Michael Grossman's model of health investment, for example, has helped us integrate and make sense of a variety of empirical observations. But it is not enough to know that parents invest differently in their children. An intervention strategy requires understanding *why* people differ so that we can specify those targets most likely to facilitate the desired changes.

In conclusion, I should note that addressing the SES link to health puts us in the business of trying to change culture, and it's a tough business. Many of the behaviors we wish to change are deeply ingrained in culture and social processes. Promoting good science about these processes is indispensable for intervention attempts. We would prefer that the goals in health we seek could be enhanced by a few basic orientations, but we know that most health behaviors are only modestly associated with one another. Indeed some are independent and even inversely related. For example, in one study we found that young people who exercise also take high risks involving danger. I suspect that underlying both is an activity factor, and those with a need to be active physically not only engage in sports and exercise, which we would encourage, but also drive their cars fast and take other risks that we would like them to avoid. Thus, in pushing in one direction, we may induce unwanted and unanticipated consequences.

Adolescence may be a particularly strategic stage for targeting interventions. It's a period in which many life-course decisions evolve that are not easily reversible later. Reaching adolescents requires interventions in family, peer groups, and school environments. It is difficult to influence families, and our notions about privacy demand we proceed with special caution in this area. A major resource, however, is the fact that no matter how disorganized the family may seem, most parents have aspirations for a better life for their children. They may not know clearly how to encourage it, or how to communicate their caring and expectations. Many youngsters fail to perceive how much their parents really care, and there may be relatively simple ways to help parents communicate more effectively.

At the community level we need much stronger supportive structures, and peer groups and schools are good places to start. Helping to develop values supportive of health and achievement and reinforcing institutions and groups that do so could be important initiatives.

The issues embedded in the SES-health link are of extraordinary importance, and the seriousness of these patterns for the welfare of individuals and for our society demands that they be addressed. The papers in this volume make it clear that we must proceed with good information, deep understanding, and much humility. But proceed we must.

NOTES

1. Adapted by the author from his Keynote Address, March 25, 1987.
2. References cited in this chapter are included with those at the end of Chapter 2.

2. Socioeconomic Status and Health: An Examination of Underlying Processes

David Mechanic

ONE OF THE more important findings of the RAND Health Insurance Experiment that has not received attention comparable to many of the other reported results was that cost sharing did not result in appropriately selective decisions about when to seek care. Financial barriers to access served to ration care in instances where care was appropriate and efficacious as well as in situations where it was unnecessary. Being somewhat perplexed, the researchers indicate that "many people may simply lack sufficient information to help them distinguish when care seeking is likely to be beneficial. Hence, they are at a disadvantage in deciding whether to seek care or forgo it. This may be a particular problem for persons who make care seeking decisions for children in lower income families. . . . Can more be done to help the economically disadvantaged discriminate better between situations when medical care would be useful and those when it would be less so?" (Lohr et al. 1986, p. 82).

The RAND group did not report on educational differences in using care appropriately; but the results noted, as in much other research on health and health behavior, suggest special problems among the disadvantaged under cost sharing. The probability of at least one episode of highly effective care for poor children was 56 percent of the free care level, while the comparable figure for nonpoor children was 85 percent. These variations may reflect differences in willingness to make health investments in children

(Grossman 1972), levels of knowledge and understanding, and differences in the capacity to cope with crisis. These findings are but one example of persistent observations in the literature of substantial relationships between social class and a wide array of measures of mortality, morbidity, well-being, and utilization of health care. Lower social status is predictive of fetal wastage and perinatal death, infant mortality, developmental problems, morbidity, psychological distress, and mortality (Mechanic 1978; Susser, Watson, and Hopper 1985; Mechanic 1982; Last 1986; Aiken and Mechanic 1986). Data supporting these relationships are comprehensively reviewed in this volume so that no further elaboration is necessary here. In exploring underlying processes that suggest hypotheses for meaningful health interventions, a variety of conceptual, methodological and substantive issues become relevant.

THE CONCEPT OF SOCIAL CLASS

Social class is typically used in sociology as a central theoretical concept indicating the individual's location in the social stratification system and access to material resources, influence, and information. This concept may be used in a highly theoretical way, as in Marxian analysis, with precise structural implications; but it is more commonly used as a descriptive indicator denoting a variety of recognized cultural and economic attributes that can be scaled in a variety of ways. In empirical analysis it is often useful to disaggregate the components of social class; but, theoretically, the concept is intended to capture in a holistic way the meaning within defined communities of occupying a particular social location and its implications not only for material welfare but also for prestige, networks of association, community influence, and cultural styles.

Qualitative studies of community stratification map the sociocultural implications of class differences, but most quantitative studies use a limited number of indicators: income, education, occupation, and occasionally, residence. These are important not only in terms of their direct implications, but also because they are substantially associated with a wide range of other factors that affect people's health, well-being, and life chances. In some instances social class, and its specific components, have direct causal influence on health factors; in others, the association is spurious, resulting from influences associated with both health and social class.

Indicators of social class only imperfectly capture its theoretical meanings, and the indicators themselves may vary across historical periods and cultures (Sewell 1982). This problem is reflected, for example, in debates concerning the effects of poverty, because income deprivation is a *relative concept* and the absolute material resources of the poor in our society may exceed those of many of the world's population, who would not so identify themselves. Similarly, the significance of a year of education, or total education attained, depends both on its meaning in a particular cultural context and the average level of education in a society overall. It would be foolish to equate the attainment of a college education among cohorts born in 1920 and 1960. Both the content and the cultural meanings change over time. Various studies of occupational prestige, however, show such prestige to be relatively invariant over time (Hodge et al. 1964), although there are clear shifts in the educational and income attributes associated with particular occupations.

The changing attributes of the labor market and occupational structures are intensively researched. The details need not concern us here. Crucial for the discussion that follows is the fact that descriptive statements between class indicators and health outcomes are bound by the time and context in which these observations are made. For example, prior to 1966, the poor used fewer physician visits and hospital bed days than the more affluent, but this relationship shifted following the introduction of Medicare and Medicaid. The limitations of descriptive findings for identifying generic interventions may be obvious, yet inappropriate generalizations from descriptive studies limited to particular periods and contexts are common. In the Medicare-Medicaid example, the intervening proximal determinants of the relationship—economic and physical access to services—are obvious, but as we examine more complex class and health linkages the underlying processes are more difficult to disentangle.

A Note on Measures of Socioeconomic Status

The major indicators of socioeconomic status are substantially intercorrelated in most populations, but each may have differential influence in varying instances. Researchers attempting to capture a more complex picture of social class may seek to develop comprehensive indices of socioeconomic status but they do so at some cost. Education, income, occupation, and residence may each have different effects on specific dependent variables, and these effects may vary as well, depending on labor force participation (Kessler 1982). Given increasingly sophisticated multivariate methods, the availability of large data sets, and the power of modern computers, whenever possible it is advantageous to disaggregate index components to examine their unique effects and interactions with other measures. Thus, for example, Kitagawa and Hauser (1973) demonstrated that education and income have independent effects on mortality, and Kessler (1982) showed that income, education, and occupational status all have independent effects on levels of psychological distress.

The Meaning of Social Class Indicators

Indicators of social class are commonly associated with cultural practices, family life, child-rearing practices, self-conceptions, community involvements, cognitive skills, and coping strategies. They are predictive as well of quality of housing, nutrition, access to medical and social services, recreation, and many other goods and services. Since the number of linkages is extraordinarily large, it is useful to think of class effects in terms of some generic categories. By doing so we can better understand linkages and also intraclass variance.

Class can be seen as affecting exposure to environmental risk, opportunities to access valued material resources and information, the development of cognitive schemas, cognitive complexity, and coping skills, and access to social networks and instrumental support. Class also has important influence on self-conceptions and problem-solving orientations, as well as values and interests. Each of these factors may bear directly on health behavior and health status or may be associated rather loosely with particular life trajectories that have many complex transition points. Choices and decisions made at varying points in the life cycle involving marriage, pregnancy, termination of schooling, and job affect the probabilities of later life chances. Class also may affect the propensity to "drift" into particular trajectories in contrast to careful information acquisition and planning. Social position of one's family at birth substantially affects the probabilities of varying life trajectories. In the remainder of the paper, I illustrate some of these processes and suggest some implications for intervention. But, first, some methodological caveats.

THRESHOLD EFFECTS AND SOCIAL SELECTION

It is common to observe that much of the observable health impact occurs below a certain threshold of social status and that once certain levels of income, education, and job status are reached, additional effects are more modest (Mechanic 1978). Hundreds of studies show that poor health, inappropriate health behavior, and social pathologies cluster significantly in the lowest socioeconomic groups, with high rates of most types of pathology in these social strata (Robins 1979, 1982). It is debatable whether it is appropriate to view these populations as part of an underclass, but it is important conceptually to differentiate such populations, which are relatively small, from all others who may be in poverty at any point in time.

Poverty is a time-limited status for a majority of the poor; within this population are subgroups characterized by long-term poverty, profound health and social risk, high levels of demoralization and anomie, and highly prevalent illness, mortality, and violence. Since most available data are cross-sectional, it is extraordinarily difficult to track how this more intractably poor population differs from the transient poor. It is difficult to link appropriately the necessary data sources, since even large representative surveys of the population do not sample sufficient numbers of the population at highest risk to allow substantial analysis. This population at highest risk is also difficult to survey, requiring us to depend to a greater degree than we would like on limited studies.

A closely associated issue involves the assortative processes that result in low socioeconomic status. In many instances, low social status is a consequence of biological vulnerability, poor health status and social pathology, and in most data sets it is impossible to identify the direction of influence. Moreover, selection effects occur through a variety of processes including assortative mating, residential drift, and job selection, complicating our understanding of the biological and behavioral predictors. How individuals come together, live together, marry, have and raise children are difficult to model, but these selective processes have influential effects on the health of children, their psychological and social development, and their future life chances.

SOCIAL STATUS AND THE PHYSICAL ENVIRONMENT

Socioeconomic status affects exposure to noxious aspects of the physical environment through its influences on residence and occupational risks. Substantial numbers of deaths and injuries occur in the workplace, and risks are significantly higher in blue-collar occupations and among unskilled labor. Such risks include accidents, as in mining and construction, or high levels of exposure to noxious substances, as in the manufacture of chemicals. There are at least nineteen chemicals or industrial processes for which there is reasonably convincing epidemiological evidence of carcinogenicity in humans, including asbestos, benzene, vinyl chloride, and chromium. Many others are highly suspect but involve less definitive evidence (Brandt-Rauf and Weinstein 1982, p. 272). Other sources of danger clearly associated with disease or disability include coal dust and tars, hot and cold temperatures, cotton dust, noise, and high exposure to metals such as lead, manganese, and tin.

Environmental hazards are found in the indoor environment, food, water, waste and sewage, and in contamination of the air. Crowding, deficient appliances, poor maintenance of housing structures, and low quality of household equipment and ventiliation all may contribute to risk through accident, fire, or environmental degradation. Although I pass over this important area quickly, it should be apparent how each of the SES indicators noted earlier is likely to affect these risks through both voluntary and involuntary behavior. Persons better educated are more likely to know the risks, can make choices that are in part informed by such awareness, and can take other preventive actions. Economic resources provide access to safer homes and neighborhoods, allow purchase of better functioning appliances and house maintenance, and give more choice of neighborhood. Residents in higher socioeconomic areas are better able to protect themselves by zoning and other political processes from traffic and other sources of exposure, not only to noxious contaminants but also to crime and other potential dangers. While SES is not the only or even the major source of exposure to environmental risk, it constitutes a significant part of the picture.

Persons in higher socioeconomic groups are less likely to be unable to work because of disability than those lower in the social hierarchy. This reflects both differences in exposure to risk contributing to disability and the fact that physical deficits are much more limiting in jobs at the lower levels of the occupational structure. While professional and technical personnel and clerical workers are greatly underrepresented among the disabled population, farm and service workers, laborers, and workers in the crafts are significantly overrepresented (Rest 1986, p. 905). Disability is also influenced, in part, by motivation: the greater prevalence of disabled at the lower ends of the occupational spectrum reflects the fact that disabilty benefits are more comparable to wages at lower income levels.

In considering occupational and environmental risk, much of the variance is explained by the specific risks inherent in particular work and living situations, irrespective of social status. Thus, physicians have high risk of drug abuse, influenced by their easy access to addicting drugs, and nurses have a high prevalence of lower back injury specific to the types of work they do. However, because the highest risks of noxious exposure and injury tend to be associated with jobs at the lower ends of the occupational spectrum and because housing conditions and neighborhood quality are closely linked with income, the socioeconomic effects in the aggregate are substantial. Nevertheless it is unlikely that we have much to learn by pursuing these aggregate relationships in contrast to targeting specific risks associated with specific jobs.

SOCIAL CLASS AND OCCUPATIONAL ATTAINMENT

From a health viewpoint, there are at least two reasons to examine briefly the literature on social class and occupational attainment. First, as a highly developed area of research (Blau and Duncan 1967) it suggests causal processes that have bearing on the questions we ask about health. Second, occupational attainment and its correlates, as we have already noted, are an important factor in health outcomes.

The Wisconsin model of status attainment is perhaps the best-developed single model and is consistent with the results of most other major studies that are less comprehensive (Sewell and Hauser 1975). The study, based on the cohort of all high school seniors in Wisconsin in 1957, included follow-up observations in 1964 and acquisition of tax records in 1965 to assess earnings. The analysis conveys the complexity and specificity of mobility processes, suggesting caution to workers in the health arena about the scope of generalization. While the Wisconsin model was highly successful in explaining educational achievement, accounting for 54 percent of the variance, it accounted for only 43 percent of the variance in occupational attainment and 7 percent of the variance in 1967 earnings. The latter result reflects in part the fact that earnings in the sample had not stabilized by 1967, but also that many factors other than the determinants of educational attainment influence earned income.

The Wisconsin model indicates that the most important influences in obtaining higher education are the decision to plan to go to college and college entry itself. Both socioeconomic origins and ability are powerful predictors of such planning and decision making. While only approximately half of high ability boys and a quarter of high ability girls of lower SES origins in the cohort studied enrolled in college, 90 percent of high SES boys and 76 percent of high SES girls of comparable ability enrolled. These influences persist through graduation. Only 38 percent of low SES/high ability boys graduated compared with 71 percent of high SES/high ability boys. Comparable figures for girls are 50 and 67 percent. Thus, while ability was important in selecting students for higher education, SES continued to be a major determinant of the selection process.

In modeling educational and occupational attainment, important intervening variables include high school performance, encouragement of educational and occupational aspirations by significant others, and the aspirations students develop, which in turn depict processes most influenced by background factors. Additional factors unrelated to ability or socioeconomic origins influence the levels of encouragement and aspirations. Socioeconomic status does not affect performance in high school independent of ability, but it strongly affects educational and occupational attainment through the influence of significant others. The ability of the student, in contrast, independently affects both high school performance and the encouragement students receive from significant others, which in turn predict educational and occupational attainment.

While SES is a powerful force in these attainment processes, much of the variation is not explained by SES, ability, and the other intervening factors. This is as it should be, since many influences contribute to attainment, such as motivation, personality, capacity for sustained effort, and luck. The complexity of these processes is worthy of some emphasis, since it realistically depicts what we should expect to find in examining SES and health outcomes. Logically, genetic health endowment, although more difficult to measure, is comparable in health models to the ability indicator in status attainment models. It would be useful to attempt better to objectify what every physician takes into account in taking a medical history—the individual's biological health stock. But the key point is that many factors other than SES or health endowment affect the intervening variables that modify health outcomes, and if we are to target interventions effectively, the challenge is to identify better those intervening variables more proximal to the health outcomes of special interest to us.

SOCIAL CLASS AND COGNITIVE AND BEHAVIORAL PROCESSES

Socioeconomic status is moderately associated with measures of intellectual ability. I would like to sidestep the acrimonious debate as to how much of this correlation can be explained by the character of ability tests as compared with social selection effects. Persons of less ability, as we have seen, have lesser educational and occupational attainments, and substantial marriage assortment occurs to bring such persons together. The evidence also demonstrates, however, that high levels of educational attainment occur in the absence of high ability when other factors are promotive.

High levels of education facilitate the acquisition of knowledge and skills, as well as the development of cognitive capacities. Similarly, certain types of work are likely to facilitate how people think about their environment and how they solve problems. Thus educational and occupational attainment are likely to be important for coping independent of the ability of individuals or the tangible and intangible rewards educational and occupational attainment bring.

Kohn and Schooler (1978) have observed that intellectual flexibility, self-direction, and greater well-being are associated with job conditions that involve more complex substance, are free of close supervision, and are nonroutine. In contrast, job conditions that lack these characteristics promote a conformist orientation. In an intriguing presentation, Spaeth (1976) argues that much of the status-attainment process could be understood in terms of the transmission of the capacity to cope with cognitive complexity. He argues that

> Statuses relevant to socioeconomic achievement can be considered as indicators of the complexity of settings to which persons are exposed. In the family of orientation, children may not only be exposed to complex stimuli; but parents may also manipulate those stimuli; serve as role and competency models and bring about treatments that increase (or decrease) the competency of their children in coping with cognitive complexity. [p. 130]

In support of his interpretive framework, Spaeth finds that the correlation between occupational complexity (as measured by Kohn) and occupational prestige is .8, which in turn is correlated .6 with schooling. He views schooling as a measure of exposure to increasingly complex educational environments, and parental SES as a proxy for the complexity of the child's cognitive environment. Parental SES is associated with a wide variety of environmental attributes, including talking and playing with the young child, talking to the child during meals, and providing explicit instructions and positive feedback (Spaeth 1976, p. 108). As Schooler (1972) has suggested, the child exposed to a more complex environment is better able to cope intellectually with complex and ambiguous situations.

Status attainment, like health behavior and health status, is best thought of as a series of contingencies, none of which completely determines the outcomes. In extending this line of thinking, Miller, Kohn, and Schooler (1986) found that schooling reproduces high socioeconomic status through "differential training of independent, self-directed orientations in students." Through initiative and independent judgment, cognitive functioning becomes enhanced.

The implications of this large body of research are intriguing. Education, for example, is one of the most consistent predictors of measures of mortality, morbidity, and health behavior. It is also associated with smaller family size and parental interest in the child (Mechanic 1980). It seems plausible to anticipate that parents with higher levels of interest and knowledge about health and those with greater interest in their children will be more likely to make investments for the health of their children, will create healthful environments for their children's development, and will provide more direct health instruction consistent with maintaining health.

It seems plausible, in addition, that educational attainment is a proxy for such diverse factors as rearing practices, attitudes and values, parental interest and nurturance, coping instruction, self-esteem, and opportunities to invest in health, but there is no empirical model available that explains the effects of education in a coherent way. Despite some serious measurement difficulties, Pratt's research on the influence of family structure on health behavior (Pratt 1971) points to coping competence as a key consideration. Pratt found that both education and family structure were associated with health behavior, but when the latter was taken into account, education had no further net effects. She argues that:

> Men and women whose family arrangements provide opportunities for autonomy and personal growth are more likely to assume full personal responsibility for caring for their own health, to seek out the best methods of health care, to strive for maximum development of their physical capacities, and to be resourceful in responding to the changing health needs of their bodies. [Pratt 1976, p. 86]

Pratt, unfortunately, does not present a sufficiently developed model to assess varying effects. In an effort to examine Pratt's hypothesis, I found some evidence in support of the importance of self-esteem and certain family processes on health behavior, but these were mostly independent of education (Mechanic 1980).

SOCIAL CLASS, HEALTH VALUES, AND HEALTH KNOWLEDGE

Social class is substantially related to values, interest in health, knowledge about health matters, and preventive health actions (Feldman 1966; Mechanic and Cleary 1980). It also affects how persons respond to illness, how they express their problems and health concerns, how they retain information and services, and how they cooperate in treatment. The literature in this area is large but highly descriptive and not very analytical. In general, education has the largest effects among class indicators on health knowledge and values, but the relative importance of education, occupation, and income depends on the specific issue under consideration. Education, for example, is most influential in the acquisition and retention of information, whereas income is often important in issues involving access to and retention of services.

Kohn (1977), in his theory of occupational self-direction noted earlier, provides the single most coherent approach to this topic. His basic thesis is that the relationship between social class and values derives from underlying conditions of life characteristic of different positions in the social structure. He emphasizes the substantive complexity of work and self-direction as his core concern, but these concepts may apply equally well to home environments and leisure pursuits. Kohn presents considerable evidence indicating that middle class parents value self-direction whereas working class parents put larger emphasis on conformity to external authority, and these attitudes in turn influence disciplinary practices as well as relative parental responsibilities in setting constraints for children. This approach suggests that children raised in environments emphasizing self-direction will be more likely to develop their intellectual and coping capacities and acquire a stronger sense of self. Kohn does not directly give much emphasis to health, but he has argued that the conditions of conformity characteristic of the working class restrict coping flexibility and put vulnerable children at risk when they are under stress. While the process Kohn posits is plausible, the links between class and the outcomes of major interest are not well developed.

On a descriptive level, education is substantially associated with greater knowledge and a greater inclination to acquire further knowledge. As Feldman (1966) has noted, those less educated are not only less informed, but also are less exposed to new information and appear to learn less when exposed. Thus knowledge and ignorance perpetuate themselves (Feldman 1966, p. 56). It is for this reason, he maintains, that health education makes only slow progress in reaching less-informed groups. It remains unclear how much educational differences reflect varying ability and openness to information in comparison with differential access. Certainly there is extraordinary informational access in American society. Few studies probe deeply enough to examine whether the varying levels of information characteristic of groups with different levels of education reflect varying exposure to and ability to understand health messages, or whether persons in varying classes differ in their capacities or inclinations to update their health knowledge over time.

Consideration of Kohn's theory in relation to descriptive data on acquisition of health knowledge suggests the hypothesis that persons of lower education are more likely to acquire health information in a prescriptive way, while those with higher levels of education are more inquiring, more open to new information, and more proactive in upgrading and updating what they know. The difference between having health information and knowing how to acquire it is an important one, because the possible stock of health knowledge is very large and changing and most people have limited need for most of it. Thus it seems important for people to have search strategies to alert them when further information is necessary and skills to acquire it. Many studies suggest that in illness behavior situations, the most common alerting factor is a change from expected or customary levels of function. The seriousness of such changes is often judged by the extent to which they interfere with goals and usual activities, and not by medically relevant criteria. These decisions are arrived at through a "common-sense" self-assessment. To the extent that a medical definition of danger is preferable, it becomes necessary to program individuals to bypass usual common-sense explanations in assessing meaning.

ASSESSMENT OF ECOLOGICAL DATA

Most of the findings discussed involve surveys and epidemiological investigations, but much data of interest come from correlating attributes of populations with rates representing these populations. Associations from such ecological analyses tend to be higher than those from data sets involving individuals and also to be more difficult to interpret clearly. Typically, income and educational characteristics of census tracts or statistical reporting areas are substantially associated with a wide range of indicators of poor health, deviant behavior, and family disorganization.

Such ecological correlations depict the culmination of a variety of selection and causative processes impossible to disentangle in such data. Ecological areas with high rates of pathology compound the noxious environmental, housing, family, and personal influences that contribute to health problems. These areas also provide the only living contexts for those who failed in a variety of social roles. Thus there are often disproportionate numbers of single-parent families, unemployed individuals, homeless individuals, decarcerated mental patients, and criminals, etc. Such data, thus, can serve as no more than clues for further investigation. By themselves they are unlikely to take our understanding much further.

A MODEST PROPOSAL FOR RESEARCH

This brief review indicates that while there is no lack of ideas about the links between social class and health outcomes, there is relatively little development of models that explain why socioeconomic indicators have the effects they do on varying health outcomes. More careful specification of intervening variables and their relationships could help target good points of leverage for health promotion. It would be preferable to study such links prospectively.

Fortunately there is available a rich data repository that has hardly been exploited. Measures of education and occupation are almost universal in surveys and other research studies and although income poses difficulties, it is also a common measure. It would not be difficult to locate existing data sets with comprehensive health information for modeling purposes. Such secondary analyses could not only help define more specifically the priority to be given to different measures in future longitudinal and other studies but could also provide clues to intervention strategies.

THE COMPLEXITY OF HEALTH PROMOTION: AN EXAMPLE

My colleague Stephen Hansell and I have been following longitudinally 1,235 adolescents, ages 12 to 17, along with a large subsample of their parents, in order to learn about the influences on their health responses (Mechanic and Hansell 1987; Hansell and Mechanic 1987). One dependent variable we study is an index of positive health behavior involving five equally weighted dimensions: smoking, marijuana use, drinking, seat-belt use, and exercise. At the zero-order level, two of the most important factors affecting good health behavior are parental education and the child's age. Older children and those whose parents are less educated have poorer health responses. These two measures are also the most important predictors of change over a year, net of the level of health behavior at the beginning of the year.

We have been successful in explaining only about half of the education effect, even using fairly complex models, but our findings are instructive in suggesting the complexity of the behavioral patterns we would like to influence. Intervening variables that explain part of the effect of parental education include levels of life stress affecting the family, levels of parental distress, degree of parental interest in the child, disagreements with the child, the child's poorer school achievement and less religious participation. In each case, families with more poorly educated parents had less favorable scores on these indicators. In contrast, peer groups had greater influence on the child in these families, as reflected in measures of involvement with peer social activities.

Our results show that adolescents who adopt a lifestyle reflecting parental values and expectations and oriented toward conventional activities such as school and religious activity practice better health behavior. In contrast, those more oriented to peer social activities exhibit poorer health behavior over time. Thus family and peer group influences are linked. The dynamics are complicated. Families under greater stress with more distressed parents demonstrate lower levels of interest in the child as perceived by the child. This phenomenon probably contributes to higher levels of disagreement and less supervision, encouraging the adolescent to make greater investments in peer activities that encourage experimentation with health risks. But the effects are probably more general, influencing school work and other activities as well. In short, health behavior is embedded in complex patterns of family life, school and peer group activities, which suggests why it is so difficult to intervene effectively. Ironically, parental encouragement of good behavior is relatively ineffectual in contrast to the quality of the emotional climate of the family.

This research leads to no single specific intervention, although it suggests various points of possible leverage depending on opportunity. One alternative is to strengthen the sense of family embeddedness and instruct parents in clear and simple ways to demonstrate interest in their children's activities and competence. Another is to make efforts to modify the health values of school peer groups. None of this is easy, nor is success assured. But such is the state of health promotion. Interventions based on deeper understanding offer greater potential.

REFERENCES

Aiken, L., Mechanic, D., eds. 1986. *Applications of social science to clinical medicine and health policy.* New Brunswick, NJ: Rutgers University Press.

Blau, P. M., Duncan, O. D. 1967. *The American occupational structure.* New York: Wiley.

Brandt-Rauf, P. W., Weinstein, I. B. 1983. Environment and disease. In Mechanic, D., ed. *Handbook of health, health care, and the health professions.* New York: Free Press.

Feldman, J. 1966. *The dissemination of health information.* Chicago: Aldine.

Grossman, M. 1972. *The demand for health: a theoretical and empirical investigation.* New York: Columbia University Press for the National Bureau of Economic Research.

Hansell, S., Mechanic, D. 1987. Adolescent lifestyles and positive health behavior. Unpublished paper.

Hodge, R. W., Siegel, P. M., Rossi, P. H. 1964. Occupational prestige in the United States, 1925–63. *American Journal of Sociology* 70:286–302.

Kessler, R. 1982. A disaggregation of the relationship between socioeconomic status and psychological distress. *American Sociological Review* 47:752–764.

Kitagawa, E. M., Hauser, P. M. 1973. *Differential mortality in the United States: a study in socioeconomic epidemiology.* Cambridge, MA: Harvard University Press.

Kohn, M. 1977. *Class and conformity: a study in values.* 2nd ed. Chicago: University of Chicago Press.

———, Schooler, C. 1978. The reciprocal effects of the substantive complexity of work and intellectual flexibility: a longitudinal assessment. *American Journal of Sociology* 84:24–52.

Last, J., ed. 1986. *Maxcy-Rosenau public health and preventive medicine.* 12th ed. Norwalk, CT: Appleton-Century-Crofts.

Lohr, K. N., et al. 1986. *Use of medical care in the RAND health insurance experiment. Diagnosis- and service-specific analyses in a randomized controlled trial.* R-3469-HHS. Santa Monica, CA: RAND Corporation.

Mechanic, D. 1978. *Medical sociology.* 2nd ed. New York: Free Press.

————. 1980. Education, parental interest, and health perceptions and behavior. *Inquiry* 17:331–338.

————. 1982. Disease, mortality, and the promotion of health.
Health Affairs 1:28–32.

————, Cleary, P. D. 1980. Factors associated with the maintenance of positive health behavior. *Preventive Medicine* 9:805–
814.

Mechanic, D., Hansell, S. 1987. Adolescent competence, psychological well-being, and self-assessed physical health. *Journal of Health and Social Behavior*: 28:364–374.

Miller, K. A., Kohn, M. L., Schooler, C. 1986. Educational self-
direction and personality. *American Sociological Review*
51:372–390.

Pratt, L. 1971. The relationship of socio-economic status to
health. *American Journal of Public Health* 61:281–291.

————. 1976. *Family structure and effective health behavior: the en-
ergized family*. Boston: Houghton-Mifflin.

Rest, K. 1986. Problems of special groups. In Last, J. et al., eds.
Maxcy-Rosenau Public Health and Preventive Medicine. 12th ed.
Norwalk, CT: Appleton-Century-Crofts.

Robins, L. 1979. Follow-up studies of behavior disorders in
children. In Quay, H. C., Werry, J. S., eds. *Psychopathological
disorders of childhood*. 2nd ed. New York: Wiley.

————. 1983. Continuities and discontinuities in the psychiatric
disorders of children. In Mechanic, D., ed. *Handbook of health,
health care, and the health professions*. New York: Free Press.

Schooler, C. 1972. Social antecedents of adult psychological
functioning. *American Journal of Sociology* 78:299–322.

Sewell, W. H., Jr. 1982. Occupational status in nineteenth-cen-
tury French urban society. In Hauser, et al., eds. *Social structure
and behavior*. New York: Academic Press.

Sewell, W. H., Hauser, R. M. 1975. *Education, occupation, and
earnings*. New York: Academic Press.

Spaeth, J. L. 1976. Cognitive complexity: a dimension underlying the socioeconomic achievement process. In Sewell, W. H.,
et al., eds. *Schooling and achievement in American society*. New
York: Academic Press.

Susser, M., Watson, W., Hopper, K., eds. 1985. *Sociology in medicine*. 3rd ed. New York: Oxford University Press.

Part II
What We Know

3. Socioeconomic Status and Health: Overview, Methodological Critique, and Reformulation

Diana B. Dutton and Sol Levine

THIS PAPER EXAMINES social and psychological factors that may help to explain the relationship between poverty and health. First, we summarize some of the main findings that emerge from existing research. Second, we consider some recent thoughts and various findings on stress and coping that may suggest some of the mechanisms by which social class affects health. Third, we raise some questions and some methodological problems in understanding the relationship between poverty and health. Finally, we consider the difficulty of altering the health status of the poor through conventional health education and health promotion approaches.

Our general thesis is that a host of factors are embedded in the phenomenon of poverty, that there is no single explanation for socioeconomic gradients in health, and indeed that the combined and interactive impact of multiple adversities, processes, and constraints undermines endurance and leads to a sense of beleaguerment and loss of control that is detrimental to health. If the cumulative effects of multiple hardships are disproportionate and synergistic, as we postulate, rather than simply additive, then conventional applications of regression-based methods for estimating these effects or adjusting for them may be inadequate. For the same reason, narrow, piecemeal strategies for improving health among lower class groups may be less effective than expected.

GENERAL PROPOSITIONS

Research to date allows certain broad generalizations about the relationship between socioeconomic status and health which, while not entirely uncontroversial, appear to be reasonably well established. We outline them here both because they summarize the phenomenon we are addressing and because they provide some clues to the underlying mechanisms that may be involved.

Different Measures of Socioeconomic Status Yield a Roughly Similar Picture of Health Inequalities

Socioeconomic status (SES) is a composite measure that typically incorporates economic status, measured by income; social status, measured by education; and work status, measured by occupation. Each of these components bears a conceptually distinct, albeit overlapping, relation to health: Income affects material conditions; education and occupation influence cultural, social, and psychological patterns; and occupation exerts a special influence in determining the physical as well as social conditions of people's major daily activity. In some cases these multiple influences can be distinguished empirically. For example, there are clear income gradients in self-reported health status at every educational level and, likewise, clear educational gradients in reported health at every income level (NCHS 10:142, 1983).

For many health measures, however, the separate effects of individual SES indicators cannot easily be distinguished, mainly because of the high degree of intercorrelation among income, education, and occupation in advanced industrial nations. The multiple components of SES affect not only each other but also have a common effect on sociopsychological factors such as alienation. But precisely because of this close correlation, distinctions among different indicators may not matter very much from a practical standpoint (we shall have more to say about this later). Whether SES is measured by income, education, or occupation, much the same picture emerges: Those at the bottom generally have the highest rates of death and disease. Race is strongly correlated with social class; although two-thirds of the people below the offical poverty level are white, almost half of all blacks are poor (Price 1984).

The relation between illness and income—unlike that with either race or education—involves a two-way effect: being poor often leads to worse health, and in turn worse health may also lead to diminished earning capacity and hence reduced income. Both directions of causation may be manifest in comparisons by income or occupational status for working-age adults. However, the fact that such comparisons generally do not differ greatly from those by education and race, even for working-age adults, suggests that gradients by income and occupation also reflect primarily the adverse effects of low SES on health, although the effect of poor health in reducing income or occupational status may also obtain.[1]

SES Gradients in Health Are Large, Widespread, and Remarkably Consistent

One of the most striking features of the relationship between SES and health is its pervasiveness and persistence over time. This relationship is found in virtually every measure of health status: age-adjusted mortality for all causes of death as well as specific causes, the severity of acute disease and the incidence of severe infectious conditions, the prevalence and severity of nearly every chronic disease, and measures of disability and restricted activity (detailed data are reported in Health Resources Administration 1979; *Black Report* 1980; Marmot et al. 1984; Dutton 1986; Whitehead 1987). It cuts across geographic boundaries, at least within industrialized nations (Marmot et al. 1987), and has been with us throughout most of recorded history.

Certain exceptions to these general patterns should be noted. Class differentials in mortality for immigrants from various developing countries are less consistent; for Caribbean immigrants to England and Wales, in fact, the highest death rates are found among the highest occupational class (Marmot et al. 1987). There is also evidence that the distribution of coronary heart disease mortality has shifted over time. Data for England and Wales suggest that in the 1930s heart disease mortality was higher among the upper classes, whereas now it is highest among the lowest social classes (Marmot et al. 1978). Possible reasons for this shift include class-related changes in smoking and diet and in diagnostic reporting. Obviously, however, these data do not tell the whole story about morbidity and mortality in non-Western countries or in earlier times.

What is conspicuous, nevertheless, is the strength and consistency of the gradients revealed today even among widely varying diseases and conditions that seemingly involve entirely different etiologies. For instance, causes of death as disparate as respiratory system diseases, heart disease, malignant neoplasms, and accidents (including poisonings and violence) all show significant class gradients in Britain (*Black Report* 1980; Marmot and McDowall 1986). The extraordinary consistency of social class gradients in diverse measures of morbidity and mortality has led some analysts to suggest that a more general process of breakdown and vulnerability may be at work that transcends disease entities (Syme and Berkman 1976). Indeed, lowered resistance may heighten the effects of specific risk factors (we will consider these points later).

Subjective and Objective Illness Measures Reveal Roughly Similar Class Gradients

Class gradients in health cannot be attributed simply to the differential *perception* of symptoms by people of different socioeconomic levels since comparable gradients occur in both subjective measures of disease and objectively defined measures. For example, data from the first National Health and Nutrition Examination Survey (HANES-I) show that people with limited education are two to three times as likely as those with some college to have arthritis, whether based on X-ray findings, physicians' clinical examinations, medical histories, or family interviews (Dutton 1986). The strongest gradients, in fact, were revealed by the most "objective" evidence—the blindly read X-ray data and the physicians' clinical examinations—rather than by reports of subjective symptomatology. Based strictly on X-ray findings, the prevalence of arthritis of the hip, sacroiliac, or knees was three times greater among adults with only a grade-school education or less compared with those with some college (5.5 percent versus 16.6 percent). Over 40 percent of adults with only a grade school education or less had some amount of arthritis, even using a rigorous and conservative definition of arthritis based on X-rays and clinical examinations.

These same data also point up another paradox in the relationship between health and SES: Although both subjective and objective measures of arthritis reveal roughly comparable class gradients for the population as a whole, there is relatively weak correspondence between the two types of measures for given individuals. Among the 1,768 people in the HANES-I sample with evidence of arthritis based on either medical examinations or X-ray findings, over a third (39.2 percent) did not report any symptoms (pain, aching, or swelling in any joints or morning stiffness). The severity of radiologic findings has been shown to correlate with the proportion of people in the HANES-I sample reporting pain in the hip and other joints, yet more than 40 percent of the people with "severe" osteoarthrosis of the hips on X-ray did not report any hip pain (NCHS 11:213). Sex differences in reporting of symptoms may account for part of this disparity (Kelsey 1984), but other possible reasons for the divergence between biological and perceptual measures of disease remain unclear. This disparity further complicates the task of explaining the mechanisms underlying the relation between SES and health.

SES Gradients in Health Occur for Both Sexes and at All Ages

Class differences in morbidity and mortality are a nearly universal feature of the entire human life span, regardless of sex. Although mortality rates for males are higher at every age than for females, the gap between the classes is substantial for both sexes (*Black Report* 1980). Morbidity, conversely, is generally higher among women, as is use of physician services; but again, the gap between the classes remains roughly comparable for both sexes. There has been some dispute about whether married women should be classified according to their husbands' SES or their own (if independently employed), but in either case health status appears to be substantially worse among women in the lower SES groups (Marmot et al. 1987).

For many measures, the health gap between rich and poor increases with age, reflecting the cumulative effects of a lifetime of impoverishment. Yet there are significant disparities even among infants and children. One study found that infant mortality rates were 50 percent higher in the poverty areas of 19 large cities than in the nonpoverty areas (Chartbook 1977). Differentials by race are also pronounced: Nonwhite babies continue to die at roughly twice the rate of white babies, despite improvements for both (Subcommittee on Oversight 1984). This differential is not confined to any single cause but is reflected in all listed causes of death (Surgeon General 1978). Moreover, it shows no signs of disappearing. Between 1950 and 1980, in fact, the overall decline in infant mortality was proportionately greater for whites than nonwhites (NCHS 30:13, 1982).

National data show that death rates among children in lower income families are from 50 to 100 percent higher than those among children in upper income families (Mare 1982). A 1983 study in Maine found that children in low income families had a death rate more than three times higher than that of other children (Maine Department of Human Services 1983). Based on a comprehensive review of the literature, Egbuonu and Starfield (1982) concluded that poor children were more likely than others to become ill, to suffer adverse consequences from illness, and to die. They found that poor children had a higher prevalence of many specific disorders, including cytomegalic inclusion disease (the most common congenital infection), iron deficiency anemia, lead poisoning, hearing disorders, and poor vision, as well as almost twice as many bed disability days and four times as many hospital days as their more affluent peers. Poor children are also more than twice as likely to be reported by their parents as having chronic conditions and only "fair or poor" health; physicians' clinical examinations tend to confirm these parental ratings (NCHS 11:129, 1973).[2] For many people, in short, the detrimental effects of poverty on health apparently begin very early in life.

Inequalities in Both Health and Economic Status Appear to Be Increasing

Data from England and Wales show that, although mortality rates for both males and females have declined steadily over the

last century, rates for the lower occupational classes have generally shown a proportionately smaller decline than those of the
upper social classes. The gap in mortality between the classes has
therefore been increasing over the past century among men of all
ages and among women ages 35–64 (*Black Report* 1980). Infant
mortality data reflect similar increases in the gap between upper
and lower occupational groups (*Black Report* 1980). Morbidity
data also reveal a widening gap between upper and lower classes.
Comparing standardized morbidity ratios for all causes, lung
cancer, coronary heart disease and cerebrovascular disease in
Great Britain over the last two decades, Marmot and McDowall
(1986) have shown that despite the general fall in mortality, the
relative disadvantage of manual compared with nonmanual
classes has increased for each of these four cause groups. Unfortunately no comparable data are available for the United States,
but it seems likely that the trends are similar.

In Great Britain, the distribution of disposable income appears to have remained essentially constant over the past twenty
years, despite changing governments, oil price rises and falls,
public expenditure cuts and spiraling unemployment (Morris
1986). The relative share of income going to the lowest and
highest pretax income groups has changed very little during this
period, although the near poor are now generally worse off than
they were two decades ago.

Income inequality in the United States appears to have increased somewhat more sharply than in Great Britain, especially
in recent years. Between 1980 and 1982, the percent of children
living in poverty in the United States rose by about 4 pecent—
an absolute increase of two million poor children (Price 1984).
In 1983, both the number and percentage of people living in
poverty reached the highest level since 1965 (U.S. Bureau of the
Census 1984). The gap between rich and poor has also been widening, reversing the gradual trend toward income equality that
prevailed from the 1950s through the late 1960s. While many
factors have contributed to this growing gap, recent federal policies have not helped: Federal tax and benefit legislation enacted
between 1980 and 1984 resulted in a net gain of roughly $17,000
for the most affluent and a net loss of roughly $1,000 for the
poor, taking inflation into account (Edsall 1984). In 1985, 43.5

percent of the nation's income went to the top 20 percent of all families, the highest level recorded since 1947; conversely, the bottom 60 percent of the population received 32.4 percent of the total income, again the lowest level ever recorded (Thurow 1987).

People at the bottom of the economic ladder suffer real deprivation. A Congressional study reported that the poorest fifth of all families had on average roughly 30 percent less real income in 1983 to meet their basic needs than in 1968 (Pear 1985). In a 1984 national survey, one out of every five adults reported not always being able to afford food for their families (Gallup 1984). The Physician Task Force on Hunger in America concluded that as many as 20 million Americans (12 million children and 8 million adults) experience hunger, largely because of federal cutbacks. Almost one half of those in poverty receive no food stamps, and those who do get them receive a benefit that health authorities judge to be inadequate to meet basic nutritional needs (Brown 1987).

From the data reviewed thus far, we draw the following conclusions: The relationship between SES and health is strikingly robust. It is found across a wide range of different diseases and conditions and for both males and females at virtually every age level in every country for which such data exist. This relationship appears in objective as well as subjective indicators of illness, and for most measures of SES. Recent evidence suggests, furthermore, that the gap in both health and economic status may be widening.

The strength, pervasiveness, and persistence of the relationship between SES and health suggests that some common dynamic may be at work. Students in the field have been frustrated by their inability to explain fully the dynamics of the relationship. The following discussion is intended to acknowledge some established findings as well as to suggest some factors and mechanisms that might provide additional insight into the relationship between socioeconomic status and health.

EXPLANATORY MECHANISMS

Socioeconomic status is a multidimensional concept encompassing many different features, including not only material conditions but also social and environmental stressors, resistance and coping resources, and psychological responses. In this section we review some of the evidence for each of these various mechanisms. We will include not only empirical findings but also some of the more tentative propositions about which there appears to be increasing agreement, including some findings and hypotheses from epidemiological and community psychiatric studies as well as some observational accounts of the life of the poor.

Although we focus on the poor, we also are interested in understanding the broader relationship between SES and health. It may be that some factors in the life of the poor may also illuminate the more generic social class gradients. For example, the poor are typically less able to control the conditions of their work and everyday life and have fewer coping resources. These factors may not only underlie the relationship between poverty and health but may also contribute to differences in health at each rung of the socioeconomic ladder.

Stressors

Studies on the relationship between stress and health have encountered numerous conceptual and methodological problems (Thoits 1981; Dohrenwend and Dohrenwend 1974; Levine and Scotch 1970). Much of the recent research on stress has been inspired by the work of Holmes and Rahe (1967), who developed the Social Readjustment Rating Scale based on the recent occurrence of such events as death, loss of job, or change in residence. While this scale represents an important innovation in measuring objective events and in relating these to the onset of subsequent illness, it suffers from various weaknesses (Dohrenwend and Dohrenwend 1974). For example, the scale does not reflect how desirable or undesirable the events included were for the respondents; students in the field have questioned "the advisability of focusing on life events requiring adaptive changes regardless of their social or personal desirability as compared with events which are experienced as threatening or distressing" (Mechanic 1974, p. 91). Moreover, although the scale measures significant acute events, it does not tap various types of chronic or ongoing stressors such as an unhappy marriage, life disappointments, and persistent financial pressures such as long-term debt.

In particular, for our purposes, the scale may omit entirely some events that are more likely to occur in the lives of poor people. For example, "taking out a mortgage would be reflected in higher stress scores . . . while going on welfare would not" (Makosky 1982, p. 36). Such omitted factors may account for some of the inconsistent findings regarding the comparative incidence of stressful events among the poor (see for example Myers et al. 1974, and Markush and Favero 1984).

Stressors may be viewed as stimuli or problems that tax or exceed the organism's routine response capacities. Whether we consider stressors as objective or subjective phenomena, as acute undesirable events, or as chronic burdens, the evidence suggests that the poor have more stressful lives. The lives of the poor appear to be characterized by more disruption and daily struggle as well as more simple physical hardships (Rubin 1976; Myers et al. 1974).

PHYSICAL STRESSORS

The poor encounter more adverse physical and psychological stressors in both their work and residential environments. Lower status jobs tend to be more noisy, hazardous, and physically taxing, as well as less rewarding emotionally and economically. Lower status jobs are more monotonous and less challenging and thus occupants are less satisfied and feel they have less control of their work environment (Berman 1978; Campbell 1981). Within each of the Census Bureau's 17 job categories, work-related accidents are more common among workers earning under $10,000 per year than those earning over $10,000; for farm laborers, the difference is almost fourfold (NCHS 10:133, 1980).

Substandard housing also presents a variety of threats to health (Rainwater 1966). Urban poverty areas are plagued by chemical and air pollution, noise, accidents, and crime. Higher mortality levels in poor neighborhoods are well documented (Nagi and Stockwell 1973; Kitagawa and Hauser 1973; Jenkins 1983).

FINANCIAL STRESSORS

It is a truism that lower status individuals also face more economic pressures and disruptions such as unemployment. These stressors may have emotional and psychological consequences as well as financial ones. People who are unemployed are more likely to report being unhappy and dissatisfied with life, to suffer from insomnia, and to report increased tension in family life (Schlozman and Verba 1978). Recent data from Wisconsin show a clear relation between unemployment and child abuse. In the 51 counties where unemployment rose between 1981 and 1982, 69 percent reported an increase in child abuse. In contrast, in the 21 counties where unemployment fell, child abuse declined 71 percent (Mills 1984).

Not all the results of job loss studies are consistent (Kasl 1984). However, it appears correct to infer that job loss that is not desired and that generates other stressors may be deleterious to health.

POOR HEALTH AS A STRESSOR

We have already discussed social class differentials in health status and have considered the possible impact of poor health on social mobility. What may be glaringly apparent but perhaps not given sufficient attention is that problems of poor health and incidents of previous illness are also stressors. They may not only tax the individual's capacity to cope with new problems but may also weaken the organism's resistance resources and make him/her more vulnerable to future physical illness.

SOCIAL INEQUALITY AS A STRESSOR

There is considerable evidence that those at the bottom of the social hierarchy experience not only greater economic and physical hardships but also differential treatment by every major institution of society. Crimes committed by poor people are more likely to be adjudicated and to be punished more severely than are the crimes of the more affluent (Haskell and Yablonsky 1983). The poor awaiting trial are less likely to be released without bail and are more likely to spend time in jail if convicted

(Light and Keller 1979). Similarly, political and educational institutions may also treat persons of varying socioeconomic backgrounds differentially. For example, schools in the United States employ the practice of "tracking," which divides children into different groupings (slow, average, and bright) based on their aptitude, achievement tests, and the recommendations of teachers. This practice tends to separate students along socioeconomic and racial lines, with the poorer children more frequently encouraged to pursue a vocational or so-called general program and the middle class children assigned to a college preparatory program (Light and Keller 1979).

The poor receive fewer amenities and in general are accorded less honor by society. Being "on the bottom" often entails humiliation in the eyes of the world and a damaging loss of self-esteem and perceived control over one's life (Lindheim and Syme 1983). In a study of 18,403 office-based civil servants in London, Marmot et al. (1984) found threefold differences in mortality between men at the lowest and highest grades of employment, for all major causes of death. The authors attributed these remarkably consistent patterns to a combination of disease-specific factors along with a more general factor related to the psychosocial stress experienced by lower status workers—a combination that increases susceptibility to all illness. We will discuss this in more detail in the next section.

While health inequalities for the poor, the working class, and those in lower status jobs may look roughly similar, we must be aware of course that these groups are not one and the same, nor is any of these groups homogeneous in its composition. In discussing the poor, especially, we must keep in mind that a special stratum of the poor, at the very bottom—what sometimes has been called the "hard core"—may experience unique and even extreme disadvantages in the social structure. Many of our observations about differences in social circumstance and health conditions by SES may be most evident when we examine the bottom stratum.

Resistance Resources and Coping Responses

Our discussion of the types of stressors that may affect health is certainly incomplete but may be sufficient to emphasize the chronicity, relentlessness, pervasiveness, and endemic nature of some of the stressors to which the poor are exposed (Fried 1982). Nevertheless, the mere existence of these stressors is only one component in the causal nexus between socioeconomic status and health.

It is not to be assumed that stressors by their very existence cause disease. As Cassel (1970), Dohrenwend and Dohrenwend (1970, 1974) and others have argued, such a formulation is simplistic, or at least incomplete. A more compelling explanation is that stressors may tend to weaken the resistance of the organism, making people more susceptible and thereby precipitating illness to which they are naturally prone or disposed.

Stressors may also contribute to illness by unleashing inappropriate or unhealthful responses by the individual. Thus, for example, an individual who has experienced the loss of a loved one may begin to smoke and drink more and to neglect his or her health. Or a man who has lost his job may react by abusing the members of his family, thus depriving himself of the support and protection of his most important primary group, thereby making himself more vulnerable to illness. There are also such mediating factors as personality and the social context in which stressors occur. We posit that because the poor suffer more serious and disruptive stressors and, as we will see, have fewer physical, social, or psychological resources with which to cope, they are more apt to become ill. Some interesting models of different causal chains have been provided by those working on the relationship between social class and mental illness, and these models are also suggestive in clarifying processes involved in the etiology of physical disease (Dohrenwend and Dohrenwend 1981).

One fruitful formulation was provided by Antonovsky (1981), who, while denying neither the importance of social stressors nor the existence of differential distributions of stressors among different social and cultural groups, drew attention to another major dimension in the causal sequence. Citing the relative ubiquitousness of stressors, he argued that a crucial question was the differential ability of individuals or groups to avoid or combat various types of stressors, a concept expressed as "generalized resistance resources." Indeed, Antonovsky went further and criticized the so-called emphasis on pathogenesis, an orientation reflecting interest in pathological elements in the etiology of disease, as opposed to salutogenesis, involving the capacities and mechanisms of individuals and groups to retain their health and to resist disease—an orientation he believed requires more attention.

PHYSICAL AND MEDICAL CARE RESOURCES

The poor lack money and other physical resources that are necessary to cope with the stressors they encounter or to follow the prescriptions of those who advocate a change in lifestyle. Poor people, for example, who would like to follow advice to eat more fish may find that the price of fish has risen. For these and other reasons, the poor are more likely to have an inadequate diet. National nutrition surveys indicate that the dietary intake of low income children is more deficient than that of upper income children on virtually every nutritional measure: for example, poor children are 10 to 60 percent more likely to receive inadequate vitamin A and C depending on age, and 30 to 175 percent more likely to receive inadequate calcium (USDHEW 1979).

Similarly, in seeking health care the poor more often encounter problems of distance, inconvenience, and less-available transportation services. By a few measures, such as hospitalization rates and annual number of physician visits, the poor now receive more care than the affluent. These measures are misleading, however, for they confound access with medical need. Measures that take need into account, such as the number of visits per disability day, show that the poor still obtain relatively less medical care than the affluent (Davis et al. 1981). The poor are also less likely to seek care for a given illness episode, and they receive less preventive care. On average, a third fewer low income women receive prenatal care in the first trimester of pregnancy than do upper income women (Aday et al. 1980), and roughly four times as many low income children have never had a physical examination (NCHS 10:110, 1977). Childhood immunizations are also less common among the disadvantaged (Davis et al. 1981; Dutton 1981).

Many of the poor go without basic forms of primary care

which, when provided, yield measurable benefits to health (Starfield 1985; Brunswick 1984; Levine et al. 1983; Hadley 1982). Preventive services are an obvious example. A study of the publicly funded Early Periodic Screening, Detection and Treatment (EPSDT) Program in Pennsylvania found that children previously screened under EPSDT had almost 30 percent fewer abnormalities requiring care upon rescreening (Irwin and Conroy-Hughes 1982). Prenatal care and nutritional supplements for pregnant women are also effective and highly cost-efficient forms of prevention. By reducing the incidence of low birthweight and other adverse outcomes, they help avoid the exorbitant costs of neonatal intensive care, not to mention the lifelong expense of institutionalizing premature babies who suffer mental retardation or other developmental disorders (Institute of Medicine 1985; Showstack et al. 1984; Norris and Williams 1984).

LIFESTYLE

Another reason for the health gap between rich and poor may relate to lifestyle. Alcohol consumption tends to be higher among the less educated (NCHS 15:1, 1981), as does cigarette smoking, at least for men. Both may be seen as maladaptive coping mechanisms. Smoking patterns among women differ, depending on whether SES is measured by education or income, and may be changing over time. In 1976, the proportion of women who smoked increased linearly with income but exhibited a strong inverse U-shaped relationship with education (NCHS 10:131, 1979). National data for 1979 are available only by education and suggest a positive linear relation with education—that is, higher rates of smoking among more-educated women (NCHS 15:1, 1981). For men, in contrast, the proportion who smoke is strongly inversely related to both income and education.

A more affluent lifestyle also typically involves more leisure-time exercise and less obesity. Yet, in at least one study, conventional risk factors did not account for much of the health gap. Michael Marmot and colleagues (1984) observed 50 to 100 percent differences in the relative risk of heart disease mortality among 18,000 London civil servants in different grades of employment, even after adjusting for age, smoking, cholesterol, blood pressure, and leisure activity.

SOCIAL RESOURCES

Social contacts, when absent, may be viewed as a stressor; when present and positive, as a resistance resource. Controlling for a number of prognostic indicators (including clinical variables), Ruberman et al. (1984) found that men who were socially isolated and who had a high degree of life stress had a risk of dying during the three years post–heart attack more than four times as high as men with low levels of both stress and isolation. Education was also a risk factor, but mainly because men with low education tended to have high levels of stress and isolation; controlling for psychosocial factors largely eliminated educational gradients in mortality.

The importance of supportive social relationships was first demonstrated empirically in 1897 by Durkheim in his classic study of factors related to suicide. Cassel (1976) extended this notion to other health problems, noting that individuals without "meaningful social contacts" also tended to have higher rates of tuberculosis, schizophrenia, alcoholism, and accidents. Data reported by Berkman and Syme (1979) suggest that social isolation is a special problem of the poor. In a nine-year study of mortality in Alameda County, California, they found that social support—ties to family and the community—reduced the age-adjusted relative risk of mortality, independent of initial health status, medical care, personal health practices, and SES. But lower income individuals were much less likely to have a large number of social contacts than their more affluent counterparts. There were also socioeconomic gradients in mortality, even within groups with high and low social contacts.

SENSE OF CONTROL

We have already alluded to the poor having less of a sense of control over the conditions of their lives. Rodin (1986), in a review of various studies, describes the positive relation between sense of control and health status and considers the proposition that the strength of the relationship increases with age. She also examines possible mechanisms that may explain the relationship between sense of control and health. These include the effects that sense of control may have on stress, on the neuroendocrine and immune systems, and on health behavior. Intervention studies with older persons lend support to the notion that sense of control contributes to health status and related variables (Rodin 1986).

In an effort to subsume and integrate the various resistance resources that people use to cope and to manage stressors, Antonovsky advanced a central concept of "coherence." He defines the concept of coherence thus: "a global orientation that expresses the extent to which one has a pervasive, enduring though dynamic feeling of confidence that one's internal and external environments are predictable and there is a high probability that things will work out as can reasonably be expected" (Antonovsky 1981, p. 10).

The concept still needs to be made operational and measurable, and reliable indicators of it must be developed. But the concept is appealing and directs our attention to the important role of general resistance resources in managing stress. The poor and other disadvantaged groups, by virtue of their long exposure to endemic and chronic stressors, are likely to have a weaker sense of coherence than those higher on the socioeconomic ladder. We know for example that blacks have much less trust than their white counterparts and tend to perceive themselves as living in a hostile environment (Campbell 1981; Teele 1970)—often with considerable justification.

Because individual preferences for control may vary widely, the most prudent recommendation would be not to force individuals to make choices but rather to offer them options consistent with their preferences for control—as over their medical regimens for example. Nevertheless, the poor will still be at a disadvantage since they tend to have fewer options for control over all aspects of their lives including health care.

Susceptibility

It is logical to assume that the greater burdens and pressures encountered by the poor and their limited resistance resources make them more exhausted and vulnerable to becoming ill and

less effective in dealing with assaults on their health. For example, crowded housing conditions lead to greater stress and less
opportunity for rest, resulting in greater susceptibility to illness
(Gove et al. 1979). That those on the bottom of the class structure may be more worn down by life stressors over time, may
have fewer reserves, and may be more vulnerable once they become ill is also suggested by some research findings. An eight-
year follow-up study of men who had experienced their first
heart attack showed significantly higher mortality from subsequent heart attacks among men on the bottom of the occupational structure, the semiskilled and unskilled, compared with
their middle-class counterparts (Croog and Levine 1982). Studies of survival rates from various forms of cancer suggest a similar pattern. Even when the stage of cancer at first diagnosis is
taken into account, there are consistently lower survival rates
among those in the lower socioeconomic levels (Funch 1985).

Some findings from laboratory studies are of interest. Particularly striking is an experiment by Riley (1975) in which environmental circumstances signficantly affected the onset of illness
in groups of genetically equivalent mice, all infected with a virus
that produces mammary tumors. One group, exposed to standard laboratory conditions, developed the tumors when the
mice were middle-aged, while a group raised in more desirable
conditions (quiet and spacious cages, a nocturnal schedule, and
minimal disturbance) did not develop the tumors until the mice
were near the end of their life span. Environmental conditions
alone determined whether fatal tumors would develop at middle
age or not until old age.

Obviously, these various findings are only suggestive. Biological and other etiological mechanisms have to be identified. We
stress the tentativeness of these findings and interpretations, but
believe that the hypothesis of greater susceptibility to disease
among lower socioeconomic groups deserves closer examination.

METHODOLOGICAL CHALLENGES IN ANALYZING THE
RELATIONSHIP BETWEEN SES AND HEALTH

As the foregoing discussion has emphasized, the various mechanisms involved in the relationship between SES and health do

not operate in isolation from one another but in combination. In other words, it is not so much any single aspect of being poor that undermines health as *the entire experience of being on the bottom of the socioeconomic ladder*, with all of the attendant material, social, and psychological disadvantages. In this section we discuss some of the methodological issues that are confronted in analyzing these potentially interacting and cumulative effects.

Untangling the Causal Nexus

Existing research points to a wide range of possible explanatory mechanisms linking SES and health but sheds little light on how they interact. Does each have a separate, incremental effect on health? Or are some effects synergistic, contingent on others? Do particular mechanisms exacerbate, or suppress, others? Does the overall number and severity of disadvantages borne by low SES groups alter the impact of additional adversities?

We have few answers to such questions. One reason is that many studies have been narrowly focused, addressing only one aspect of the complex causal web of factors linking SES and health—e.g., the effect of exercise on health, occupation on health, etc.—while ignoring other confounding influences. In many cases this narrow focus has been dictated by the limited scope of the data available.

A second reason has to do with the prevailing emphasis on multiple regression-based methods in health services research and contemporary social science. The primary use of such methods has been for estimating the "independent" (also called partial, conditional, or direct) effects of multiple explanatory variables on another so-called "dependent" variable, given certain assumptions about the relationships among these variables. With these methods and with the aid of computers, social scientists seek to approximate statistically the reductionist model of natural science experiments, which assesses what happens if only one thing changes—that is, a single treatment is given in an otherwise controlled environment. The results, however, may be quite different from what a natural or laboratory experiment would yield.

Amid the enthusiasm over the very real advance this capability

conveys, its equally important limitations and assumptions are
frequently overlooked. Too often this powerful new methodology is simply applied to the problem at hand, with little regard
for the assumptions it entails and little effort to determine
whether the statistical model fits the data.

In the case of poverty and health, for example, the assumption
of linear, additive relationships among various correlates of
poverty hypothesized to influence health reflects a particular theoretical view of the cycle of poverty and illness that is empirically unproven and theoretically rather implausible. Indeed,
there is considerable evidence that people may have a kind of
threshold of tolerance beyond which further difficulties take a
disproportionate toll by depriving them of a sense of control. As
we have discussed, the feeling of control appears to be an important determinant of health. If the multiple hardships of poverty
result in a cumulative overload situation with which individuals
are unable to cope, as we propose, then each additional hardship
may have a disproportionate impact on physical or psychological well-being. Because such cumulative effects would be dependent on the overall level and number of other burdens borne,
they would not be captured in the standard linear additive
regression model. They could, of course, be explicitly included
in the regression model with terms representing higher-order
interactions among the various explanatory variables (if the
sample size were large enough), but this is not common practice
among most analysts. Uncritical assumptions of linearity and
additivity too often thwart the search for more complex nonlinear or synergistic effects. In short, the regression model needs to
be chosen with care, and the linear additive model may often be
inappropriate.

Important contingent effects may also exist *among* specific
mechanisms as well as with the overall level of burdens. For example, it was recently reported that, contrary to the assumptions
of most prior empirical research, race and social class interact
significantly in affecting mental health: Race differences in psychological distress are particularly pronounced among people
with low incomes (Kessler and Neighbors 1986). Most prior
studies had been based on the assumption that the effects of race

and social class are additive and thus had estimated these effects estimated with a linear additive regression model. By failing to account for the interaction between class and race, these studies had misestimated the true effects associated with both race and class: Racial effects were underestimated among lower class groups and overestimated among upper class groups, while class effects were underestimated among blacks and overestimated among whites.

Similar contingent relationships are evident in data on infant mortality (Wise 1985) and probably occur for other measures of physical health, as well as for other correlates of class besides race. It seems quite likely, for example, that the effects of adverse environmental conditions are particularly pronounced among low income groups, who lack adequate health monitoring. Poor personal health habits may further magnify these contingent effects. It is not hard to think of many other potential contingent relationships. If not represented explicitly in a multiple regression analysis, such interrelationships will remain hidden and may result in a distorted view of the data.

Even though understanding the causal nexus is one of the central challenges for research on SES and health, relatively few regression-based studies have looked specifically for possible contingent relationships among explanatory mechanisms, and even fewer have incorporated such relationships in multiple regression analyses. Typically, regression analyses simply assume that such interactions do not exist. That is, they assume, often without empirical verification, that each explanatory variable analyzed has an additive, linear effect on health that is unaffected by and unrelated to any of the other variables in the regression equation. This assumption underlies analyses that estimate multiple predictors of health and also analyses that use regression methods to "adjust" for the effects of multiple explanatory variables. Thus, studies with a wide range of explanatory variables may fail to clarify the mechanisms linking SES and health if these mechanisms involve contingent relationships. Even the effectiveness of statistical adjustment procedures is open to question when potential interactions among explanatory variables remain unexamined and unanalyzed.

Typical Limitations of Multiple Regression Applications

It is also worth noting certain common limitations in the application of multiple regression methods that are frequently ignored. First, we often rely on cross-sectional data (data collected at a single point in time) in health services research and the social sciences to estimate effects we would like to interpret as causal; health, for instance, is regressed on income and other variables and the results are interpreted as estimates of how health would be affected if income changed by a certain amount while the other variables in the equation remained constant. In fact, these estimates are based on the relation between income and health at one point in time across the population as a whole. The actual causal relation—how a given individual's health would be affected by a *change* in his or her income—might be quite different for a variety of reasons. Although this distinction is well known to statisticians, it is often neglected in the interpretation of multiple regression results.

A second common limitation is that the assumptions necessary for determining the statistical significance of regression results may not be met by the data being analyzed. These assumptions are quite strict: the dependent variable is assumed to be distributed normally, with constant variance for all values and combinations of the explanatory variables analyzed. Violation of these assumptions will not distort the coefficient estimates themselves, but it can invalidate the associated significance statistics (p-values).

A third limitation stems from the gap that often exists between the effects estimated by regression results and those likely to occur in real life. The regression results are estimates of the changes that would occur if the variables were entirely independent of one another—as for example hair color and first letter of one's surname. It is surprisingly difficult to think of many things that are truly independent in this strict sense, and applications of regression analysis routinely include a number of so-called "independent" variables that do not meet this standard. In practical terms, this means that the supposedly "independent" effects being estimated may not in reality be entirely independent—that is, a change in one variable is unlikely to occur without changes also occurring in the others. Unless the independence of these explanatory variables is substantively plausible—that is, unless it is possible to imagine one factor changing while the others remain the same—then the estimated independent effects are estimates of changes that are never realistically expected to occur.

For most complex social phenomena, single-factor changes are relatively rare. It may be argued, in fact, that even such conceptually distinct components of SES as income, education, and occupation are unlikely, in present society, to change separately, especially without inducing changes in the other components. Across the population as a whole, people with more education tend to have better jobs and higher incomes, and vice versa—a pattern that seems likely to continue for the foreseeable future. For a given individual, furthermore, even if only one component, such as education, changes, it will often produce, at least over time, a change in the others. Thus, when people get more education, they tend to earn more money; and when people earn more money, they (or at least their offspring) frequently seek more education. Such cross-sectional correlations and longitudinal effects highlight the dangers of interpreting regression results as estimates of causal, single-factor changes. In some cases, it may be safer to estimate the effects of changes over time from small-scale longitudinal experiments rather than from large cross-sectional surveys.

A final limitation of multiple regression methods in unraveling the association between poverty and illness is perhaps the most important one. We find, paradoxically, that the estimation of independent effects clarifies mainly what we do *not* understand rather than helping to delineate linkages among the variables measured. An estimated independent effect indicates how much of the total association between a given explanatory variable (say, income) and the dependent variable (say, health), *cannot* be attributed to other variables in the equation—that is, the residual association between income and health not accounted for by the other variables analyzed. Thus, adding successively more explanatory variables to an equation estimating the relative effects of various socioeconomic factors on health steadily reduces the estimated independent effect of income as components of that effect are parceled out among the other variables being added, themselves correlated with income. For variables like income, which are not, strictly speaking, causal but are only proxies for the real causal mechanisms, the estimated independent effects leave both causal as well as correlational linkages entirely unexplained. Many, perhaps most, explanatory variables are not causal in the strict sense; hence their estimated independent effects represent mechanisms the analysis *cannot* explain rather than those it can.

Causal Mechanisms versus "Independent" Effects

Of equal or greater interest, especially for policy purposes, are the effects that *can* be explained by the variables analyzed— namely, the various indirect mechanisms that link explanatory variables to the outcome. In the case of income and health, for example, these mechanisms ("indirect effects") would indicate how income affects health through its association with intervening factors such as medical care, diet, etc. If any of these factors are amenable to policy intervention, they suggest intermediate strategies for reducing illness among low SES groups in the event that the most straightforward approach—improving income, education, or occupation—is politically or socially infeasible.

There are many ways to explore the causal mechanisms linking poverty and illness. The most reliable information can probably be obtained from field research or demonstration projects in which the effects of given changes are assessed through planned social interventions. Head Start, the Neighborhood Health Center Program of the Office of Economic Opportunity, the RAND Health Insurance Experiment, and the Income Maintenance Experiments conducted in the late 1960s and early 1970s are well-known examples of large-scale social experiments (Hunt 1985). Smaller-scale interventions and observational studies may also be useful in revealing the nature of particular mechanisms in local settings.

Another valuable source of information is survey or other data on changes over time. We know relatively little about the specific conditions and circumstances that drive people into poverty in the first place, or those that enable them to escape it. Furthermore, it seems likely that the factors affecting health might differ considerably between families that are newly poor versus those that have been poor for generations. The dynamics of the relationship between poverty and health are poorly understood at present, yet could well be essential in understanding the causal mechanisms involved. Several national data sets include follow-up on the same individuals over time, including the National Health and Nutrition Examination Survey and, by present plan, the National Health Interview Survey conducted annually by the National Center for Health Statistics. In addition, major policy or social changes likely to affect health, which in effect constitute "natural experiments," cry out for longitudinal analysis. State and even national health policy initiatives sometimes change dramatically virtually overnight, too often with little or no systematic evaluation of their impact. Careful assessment of such changes could provide a wealth of information concerning the dynamics of cause and effect among different population groups.

Finally, it may be possible to learn more about causal mechanisms when analyzing cross-sectional data simply by using analytic techniques other than multiple regression. Path analysis and LISREL are two such techniques (Blalock 1971; Joreskog and Sorbom 1984). Both provide formal statistical methods for estimating indirect as well as independent ("direct") effects. They require the analyst to specify a set of multiple regression equations representing the hypothesized causal structure among the variables of interest, including all causal mechanisms, intervening variables, contingent relationships, synergistic effects, etc., believed to exist. This technique often exposes the profound limitations in our understanding of causal mechanisms, but at least it forces us to consider these mechanisms explicitly rather than simply ignoring them and by default assuming linearity and additivity, as in many applications of multiple regression.

Given the hypothesized causal structure, path analytic techniques divide an observed association into direct, indirect, and total (i.e., not due to spurious and/or joint association) effects. The results provide specific estimates for each of the causal pathways represented in the model and also measures of the amount of variance explained. Even if the hypothesized causal structure is crude and incomplete, the estimates may still provide useful insights into the complex network of relationships that underlie most social phenomena. In particular, path analytic techniques proceed from the assumption that variables do not change in isolation from one another but rather as a network of embedded and interacting effects encompassing both the indirect as well as direct components of a given association. They delineate causal mechanisms among measured variables and provide a model of multiple interacting causal relationships that is probably more appropriate for many social phenomena than the assumption of single-factor changes implicit in multiple-regression estimates of independent effects.

Whether we use path analysis or other simpler methods, analyses of the relationship between SES and health would benefit greatly from a more explicit causal conceptualization of the interaction among variables than that offered by the simple linear additive multiple regression model. This is especially important in analyses of large-scale, cross-sectional data sets, where causal inferences depend critically on the validity of the conceptual model employed by the investigator.

The above remarks are intended not as a criticism of multiple regression methods per se, but merely as an effort to underscore some common pitfalls in their application to complex social phenomena like the determinants of health. The assumptions of multiple regression, path analysis, and related methods are demanding; rarely do the complex interrelationships of social reality yield clearly and simply to the strictures of parametric statistics. Compromises are inevitable. But in some cases the very complexity of social reality may hold critical clues to causal mechanisms. We suggest that the potentially cumulative, non-linear, and synergistic effects of the multiple dimensions of poverty offer a fruitful area for further investigation.

Implications for Health Promotion

The view of socioeconomic status as a constellation of features that have an interacting and cumulative impact on health also has implications for strategies of intervention. It suggests, for example, that efforts to counter the health-damaging consequences of poverty will have to be broadly conceived and implemented in order to modify the multiple circumstances and behaviors of the poor that seem to influence health. While traditional forms of health promotion and disease prevention have clearly helped to improve health practices and to ameliorate some of the health problems of the disadvantaged, it is vital to attack the roots of those problems—the social, economic, and environmental conditions of poverty that compromise health and exacerbate illness.

The most obvious and straightforward approach would appear to be simply to abolish poverty and reduce social inequalities. Yet while virtually everyone deplores the greater prevalence of illness among the poor, there is a lack of consensus about proposed approaches. Do we take aim primarily at economic circumstances or at broader measures of inequality? Do we attempt to achieve greater equality in conditions or in opportunity? How much would we wish to compress social stratification? What would the consequences be? Is it a zero-sum situation? And "what is the minimum economic floor to which you will let any individual or family sink regardless of the cause of their failure?" (Thurow 1980, p. 211).

While these questions are certainly beyond the scope of this paper, they indicate how difficult it is to address the problems of social inequality frontally, especially during times when the political climate is unsympathetic. Still, the accomplishments of past social programs are worth remembering. The benefits of Head Start and other special educational programs designed to promote educational attainment have been widely documented (Rohter 1985; Horacek 1985; Geiger 1984; Schorr 1988). Job-training programs and policies to promote full employment have also had an impact, at least within limited population groups; decent jobs are probably what are most missed and wanted by the unemployed and people on welfare. Even some redistribution of income might merit consideration. Most of the investigators involved in the guaranteed-income experiments of the 1960s and early 1970s concluded that the results showed that a guaranteed income would be both economically manageable and socially beneficial (Hunt 1985).

Medicine itself, when freed from its conventional bonds, can help to foster the kinds of fundamental social changes necessary to break the cycle of poverty and illness. Perhaps the most notable example of such an effort was the Neighborhood Health Center Program launched in the mid-1960s. The most ambitious centers—such as the one in Mound Bayou, Mississippi, an extremely poor region of the Mississippi Delta—offered not only the usual clinic services but also a wide variety of basic social and environmental services, ranging from sanitation and housing to transportation and education. For nutritional problems, center doctors wrote prescriptions for food, while other staff helped organize a cooperative vegetable farm. The hope was to create self-sustaining initiatives that would permit the community to lift itself out of impoverishment and dependency (Geiger 1984). While not all of Mound Bayou's pioneering programs survived, its achievements have been impressive. The infant mortality rate dropped 40 percent during the center's first four years, hundreds of residents obtained better housing and sanitary water, and over 100 people earned postsecondary school degrees, including 13 M.D.s, because of health center-sponsored programs in a community where the average education had been four years of school.

The Community Health Center Program (as it is now called) has grown dramatically during the last two decades, surviving both political and professional challenges. By 1982, there were 872 centers around the country serving 4.2 million people (Geiger 1984). These centers have clearly increased access in underserved areas and have improved the health of the populations served (Anderson and Morgan 1973; Gold and Rosenberg 1974; Goldman and Grossman 1981). Studies have shown the quality of medical care to be equal to or better than that provided in traditional settings (Morehead et al. 1971; Sparer and Johnson 1971), and center users have more appropriate and lest costly patterns of utilization: reduced hospitalization, fewer operations, and more ambulatory and preventive care (Reynolds 1976; Davis and Schoen 1978; Freeman et al. 1982; Schwarz and Poppen 1982). Although Community Health Centers have not been uniformly successful, they have shown that medical care, if broadly defined, can attack the roots of disease, as well as the symptoms.

Numerous studies have shown that removal of financial and organizational barriers to medical care reduces or eliminates traditional socioeconomic and racial gradients in access (Shapiro et al. 1982; Dutton 1978; Reissman 1974). But conventional medical care, even if equitably distributed, will not solve the health problems of the poor. Patterns of utilization in Great Britain's National Health Service have been considerably more equal than in the United States for over three decades, yet the 1980 *Black Report* showed that social class differentials in health are wider now than they were when the Health Service was established in 1948. The report attributed these differentials not to failings of the Health Service, but rather to the many other social inequalities that impinge on health, and it called for a broad strategy of social policy measures to combat them. It is just such a multifaceted approach, of course, that Community Health Centers have tried to take.

Health promotion programs can also attack dysfunctional health practices and certain largely nonmedical problems, but they too must be broadly defined and implemented if they are to counteract the formidable and pervasive effects of lower socioeconomic status. Changes in health status are unlikely to be achieved by piecemeal efforts or by the mere dissemination of information. Despite the abundant evidence from social science research demonstrating the limits of the transmission of information as a way of modifying behavior—behavior which is deeply embedded in the social and cultural structure of people's lives—health promotion efforts too often rely heavily, sometimes solely, on information as the major change strategy (Becker 1979). Information is important, of course, but mainly when individuals perceive the need to make use of the information they receive.

The importance of a broadly conceived approach aimed at changing attitudes as well as modifying behavior is illustrated by the success of a number of anti-cigarette-smoking campaigns carried out in the past twenty years. Sparked by the Surgeon General's 1964 Report, these campaigns have not been one-shot affairs but persistent efforts from many different sources. The people who were encouraging the cessation of smoking were highly credible and enjoyed considerable prestige in society; important values were appealed to, such as the health effects on children; the campaign took place in the context of an emphasis upon ecology; people were rewarded for stopping smoking; and the important primary group, the family, was often involved in the effort. Finally, laws and regulations were instituted. All these, together, made the anti-cigarette-smoking campaigns effective among most population groups (Levine 1981).

It is important to observe, however, that males in the lower socioeconomic groups continue to smoke (and drink) disproportionately. As Hart states, "The failure of health education to make the same impact on the manual working class as elsewhere in the population may be because smoking remains closely interwoven with the culture of everyday life" (Hart 1986). Hart points out that "manual workers are younger when they make the transition from school to work—perhaps this is why they have greater need of external symbols of status and change." She contrasts this transition with that of the middle class, for whom job entry is less likely to be a one-time event but instead to involve continuing career developments and additional education and training. Accordingly, Hart argues that there is less symbolic value for smoking in the middle class. In short, attention must be paid to ways in which behavior is embedded in the social and cultural aspects of life. One must also consider the social forces that tend to propagate smoking and other unhealthful behaviors. Syme and Guralnick (1986) draw attention to the heavy advertising efforts and the extent to which the tobacco industry has gone to create an attractive atmosphere for smoking by young people.

If, as we suggest, working-class people, especially the poor, are constantly dealing with overwhelming and persistent stressors and have limited resources with which to cope, they may not be as able or willing to heed the advice of health educators and health promoters. Pervasive and sustained health education programs are required. Yet it is important to realize that people may want very much to follow desirable health practices but are impeded by circumstances they cannot control. As Brown (1987) reminds us, while there may be inadequate information about nutrition in the general population, there is little evidence that the problem of misinformation is markedly more severe among the poor. The poor certainly know about smoking as a health hazard and they also have some good information about nutrition. Indeed, as Brown points out, some evidence suggests that poor people actually purchase more nutritious food than the rest of the population and think a lot about how to stretch their food dollar. He argues that the recent surge of hunger in the United States cannot be explained by the presumed ignorance of the poor.

From our analysis of the stressors and resistance resources of the poor, we offer the following propositions:

- Poor health is interwoven with the position of the poor in the social structure and the larger cultural system to which they belong. As social and economic inequality changes, the relative health status of the poor will change. This is not easily achieved in some political climates, but is worth working toward.

- A second line of approach that may be easier to implement is to modify some of the key social circumstances that impinge disproportionately on lower income groups and affect health status. For example, it may be possible to mitigate the stress of manual and clerical workers by appropriate modifications in the work environment. It may also be possible to lessen the tensions working parents face through provision of child-care services. Other critical interventions could include providing poor children with nutritious school lunches and removing impediments to the receipt of adequate health care by needy populations.

  Attention could also be given to the environments of the poor that may undermine their sense of control and coherence. For example, people who seek assistance from public service agencies often encounter endless delays and frustration that tend to undermine their sense of control and coherence. It may be possible to strengthen the coping skills of the disadvantaged and their sense of control by designing health and other human service organizations that are more responsive and dependable.

- Finally, we must use consistent and sustained approaches that address the daily concerns and life circumstances of the poor. We know that established health practices are not eas-

ily altered by one-shot educational campaigns. Policies intended to improve the health of the poor must be consistent. As we are imploring the poor to relinquish cigarettes,
we should demonstrate our consistency by removing carcinogens in the workplace and in the residential environment. As we ask the poor to avoid fatty foods and excessive
sodium, we should make sure that the poor have enough to
eat in the first place. By demonstrating consistency in various aspects of health policy, we may not only be more effective in encouraging the poor to improve their health
practices but may also achieve health benefits over which
they as individuals have no control.

Although there is much that we do not understand about the
mechanisms linking socioeconomic status and health, we do
know that the relationship is strong, persistent, and virtually
ubiquitous. To alter that relationship will no doubt require action on numerous fronts. While some improved health practices
can be achieved through health promotion efforts, this would
solve only part of the problem. Changes are also needed in the
multiple social, psychological, and environmental circumstances that reinforce and perpetuate the cycle of poverty and illness.
Only through such broadly structured interventions is this vi-
cious cycle likely to be be broken.

NOTES

1. It should be noted that poor health *in utero* and in the early
   years of life may both reduce educational attainment and
   lead to ill health later in life, another form of reverse causation. However, an empirical investigation of the relation
   between early life cycle health and schooling found no firm
   evidence that the disabled differed significantly in either
   their educational choices or rates of attrition (Shakotko and
   Grossman 1982). The relationship between health and race,
   of course, is not subject to these mutually reinforcing effects, since race does not change.
2. A few children's conditions reported by parents appear to be
   more prevalent among affluent children than among the
   poor (e.g., allergies and tension), although this may be due

in part to differential recognition and reporting by the parents (Edwards and Grossman 1982).

REFERENCES

Aday, L. A., Andersen, R., Fleming, G. 1980. *Health care in the U.S.: equitable for whom?* Beverly Hills, CA: Sage.

Anderson, R. E., Morgan, S. 1973. *Comprehensive health care: a southern view.* Atlanta: Southern Regional Council.

Antonovsky, A. 1980. *Health, stress, and coping.* San Francisco: Jossey-Bass.

Bailit, H., Newhouse, J., Brook, R., et al. 1987. *Does more generous dental insurance coverage improve oral health?* Santa Monica, CA: The RAND Corporation.

Becker, M. 1979. Psychosocial aspects of health-related behavior. In Levine, S., Freeman, H. E., Reeder, L. G., eds. *Handbook of medical sociology.* 3rd ed. Englewood Cliffs, NJ: Prentice-Hall.

Berkman, L. F., Syme, S. L. 1979. Social networks, host resistance, and mortality: a nine-year follow-up study of Alameda County residents. *American Journal of Epidemiology* 109(2): 186–204.

Berman, D. M. 1978. *Death on the job: occupational health and safety struggles in the United States.* New York: Monthly Review Press.

Black Report. Inequalities in health: report of a research working group. 1980. Great Britain: Department of Health and Social Services.

Blalock, H. M., Jr. 1971. *Causal models in the social sciences.* Chicago: Aldine.

Brown, J. L. 1987. Hunger in the U.S. *Scientific American* 256(2):37–41.

Brunswick, A. F. 1984. Effects of medical intervention in adolescence: a longitudinal study of urban black youth. *Youth and Society* 16(1):3–28.

Campbell, A. 1981. *The sense of well-being in America: recent patterns and trends.* New York: McGraw-Hill.

Cassel, J. 1970. Physical illness in response to stress. In Levine, S., Scotch, N. A., eds. *Social stress.* Chicago: Aldine.

———. 1976. The contribution of the social environment to

host resistance. *American Journal of Epidemiology* 104(2):107–
123.

Chartbook, Sept. 1977. PHS, Office of Health Resources Opportunity, Health of the Disadvantaged. DHEW Pub. No.
(HRA)77–628. Hyattsville, MD: Dept. of Health, Education, and Welfare.

Croog, S. H., Levine, S. 1977. *The heart patient recovers.* New
York: Human Sciences Press.

———. 1982. *Life after a heart attack.* New York: Human Sciences
Press.

Davis, K., Schoen, C. 1978. *Health and the war on poverty: a ten-
year appraisal.* Washington, D. C.: The Brookings Institution.

Davis, K., Gold, M., Makuc, D. 1981. Access to health care for
the poor: does the gap remain? *Annual Review of Public Health*
2:159–182.

Dohrenwend, B. S., Dohrenwend, B. P. 1970. Class and race as
status-related sources of stress. In Levine, S., Scotch, N. A.,
eds. *Social stress.* Chicago: Aldine.

———, eds. 1974. *Stressful life events: their nature and effects.* New
York: Wiley.

Dohrenwend, B. P., Dohrenwend, B. S. 1981. Socioenvironmental factors, stress, and psychopathology. *American Journal
of Community Psychology* 9(2):128–159.

Dutton, D. B. 1978. Explaining the low use of health services by
the poor: costs, attitudes, or delivery systems? *American Sociological Review* 43:348–368.

———. 1981. Children's health care: the myth of equal access.
In *Better health for our children: a national strategy.* The report of
the select panel for the promotion of child health to the U.S.
Congress and the Secretary of Health and Human Services,
Vol. IV—Background papers (January): 357–440.

———. 1986. Social class, health, and illness. In Aiken, L. H.,
Mechanic, D., eds. *Applications of social science to clinical medi-
cine and health policy*, pp. 31–62. New Brunswick, NJ: Rutgers
University Press.

Edsall, T. B. 1984. *The new politics of inequality.* New York:
W. W. Norton.

Egbuonu, L., Starfield, B. 1982. Child health and social status
Pediatrics 69(5):550–557.

Freeman, H. E., Kiecolt, K. J., Allen, H. M. 1982. Community health centers: an initiative of enduring utility. *Milbank Memorial Fund Quarterly/Health and Society* 60(2):245–267.

Fried, M. 1982. Endemic stress: the psychology of resignation and the politics of scarcity. *American Journal of Orthopsychiatry* 52(1):4–19.

Funch, D. P., 1985. A report on cancer survival in the economically disadvantaged. Report prepared for the American Cancer Society Subcommittee on Cancer in the Economically Disadvantaged.

Gallup, G. 1984. One of every 5 adults in U.S. can't always afford food. *San Francisco Chronicle*, March 19, p. 7.

Geiger, H. J. 1984. Community health centers: health care as an instrument of social change. In Sidel, V., Sidel, R., eds. *Reforming medicine: lessons of the last quarter century*. New York: Pantheon.

Gold, M. R., Rosenberg, R. G. 1974. The use of emergency room services by the population of a neighborhood health center. *Health Services Reports* 89:65–70.

Goldman, F., Grossman, M. Nov. 1981. The responsiveness and impacts of public health policy: the case of community health centers. Paper presented at the American Public Health Association Annual Meeting. Los Angeles.

Gove, W. R., Hughes, M., Galle, O. R. 1979. Overcrowding in the home: an empirical investigation of its possible pathological consequences. *American Sociological Review* 44:59–80.

Hadley, J. 1982. *More medical care, better health?* Washington, D.C.: Urban Institute Press.

Hart, N. 1986. Inequalities in health: the individual versus the environment. *Journal of the Royal Statistical Society*, Series A (general), 149(3):228–246.

Haskell, M. R., Yablonsky, L. 1983. *Criminology*. 3rd ed. Boston: Houghton-Mifflin.

Health Resources Administration. 1979. Health status of minorities and low-income groups. DHEW Pub. No. (HRA) 79–627. Washington, D.C.: G.P.O.

Holmes, T. H., Rahe, R. H. 1967. The social readjustment rating scale. *Journal of Psychosomatic Research* 11:213–218.

Horacek, H. J. Nov. 1985. Predicting school failure before birth.

Paper presented at the Robert Wood Johnson Annual Meeting, Scottsdale, AZ.

Hunt, M. 1985. Twenty thousand volunteers. In *Profiles of social research: the scientific study of human interactions*, pp. 247–296. New York: Russell Sage Foundation.

Institute of Medicine. Jan. 1985. The prevention of low birthweight. Report of the Committee to Study the Prevention of Low Birthweight. Washington, D.C.: National Academy Press.

Irwin, P. H., Conroy-Hughes, R. 1982. EPSDT impact on health status: estimates based on secondary analysis of administratively generated data. *Medical Care* 20(2):216–234.

Jenkins, C. D. 1983. Social environment and cancer mortality in men. *New England Journal of Medicine* 308(7):395–398.

Joreskog, K. G., Sorbom, D. 1984. *LISREL VI: analysis of linear structural relationships by the method of maximum likelihood (user's guide)*. 4th ed. Mooresville, IN: Scientific Software.

Kasl, S. V. 1984. Stress and health. *Annual Review of Public Health* 5:319–341.

Kelsey, J. L. 1984. Prevalence studies of the epidemiology of osteoarthritis. In Lawrence, R., Shulman, L., eds. *Epidemiology of the rheumatic diseases*, pp. 282–288. New York: Gower Medical Publishing.

Kessler, R. C., Neighbors, H. W. 1986. A new perspective on the relationships among race, social class, and psychological distress. *Journal of Health and Social Behavior* 27:107–15.

Kitagawa, E. M., Hauser, P. M. 1973. *Differential mortality in the United States*. Cambridge, MA: Harvard University Press.

Levine, S., Scotch, N. A. 1970. *Social stress*. Chicago: Aldine.

Levine, S. 1981. Preventive health behavior. In Wechsler, H., Lamont-Havers, R., Cahill, G., eds. *The Social context of medical research*. Cambridge, MA: Ballinger.

———, Feldman, J. J., Elinson, J. 1983. Does medical care do any good? In Mechanic, D., ed. *Handbook of health, health care, and the health professions*. New York: The Free Press.

Light, D., Jr., Keller, S. 1979. *Sociology*. 2nd ed. New York: Alfred A. Knopf.

Lindheim, R., Syme, S. 1983. Environments, people and health. *Annual Review of Public Health* 4:335–359.

Maine Department of Human Services. Children's deaths in Maine. America's Children Project, Office of the Commissioner, Maine Department of Human Services. State House Station 11, Augusta, ME 04333.

Makosky, V. P. 1982. Sources of stress: events or conditions? In Belle, D., ed. *Lives in stress.* Beverly Hills, CA: SAGE Publications.

Mare, R. D. 1982. Socioeconomic effects on child mortality in the United States. *American Journal of Public Health.* 72(6):539–547.

Markush, R. E., Favero, R. V. 1974. Epidemiologic assessment of stressful life events, depressed mood, and psychophysiological symptoms—a preliminary report. In Dohrenwend, B. S., Dohrenwend, B. P., eds. *Stressful life events: their nature and effects.* New York: Wiley.

Marmot, M. G., Adelstein, A. D., Robinson, N., Rose, G. A., 1978. Changing social-class distribution of heart disease. *British Medical Journal* (October 21):1109–1112.

Marmot, M. G., Shipley, M. J., Rose, G. 1984. Inequalities in death: specific explanations of a general pattern? *Lancet* 1:1003–1006.

Marmot, M. G., McDowall, M. E. 1986. Mortality decline and widening social inequalities. *Lancet* 2: 274–76.

Marmot, M. G., Kogevinas, M., Elston, M. A. 1987. Social/economic status and disease. *Annual Review of Public Health* 8:111–135.

Mechanic, D. 1974. Discussion of research programs on relations between stressful life events and episodes of physical illness. In Dohrenwend, B. S., Dohrenwend, B. P., eds. *Stressful life events: their nature and effects.* New York: Wiley.

Mills, D. 1984. *Statement on impact of unemployment on children and families.* Hearing before the Subcommittee on Labor Standards of the Committee on Education and Labor, House of Representatives, 98th Congress, 1st Session, January 31, 1983, pp. 14–24. Washington, D.C.: G.P.O.

Morehead, M. A., Donaldson, R. S., Servall, M. R. 1971. Comparisons between OEO neighborhood health centers and other health care providers of ratings of the quality of health care. *American Journal of Public Health* 61:1294–1306.

Morris, N. 1986. All change on Thatcher's poverty line. *Guardian*, November 26, p. 27.

Myers, J. K., Lindenthal, J. J., Pepper, M. P. 1974. Social class, life events and psychiatric symptoms. In Dohrenwend, B. S., Dohrenwend, B. P., eds. *Stressful life events: their nature and effects*, pp. 191–205. New York: Wiley.

Nagi, M. H., Stockwell, E. G. 1973. Socioeconomic differentials in mortality by cause of death. *Public Health Reports* 88(5):449–456.

National Center for Health Statistics. 1973. Examination and health history findings among children and youths 6–17 years, United States. Series 11, No. 129, Public Health Service. Rockville, MD.

———. 1977. Use of selected medical procedures associated with preventive care, United States, 1973. Series 10, No. 110, Public Health Service. Rockville, MD.

———. 1979. Use habits among adults of cigarettes, coffee, aspirin and sleeping pills, United States, 1976. Series 10, No. 131, Public Health Service. Rockville, MD.

———. 1979. Basic data on arthritis: knee, hip and sacroiliac joints in adults ages 25–74 years, United States, 1971–75. Series 11, No. 213, Public Health Service. Rockville, MD.

———. 1980. Selected health characteristics by occupation, United States, 1975–76. Series 10, No. 133, Public Health Service. Rockville, MD.

———. 1981. Highlights from wave I of the national survey of personal health practices and consequences: United States, 1979. Series 15, No. 1, Public Health Service. Rockville, MD.

———. 1982. Annual summary of births, deaths, marriages, and divorces: United States, 1981. Series 30, No. 13, Public Health Service. Rockville, MD.

———. 1983. Americans assess their health: United States, 1978. Series 10, No. 142, Public Health Service. Rockville, MD.

National Health Law Program. 1982. Factual memorandum and arguments in support of petition for rulemaking: for rules and regulations to declare prenatal care a public health service and to establish standards for access to such care by low-income women. Xerox copy, National Health Law Program, Los Angeles.

Norris, F. D., Williams, R. L. 1984. Perinatal outcomes among medicaid recipients in California. *American Journal of Public Health* 74(10):1112–1117.

Pear, R. 1985. Study finds poverty among children is increasing. *New York Times*, May 23, p. 1.

Price, D. 1984. U.S. families face more poverty. *San Francisco Examiner and Chronicle*, March 11, p. A9.

Rainwater, L. 1966. Fear and the house-as-haven in the lower class. *Journal of the American Institute of Planning* 32:23–31.

Reissman, C. K. 1974. The use of health services by the poor. *Social Policy* 5:41–49.

Reynolds, R. A. 1976. Improving access to health care among the poor—the neighborhood health center experience. *Milbank Memorial Fund Quarterly/Health and Society* 54(1):47–82.

Rhoter, L. 1985. Study stresses preschool benefits. *New York Times*, April 9, p. 15.

Riley, V. 1975. Mouse mammary tumors: alteration of incidence as apparent function of stress. *Science* 189:465–467.

Rodin, J. 1986. Aging and health: effects of the sense of control. *Science* 233:1271–1276.

Rose, G., Marmot, M. G. 1981. Social class and coronary heart disease. *British Heart Journal* 45:13–19.

Ruberman, W., Weinblatt, E., Goldberg, J. D., Chaudhary, B. S. 1984. Psychosocial influences on mortality after myocardial infarction. *New England Journal of Medicine* 311(9):552–559.

Rubin, L. B. 1976. *Worlds of pain: life in the working-class family.* New York: Basic Books.

Schlozman, K. L., Verba, S. 1978. The new unemployment: does it hurt? *Public Policy* 26(3):333–358.

Schorr, L. B., with Schorr, D. B. 1988. *Within our reach: breaking the cycle of disadvantage.* New York: Anchor Books.

Schwarz, R., Poppen, P. 1982. Measuring the impact of CHCs on pregnancy outcomes. Final Report, Contract No. 240-81-0041, Health Resources and Services Administration, Rockville, MD.

Shakotko, R. A., Grossman, M. 1982. Physical disabilities and post-secondary educational choices. In Fuchs, V., ed. *Economic aspects of health*, pp. 185–203. National Bureau of Economic Research. Chicago: University of Chicago Press.

Shapiro, S., Venet, W., Stax, P., et al. 1982. Prospects for eliminating racial differences in breast cancer survival rates. *American Journal of Public Health* 72(10):1142–1145.

Showstack, J. A., Budetti, P. P., Minkler, D. 1984. Factors associated with birthweight: an exploration of the roles of prenatal care and length of gestation. *American Journal of Public Health* 74(9):1003–1008.

Sparer, G., Johnson, J. 1971. Evaluation of OEO neighborhood health centers. *American Journal of Public Health* 61:931–942.

Starfield, B. 1985. *Effectiveness of medical care: validating clinical wisdom*. Baltimore, MD: The Johns Hopkins University Press.

Subcommittee on Oversight and Investigations of the Committee on Energy and Commerce. 1984. Infant mortality rates: failure to close the black-white gap. U.S. House of Representatives, 98th Congress, Second Session, Serial No. 98–131. Washington, D.C.: G.P.O.

Surgeon General. 1979. Healthy people: the Surgeon General's report on health promotion and disease prevention, 1979. DHEW, Public Health Service, Pub. No. 79–55071. Washington, D.C.: G.P.O.

Syme, S. L., Berkman, L. F. 1976. Social class, susceptibility, and sickness. *American Journal of Epidemiology* 104:1–8.

Syme, S. L., Guralnik, J. 1987. Epidemiology and health policy: coronary heart disease. In Levine, S., Lilienfeld, A., eds. *Epidemiology and health policy*. New York: Tavistock Publications.

Teele, J. 1970. Social pathology and stress. In Levine, S., Scotch, N. A., eds. *Social stress*. Chicago: Aldine.

Thoits, P. 1981. Undesirable life events and psychophysiological distress: a problem of operational confounding. *American Sociological Review* 46(1):97–109.

Thurow, L. C. 1980. *The zero-sum society*. New York: Basic Books.

———. 1987. A surge in inequality. *Scientific American* 256(5):30–37.

Townsend, P., Davidson, N., eds. 1982. *Inequalities in health: the Black Report*. Harmondsworth, England: Penguin Books.

U.S. Bureau of Census. Aug. 1984. Current Population Reports, Series P-60, No. 145: Money income and poverty status of families and persons in the U.S.: 1983, p. 1. Washington, D.C.: G.P.O.

USDHEW. Sept. 1979. Dietary intake source data, U.S. 1971–74. DHEW Pub. No. (PHS)79–1221. Hyattsville, MD: Department of Health, Education, and Welfare.

Whitehead, M. 1987. *The health divide: inequalities in health in the 1980s*. London: The Health Education Council.

Wise, P. H., Kotelchuck, M., Wilson, M. L., et al. 1985. Racial and socioeconomic disparities in childhood mortality in Boston. *New England Journal of Medicine* 313:360–366.

Comments on Chapter 3

Mark R. Cullen

After reviewing the basic data that proves the inverse and robust relationship between measures of SES and measures of health outcome, this paper focuses on several potential methodologic problems in attempting to elucidate the roles of specific, and ideally more remediable, factors that contribute to the relationship. The two major limitations identified—the necessary simplification inherent in multiple regression analyses, and the limitation of cross-sectional data sets in making inferences about causality—are unarguable, and the authors make a cogent case for the fact that these methodologic difficulties may be particularly troublesome in the study of health effects caused by the complex circumstances involved in poverty.

Having laid this foundation, however, the inferences the authors draw do not necessarily follow. If indeed the causal variables are themselves mutually interactive, then it is true that modification of some in isolation of others may be *difficult* (this is not original). If, on the other hand, the variables are interactive (e.g., synergistic) regarding their impact on the outcomes (i.e., health), the implication that individual interventions are unlikely to affect outcome is incorrect. In fact, synergy of this type implies that small changes in any one variable will have a disproportionate, magnified impact on outcome, such as the value of smoking cessation in workers previously exposed to asbestos.

Thus, while I agree that understanding the interactions among causal and outcome variables is crucial if health of the lower SES groups is to be modified (short of modifying their SES itself), the goal should be isolation of those factors that are large contributors, *especially* if they interact with other factors less amenable to changes.

Mary N. Haan

The central theme of this paper seems to be that those in the lowest SES strata are beset with a multiplicity of social, psychological, and physical problems and that they lack the psychological, social, and material resources needed to cope with them. While I certainly agree that the association between SES and health is a multifaceted one, I think that the focus on the poor—on those at highest risk—will lead us toward different research questions and interventions than a focus on the overall SES health gradient.

Recognition of this gradient in research and intervention is important because first, it tells us that the risk is widely distributed, albeit unevenly, and is unlikely to be due to endogenous individual characteristics of members of the highest risk group; second, it tells us that whatever combinations of risk factors could be "causing" this association must be distributed across SES strata in a way consistent with the risk distribution.

In other words, one might ask the question: even if the poor are at highest risk because they lack coping ability or they can't get medical care, why are the middle strata at higher risk than the upper strata? Is there any reason to assume that coping ability or medical care is inferior in the middle compared to the upper strata? This seems unlikely. In short, there needs to be some explanatory strategy that can encompass all dimensions of the SES-health association.

A focus on the high-risk bottom also leads us toward examining charactersitics of members of that group and designing interventions that will shore up the poor by, for example, training them to cope better with inevitable problems they face as members of a high-risk group. The intervention once again becomes an issue of changing the way the poor handle problems rather than changing the definition of the problem and the kind of problems faced by the poor (or anyone else lacking perfect freedom). If we focus on the gradient, the SES-health link becomes at least somewhat of a problem for virtually everyone. If it is a problem for virtually everyone, then social welfare programs, for example, will reflect this by providing for minimum standards of income, health care, and other benefits for all members of society. If SES is seen as a problem just for the poor, the intervention must seek to discriminate between the poor and non-poor, e.g., means tests, and prevent the near poor or the lower middle class from seeking help from entitlement programs. If the problem belongs to everyone, either directly or indirectly, then the solutions will not lie principally in investigating and changing individual or group characteristics of the poor, but in identifying and changing environmental characteristics that produce increased risk for everyone.

George A. Kaplan

At the core of Dutton and Levine's approach to explaining the association between SES and health is the notion of lower socioeconomic status leading to a sense of "beleaguerment"/loss of control. Although I have little disagreement either with much of the evidence they present or with some of their conclusions, the focus on this phenomenological endpoint leads to certain problems.

How are we to understand the beleaguerment/loss of control (B-LOC) notion? The most common approach is one that conceptualizes it as a generalized cognitive state with which the individual views the world. This is a very popular model in contemporary psychology and one that has led to numerous interventions to change the ways in which people think about problems. Thus individuals are seen as having generalized modes of cognition that guide their attempts to explain the world. If these modes are maladaptive, then the solution is psychotherapy of one sort or another.

It is instructive to consider some of the history of related notions. In the mid-1960s, Seligman and his colleagues at the University of Pennsylvania performed a number of experiments in which they subjected dogs to uncontrollable shock. Compared to dogs exposed to the same and controllable amount of shock, these animals adopted a particular form of behavior that was labeled "learned helplessness." Thus an environmental manipulation induced a "cognitive-behavioral" state in the animal. In the

years since these experiments, the notions of learned helplessness, sense of control, self-efficacy, and other similar concepts
have become very popular. But instead of being viewed as a
consequence of an environmental manipulation, these states are
now seen as personality-type attributes. Thus an environmental
problem is transformed into an individual problem.

I do not think that Dutton and Levine intend to take on such a
focus, but I would submit that concepts such as B-LOC very
often lead to a conceptualization of the problem as residing
within the individual rather than in the environment. This view
of course ignores the fact that individuals come and go, but the
groups they belong to continue to show high risk. When such a
view is adopted, the observation that these patterns of cognition
are socially patterned and that they are consequences of social
structure is lost. Interventions then get directed at the consequences of the problem, not the source. Although changing
how people feel, empowering them, may have many positive
consequences, discussions that focus on the phenomenological
outcome of deprivation may end up excluding the physical and
social environment as a locus of intervention. This is a position I
believe we need to guard against adopting.

In another vein, much of Dutton and Levine's discussion centers on those at the bottom of the socioeconomic scale. Yet we
see gradients almost everywhere we look. These gradients present a real challenge to our understanding, and a test of any explanatory attempt. Is it the case, for example, that there are gradients of B-LOC by socioeconomic level? If there are such data,
it would be nice to know.

Finally, I would agree that the statistical modeling of socioeconomic effects on health must adopt more than a simple main-
effects approach. However, I would add that a statistical model
is not to be confused with the underlying biological process that
converts different levels of socioeconomic position to better or
worse health. In my view, such models should be taken as high-
lighting the conceptual relationships involved. The true causal
model will have to be one that specifies the social and environmental pathways that allow socioeconomic position to get under
the skin.

Lincoln Moses

Let me begin with two apparently unrelated remarks, which however lead me to look in the same direction.

First, we are told early in the paper that the "separate influences" of education and income can be distinguished because at fixed levels of either a trend of health upon the other can be seen. The data (these trends) do not imply (necessarily) separate influences of either one. For example, suppose there is a single underlying quality u (competence? coherence? social privilege? information-processing skill? . . .) and that income, education, and health all have positive linear correlations with u, and no other dependence whatsoever. Then at any fixed level of income a positive trend of health upon education will will be seen, etc. The reason is that when we fix income we do not entirely fix u, we only restrict its range to some extent; and at the various values of u among those subjects at the fixed income level, education and health will vary together and a trend will be seen. (The argument can be confirmed algebraically by computing the partial correlation of education and health for fixed incomes, when all three simple correlations arise solely from each variable consisting of some multiple of u plus error.

Second, in the section on SES gradients relating to sex and age, it is indicated that poverty takes hold on health very early in life because poor infants and children have adverse rates of various kinds. This seems to me to gloss over the nature of the probable situation—viz, by the time poor people become parents they have arrived at a state where adverse experience among their offspring is more common than average. This formulation allows that the processes *may* begin in infancy, or that they *might* be wholly delayed until young adulthood, or yet to some intermediate age.

It seems to me that we may gain from looking for *one* (or possibly as many as two or three) complex constructs, high values of which tend to promote high educational status, high income, and good health. Such a complex construct might be: "coherence," information-seeking and information-processing behavior, "physiological reserve," access to successful life models, absence of self-destructive orientation, ...

If we had a few such promising constructs to work with, then how should we proceed further? Deep biographical interviews? Questionnaire studies? Experiments? (I doubt statistical analysis of existing data could take us far.) Sooner or later we would need to give an operational definition to the constructs, and learn how to measure them. If very fortunate, we might eventually even see how to modify and improve a person's (or a population's) values of the underlying variables.

4. Socioeconomic Status and Health: Old Observations and New Thoughts

Mary N. Haan, George A. Kaplan,
and S. Leonard Syme

INTRODUCTION

Observations of a positive association between socioeconomic position (SES) and health are not new, extending back to the 12th century (Antonovsky 1967; Syme and Berkman 1976). Inquiry into these matters is found in the 1826 investigation of Villerme into the relationship between rent level and mortality in Paris and in Farr's work in 1851 on differences in mortality in England by occupation (Susser et al. 1985). Since these early reports, variations in disease risk by level of SES have been noted but seldom explained. Indeed, the ubiquitous nature of these findings paradoxically has led to the exclusion of SES as a subject of inquiry. Instead of being the subject of investigation in its own right, SES is often seen as a background characteristic similar to age and sex, a characteristic that must be included in analyses but that is seldom addressed directly.

The purpose of this paper is to refocus attention on the association between SES and health in hopes of stimulating explanations for this phenomenon. First, we will consider the consistency over time and place of the relationship between SES and health. From this review, we will identify features of the association that can guide a search for explanations. Finally, we will assess alternative explanations currently being proposed and offer our own. In order to facilitate discussion, this report also includes a chartbook of selected studies (Figures 1–26), which appears at the end of this chapter, and an annotated bibliography of recent reports on SES and health, which appears at the end of this volume.

REVIEW

We have found it both convenient and instructive to organize our review of SES and health according to stages of the life span. Not only is this organization logically clear, it illustrates the continuing influence of SES on health throughout the life span.

Infancy and Childhood

We have found evidence that the association between SES and health status persists from birth to death. With regard to infants and children, there are a large number of studies that indicate variations in health risk by level of SES. Figure 1 presents a good example from Sweden of the associations often observed between birth outcomes and SES (Ericson et al. 1979). In this study of almost 200,000 births that occurred in 1976–1977, SES was inversely associated with perinatal mortality, prematurity, low birthweight, small size for gestational age, and late (>43 weeks) birth. These results from Sweden are particularly impressive when one considers the low rates of these outcomes in Sweden relative to other countries. This study used a summary measure of SES based on census information on mother's education, family income, quality and type of housing, and number of family members.

Other studies have reported similar findings based on mother's or father's occupation (Antonovsky and Bernstein 1977; Murrells et al. 1985; Rantakallio 1979; Rush and Cassano 1983), income (Antonovsky and Bernstein 1977; Starfield and Budetti 1982), or education (Antonovsky and Bernstein 1977; Gortmaker 1979; Kitagawa and Hauser 1973; McCormick 1985; Rantakallio 1979), or on census tract or other area indicators of these measures (Antonovsky and Bernstein 1977; Brennen and Lancashire 1978; Brooks 1975; Ericson et al. 1979; Hadley and Osei 1982; Kraus and Redford 1975; Simpson 1984). Figure 2 shows the relationship between maternal and paternal education and rates of perinatal death for six states in the United States in 1973

(World Health Organization 1985). Similar results for education, social class, and income, respectively, are presented in Figures 3–5 for Finland (Rantakallio 1979); England and Wales
(Morris 1979); and San Antonio, Texas (Markides and Barnes
1977). Other studies have shown that SES is related to a large
number of other mortality and morbidity outcomes in children
(Brennen and Lancashire 1978; Dutton 1985; Lines 1977; Mare
1982; McWhirter et al. 1983; Morgan and Chin 1983; Spiers et al.
1974; Starfield and Budetti 1982).

Adolescence and Early Adulthood

From early childhood to the forties, the major causes of death
are those associated with injury, which account for more deaths
than all other causes combined. Here, too, there are substantial
gradients of risk associated with SES (Mare 1982; Baker et al.
1984). Figures 6 and 7 show the association between death rates
from injuries and per capita income of area of residence. For
deaths from unintentional injuries, which account for roughly
two thirds of all injuries, there is a strong gradient of risk associated with SES, and this gradient is found for whites, blacks,
and Asians. Homicides also decline with income. Motor vehi-
cles are the major source of injury up to age 44; drowning is the
next most prevalent. For each of these outcomes, there is a
strong gradient of risk associated with SES (Figure 8).

A variety of other studies of those in this age group also shows
a positive association between health and SES. Lower SES is associated with higher prevalence of heart disease and high blood
pressure (National Center for Health Statistics 1983), higher incidence of diabetes (Medalie et al. 1974; Figure 9), and higher
prevalence of orthopedic impairments associated with injury
(National Center for Health Statistics 1986). In addition, for
both blacks and whites, there is an association between SES
level, days of restricted activity, acute conditions, bed days, and
short-stay hospital days (National Center for Health Statistics
1985, 1986, 1987; Figures 10 and 11).

The Middle Years

As the incidence and prevalence of chronic conditions begin
to increase from age 40 on, the association between SES and

health continues to be observed. Strong negative associations are found between SES and all-cause mortality (Antonovsky 1967; Kaplan 1987; Kitagawa and Hauser 1973; Metro Life 1977; Nagi and Stockwell 1973; Nayha 1977; Pearce et al. 1983a, 1983b, 1985; Syme and Berkman 1976). A number of studies, using different measures, have reported an association between SES and cardiovascular outcomes (Marmot et al. 1984; Rose and Marmot 1981; Salonen 1982). Figure 12 presents this relationship as observed in the Whitehall study of British civil servants (Marmot et al. 1978, 1984; Rose and Marmot 1981). Similar SES gradients for death and cardiovascular endpoints have been observed in Finland (Koskenvuo et al. 1979; Nayha 1977; Notkola et al. 1985; Salonen 1982; Figure 13), Sweden (Haglund 1985; Lapidus and Bengtsson 1986), Norway (Arnesen and Forsdahl 1985; Forsdahl, 1977; Holme et al. 1981; Leren et al. 1983), England and Wales (Black et al., 1980; Morris 1979; Figure 14), and, within the United States, in Los Angeles (Frerichs et al. 1984; Figure 15), Birmingham, Buffalo, and Indianapolis (Yeracaris and Kim 1978), Alameda County (Kaplan 1985), Baltimore (Kuller 1972), Washington County, Maryland (Comstock and Tonascia 1978), and in Australia and New Zealand (Dobson et al. 1985; Fisher 1978; Pearce et al. 1983a; Figure 16).

A negative association between SES and prevalence of disease, for those aged 40 to 60, is also found for arthritis, heart disease, ulcers, diabetes, high blood pressure, chronic bronchitis, and emphysema (National Center for Health Statistics 1983; Figure 17), gallbladder disease (Diehl et al. 1985), incidence of cervical and lung cancer (Devesa and Diamond 1980; Hakama et al. 1982; Figures 18 and 19), and mortality from all sites of cancer (Dayal et al. 1984; Hathcock et al. 1982; Holme et al. 1981a; Jenkins 1983; Moser et al. 1984; Salonen 1982). As to the burden of injury in these years, injuries from falls and house fires begin to add significantly to those due to motor vehicle accidents, and for all these there is an inverse association with SES (Baker et al. 1984).

Old Age

After age 60, a negative association between SES and all-cause mortality continues to be seen in most studies. As deaths from

malignancies begin to rise overall, SES is inversely associated
with cancer of the esophagus, pancreas, lung, stomach, prostate,
and other sites (Dayal et al. 1984; Devesa and Diamond 1983;
Mack and Paganini-Hill 1981; Marmot et al. 1984, Steinhorn et
al. 1986). Overall cancer survival is poorer in lower SES patients
compared to higher SES patients (Blane 1985; Chirikos and Horner 1985; Dayal et al. 1982, 1985; Lipworth et al. 1970; Savage et
al. 1984; Smith and Day 1979; Wegner et al. 1982). Kitagawa and
Hauser (1973) in their study of deaths in the United States among
those over 65 years of age found negative associations between
SES, measured by education level, and mortality in those over 65
years old from diabetes, major cardiovascular-renal diseases, vascular lesions affecting the nervous system, arteriosclerotic and
degenerative heart disease, influenza and pneumonia, and accidents. In analyses from the National Health Interview Survey, for
those 65–74 years old, there is a negative association between
family income and prevalence of arthritis, diabetes, hypertension, chronic bronchitis, and emphysema (National Center for
Health Statistics 1983). For those 65 years old and over, there is an
inverse gradient between SES and acute conditions, activity limitations due to chronic conditions (National Center for Health
Statistics 1985), bed disability, days of restricted activity (National Center for Health Statistics 1987), hearing impairments,
and orthopedic impairments of the back and lower extremities
(National Center for Health Statistics 1986, Figure 20).

   All of these studies indicate the pervasive and consistent relationship between SES and health, a relationship that is found
throughout the life course and across a wide variety of diseases and
organ systems. Although any one of these studies could be criticized, the consistency of the evidence clearly is sufficient to merit
a serious search for explanations. This consistency is all the more
impressive because it is generally observed regardless of the way
in which SES is assessed. Thus, SES is linked to disease whether
one uses measures of income, occupation, education, area of
residence, or prestige ranking—either alone or in combination.

What Needs to be Explained?

   In addition to addressing the basic observation of an association between SES and health, any proposed explanation ideally

should address four key issues. We will examine each of these in some detail.

SES GRADIENTS

The usual focus on the SES-health link has been on those at the very bottom of the SES hierarchy. This focus is understandable because occupants of the lowest position are subjected to a wider variety of and greater exposure to physical, psychological, social, and economic insults. Nevertheless, most of the evidence we have reviewed shows that the health disadvantage associated with lower SES is not restricted to those at the bottom. It appears that there is an SES gradient of health. Even persons in the upper middle class are at higher risk for disease than those at the very top of the scale. This gradient persists for different measures of SES, in different populations, and in different countries. It consistently shows that as we descend the SES hierarchy, rates of ill health increase. This observation is important because whatever single or multiple factors are responsible for the SES-health association should take this gradient into consideration.

LIFE–SPAN EFFECTS

The SES-health link persists throughout the life span, manifesting itself in differential infant mortality rates, accidental deaths among youth and young adults, in cardiovascular mortality rates among middle-aged adults, and in all-cause mortality across all ages. It may be true, as Marmot suggests in his comments in chapter 7, that the health disadvantage associated with lower SES begins at or before birth. For example, poor nutrition *in utero* or exposure to environmental lead in early childhood leads to compromised health and poorer educational performance. Poorer educational performance, in turn, could lead to continuing social and economic disadvantage and again to higher exposure to social and environmental risks.

Given that the health disadvantage associated with lower SES may begin early and may be cumulative over the life span, it is still possible that different risk factors may be responsible for the poor health of lower SES people at different stages of life. It is important for our understanding of this phenomenon to exam-

ine the *pattern* of such etiologic risk factors in addition to looking at them singly.

TEMPORAL TRENDS

The SES-health link appears to persist over time and may be
increasing in strength. The pattern of risk factors that might
"explain" the link must also persist over time, even though single factors composing the pattern could change. The overall pattern should also change accordingly where there have been shifts
in the SES-health relationship.

INTERNATIONAL CONSISTENCY

As is clear from the introductory material and the chartbook,
the association between SES and health has been observed in a
wide variety of countries, cultures, and economic systems.
Again SES-related patterns of risk factors should demonstrate
some level of cross-national consistency and interpretability.

We think that the gradient, the persistence over the life span
and over time, and the international consistency of the association are basic to our understanding of SES and health. These are
central characteristics of the SES-health association, and any effort to explain it should adequately examine them. Our review
has covered 300 studies on this topic. In our writing we have not
attempted to account for every study of SES and health; instead
we have focused on the major examples. We believe that such an
"unbalanced" approach is defensible when the weight of the evidence is as convincing as it is in this case. Nevertheless, we recognize that exceptions will also need to be addressed.

CURRENT EXPLANATIONS

As noted in the *Black Report* (Townsend and Davidson 1982) and
elsewhere, several major themes predominate in research and
speculation about the association between SES and health. The
most frequent of these themes is the idea that SES differences in
behavioral risk factors such as smoking, alcohol consumption,
and diet account for the link between SES and mortality. Another view is that the SES link to health reflects the influence of

health on SES. In other words, ill persons lose income and "drift" into lower social positions. Others hold that there are personal or social characteristics of individuals that keep them in poverty and that these characteristics are "cycled" from generation to generation. A fourth approach identifies socioeconomic or material factors as determinants of the SES-health link. For example, deprivation of access to medical care, to food, transportation or education are identified as the causative factors. Finally, a fifth approach theorizes that SES differences in exposures to noxious social and physical environments may lead to higher rates of morbidity and mortality in lower SES groups.

In the following sections, we will consider the usefulness of these themes in accounting for the SES-health association.

Individual Behaviors

It is often proposed that the gradients of health associated with SES are due to different levels of high risk behavior among those in different SES strata. According to this view, the SES-health link can be accounted for by differences in smoking, diet, alcohol consumption, and similar lifestyle factors. Since a substantial body of knowledge links such risk behaviors to poor health, this is an attractive proposal. Such a view, however, needs to be critically examined from a number of perspectives.

First, even if the magnitude of the association between measures of SES and health outcomes is reduced after adjusting for behavioral risk factors, the interpretation of such a finding is not without its problems. Such a pattern of results may very well indicate not that SES is irrelevant and that we should focus on these risk factors, but rather that it is an antecedent, causal variable that is involved in the adoption and maintenance of high risk behaviors.

Second, even if high risk behaviors are distributed in a graded fashion by SES strata, it still would remain to be seen whether or not the differential distribution of these factors actually did account for the increased risk in these strata.

Unfortunately, there are only a limited number of studies that have examined the association between health outcomes and SES, taking into account the practice of high risk behaviors.

One such analysis comes from the Human Population Laboratory's ongoing follow-up of a sample of residents of Alameda
County, California (Kaplan et al. 1986). Figure 21 presents survival curves for county residents followed for 19 years as a function of baseline income (Figure 21–A) and education (Figure 21–
B). Family income, adjusted for family size, is grouped into four
categories (inadequate, marginal, adequate, very adequate) by
reference to federal standards at the time (1965), and education is
grouped into three levels (0–11 years, 12 years, 13 years or
more). The ordinate represents the proportion surviving at each
year of follow-up. With adjustment for age and sex, those in the
lowest income category had 2.23 times the risk of death compared to those in the top category ($p<.00001$), and those with
0–11 years of education had 1.57 the risk of those with some college ($p<.001$). Parts C and D of the figure illustrate that the increased risk associated with both income and education remains
when there is adjustment for a number of high risk variables, in
this case smoking, alcohol consumption, physical activity level,
relative weight, and amount of sleep. There is also adjustment
for race and prevalent chronic disease (hypertension, heart trouble, cancer, diabetes). As can be seen in this figure, there is still
a strong gradient associated with both measures. Those in
the inadequate, marginal, and adequate categories are at 1.78
($p<.0012$), 1.56 ($p<.004$), and 1.30 ($p<.025$) times the risk, respectively, of those with very adequate incomes. Those with 0–
11 years of education are at 1.30 ($p<.03$) times the risk of those
with some college. Although in each case there is some reduction in the pattern of risk associated with SES, a substantial, increased risk associated with low SES remains, and, in the case of
family income, a strong gradient persists.

Several analyses of the association between SES and cardiovascular outcomes have come to similar conclusions. The
Whitehall study (Marmot et al. 1984) observed a substantial gradient in cardiovascular risk associated with employment grade
in its 10-year study of British civil servants. Although levels of
smoking, high blood pressure, physical inactivity, and other risk
factors were higher in the lower grades, adjustment for these factors accounted for less than one half of the observed association.
Those in the lowest grade were at a fourfold increased risk when

these other factors were taken into account (Marmot et al. 1978; Rose and Marmot 1981). Increased cardiovascular risk associated with lower employment grade was also found for other outcomes not particularly related to smoking (Marmot et al. 1984). Similar conclusions were reached in studies in Finland and Norway. Salonen (1982) found increased risk of death from ischemic heart disease associated with low education and income in a 7-year study of men in Eastern Finland. This increased risk persisted after adjustment for age, serum cholesterol, diastolic blood pressure, and amount of smoking. In another prospective study in Norway, Holme et al. (1981b) found that less than half of the gradient in risk of coronary heart disease associated with low income and education could be explained by levels of serum cholesterol, triglycerides, blood pressure, cigarette smoking, physical activity, and other risk factors. Thus, there is a consistent body of evidence that finds that differences in the distribution of behaviors related to cardiovascular disease do not explain fully the association between SES and cardiovascular outcomes.

Turning to reproductive health outcomes, a similar picture emerges. Although smoking is associated with low birthweight (National Academy of Sciences 1985) and higher rates of perinatal and postneonatal mortality (Bakketeig et al. 1984; Rush and Cassano 1983), and although there tend to be gradients of smoking related to SES, these variations in smoking do not seem to account for the association between SES and these outcomes. Rush and Cassano (1983), for example, studied the association between SES measured by occupational grade and both low birthweight and perinatal mortality in 16,688 singleton births occurring in Britain in one week's time in 1970. Although maternal smoking was an important predictor of both outcomes, it did not fully account for the association between these outcomes and SES. For example, 63 percent of the association between occupational grade and low birthweight remained after statistical adjustment for maternal smoking, age, gravidity, height, and marital status. Similarly, 75 percent of the SES-perinatal mortality association remained after adjustment for maternal smoking and other factors. Rantakallio (1979), in a Finnish study, also found that low maternal education was associated with lower birthweight and higher perinatal and postneonatal mortality, as well as higher rates of hospital admissions during the first five years of life. These differences were not attributable to higher rates of smoking in low SES women.

Finally, van den Berg and Oechesli (1984), in a study of 11,000 pregnancies that went beyond 22 weeks, found that rates of prematurity (e.g., delivery in first 37 weeks) were related to maternal education. This finding held when there was statistical adjustment for maternal smoking, weight gain, first trimester bleeding, time since last pregnancy, length of gestation of previous pregnancy, sex of infant, and father's education. Again we see a picture consistent with that for cardiovascular diseases. Although certain high risk behaviors may be more prevalent among those in the lower SES strata, they do not seem to account fully for the gradient of association between SES and reproductive outcomes.

There seems to be an "independent" role for SES, even when it comes to lung cancer. Although smoking is undoubtedly the most important factor in lung cancer incidence, several studies suggest that SES is related to lung cancer incidence even when variation in levels of smoking by SES strata are taken into account. For example, Marmot et al. (1984) found a similar gradient for occupational grade and lung cancer when they compared ex-smokers and smokers who consumed 1–9, 10–19, and 20 or more cigarettes per day. (As would be expected, there were too few lung cancer deaths in nonsmokers to complete the full set of comparisons.) Similarly, Salonen (1982) found a significant association between education level and risk of cancer mortality, approximately 60 percent of which would be due to lung cancer, when there was adjustment for smoking and other variables. Comstock and Tonascia (1978), in their studies in Washington County, Maryland, also found a trend indicating that low education was associated with increased risk for lung cancer death even after adjustment for smoking status.

Finally, recent analyses of the 18-year cancer incidence experience of respondents in the Alameda County Study (Kaplan et al. 1986) have indicated a surprisingly strong relationship between SES and lung cancer incidence and mortality. Women who were in the bottom quartile of the distribution of family income adjusted for family size, had an 11.0 ($p<.03$)- and 16.6

($p<.01$)-fold increased risk of lung cancer death or incidence, respectively, when compared with women in the top quartile of adjusted family income, with adjustment for age, race, and pack-years of smoking. No such association was found for men. These results should not be taken as indicating that smoking is not important in the etiology of lung cancer. In all analyses, smoking remains an important predictor. Rather, in the case of lung cancer where tobacco consumption is such a strong predictor, the independent risk associated with SES indicates the strength of the SES-disease association.

Unfortunately, few studies have examined the joint influence of measures of SES and other risk factors, so we cannot come to any definitive answers regarding the independent influence of SES on most disease outcomes. Considering individual SES factors, however, can provide some insight. In analyses of occupational stress and ischemic heart disease, for instance, Haan (1985) reported that persons who smoked and were exposed to high levels of job strain were at a fourfold risk of ischemic heart disease compared to those who were nonsmokers and had low strain jobs. These and other analyses suggest that behavioral risk factors may interact with SES in the disease process but not account fully for the association.

Selection

Some have interpreted gradients of health associated with SES as reflecting the influence of health on SES, rather than vice versa (Illsley 1955; Stern 1984; Wadsworth 1986). Because it is undoubtedly true that illness is often accompanied by declines in some measures of SES such as income, it is important to examine this reverse causation argument thoroughly. Analyses of the dynamics of income change in a panel of 5,000 families indicated that 28 percent of married men experienced a work loss due to illness during an 11-year period (Duncan 1984). Kitagawa and Hauser (1973) in their study of all deaths in the United States in a 4-month period in 1960, reported that decedents aged 25–64 years old had worked less in the preceding year than those who survived, and thus had lower incomes.

It is also likely that changes in occupational status occur in response to health problems. In some cases—schizophrenia, for example—there is good evidence for a drift into lower occupational groups due to such a disorder. Drift into lower occupational groups is also more prevalent in those who were seriously ill during childhood (Wadsworth 1986). In an example of the same phenomenon occurring later in life, Illsley (1955) found that women who experienced intergenerational upward mobility, defined with respect to the occupational group of their fathers compared to their husbands, were healthier before marriage than those who did not move upward via marriage. In short, health may influence social status in both a positive and negative direction.

Given that there is some impact of health on SES, it is necessary to establish to what extent this influence makes an important contribution to the observed association between SES and health. Based on our review of the evidence, we do not feel this explanation is of major importance. First, a comprehensive discussion of the contribution of health-related mobility to SES gradients observed in England and Wales has been provided by Wilkinson (1986), who concludes that the impact of such selection is unimportant.

Second, the selection argument depends on shifts in income and occupation but does not take education into account. Because educational attainment occurs relatively early in life, it is temporally impossible for it to be influenced by health status measured decades later. For this reason, when the SES-disease link is assessed in terms of education level, this link cannot be due to poor adult health influencing amount of education. For the vast majority of disease outcomes among adults, there is an inverse gradient related to level of education. Marmot (1987) has pointed out that poor health in early childhood due to low SES may lead to poorer educational and occupational attainment in adulthood. This phenomenon is not an example of initial poor health leading to downward drift but is, instead, an example of the cascading effects of lower SES on health throughout the life span.

Third, if the SES-health link were a result of drift due to poor health, then we would not expect to see an SES-health association for family members. Yet there are a number of studies that find gradients of health for children or wives related to the SES circumstances of their fathers or husbands.

Fourth, the drift hypothesis cannot explain the observed gradients of health among retired individuals for whom income is no longer as dependent on health. Yet, in some analyses, for some measures of SES, the gradients are actually stronger among older persons.

Fifth, if these gradients reflect a bias that transfers the sick to lower and lower levels of SES, then in longitudinal studies we should expect that the gradients would be greatest during the years immediately following the beginning of follow-up, and they should decrease over time. Fox et al. (1985) in their 10-year follow-up of a 1 percent sample of the population of England and Wales in 1971, found just the opposite effect with increasing length of follow-up—that is, the SES gradient, defined with respect to occupational groupings, was actually larger in the second five years of follow-up than in the first.

The drift hypothesis is further contradicted by the observation that for many outcomes it is incidence of disease that is inversely related to SES. Given that incidence represents the time at which the disease is first diagnosed, it is less likely that there has been any major earlier impact of the disease on SES. The gradients of mortality from unintentional injuries related to SES also cannot be due to downward drift, especially since they occur with greatest frequency among the young. Survival from a number of conditions also appears to be related to SES, and better survival is associated with higher SES even when prognostic factors have been taken into account.

Finally, we were able to examine the joint impact of health changes and income changes on mortality risk using data from the Alameda County Study (Kaplan et al. 1986). In a sample of healthy persons aged 50 and over, income loss was associated with higher risk of subsequent death, and this association was not due to worsening health coincident with income loss. Even if poor health were associated with movement into lower SES, one would still want to know what antecedent conditions were associated with this poorer health. Given the pattern of evidence surveyed, it seems likely that a good proportion of downward drift in SES due to health may in fact be due to an etiologic role in early life for SES.

In summary, although it is true that poor health can lead to lower SES, the bulk of evidence surveyed does not indicate a major role for this pathway in accounting for the graded relationship between SES and health outcomes.

Medical Care

The central question to be addressed in this section is not whether there are inequities in access to and quality of medical care by SES, as clearly there often are, but rather whether SES inequities in medical care access or utilization could explain the SES-health link. The real question is whether lack of access to medical care is the *reason why* lower SES people have higher rates of incident disease, higher mortality, and poorer survival. Even with this limited definition, it will be difficult in this brief discussion to examine in depth the impact of access to and quality of medical care on the SES-health link.

Although lack of access to medical care is frequently cited as a cause of poorer health and higher mortality in lower SES groups (Starfield and Budetti 1982), research in a number of countries where access to medical care is relatively equitable has still revealed substantial SES differences in health (Holme et al. 1981a, 1981b; Koskenvuo et al. 1979; Pearce et al. 1983a; Rantakallio 1979; Rose and Marmot 1981). Of course, as several reviewers pointed out, potential equality of access is not the same as actual equality of access. Even in countries where medical care is free to all, there may still be more subtle barriers to quality care for lower SES people. The *Black Report* (Townsend and Davidson 1982) failed to find improvement in the SES-health differential, even with improved access to medical care afforded by the British National Health Service.

The SES gradient is important to take into consideration in examining the possible role of medical care in accounting for the SES-health link. Differences in medical care access, quality, and utilization are unlikely to account for the health status difference between the top of the SES scale and the level just below it.

We have reported SES differences in both incidence and survival. In general, medical care is less efficacious than other interventions in the prevention of new chronic diseases in adults (incidence) (McKeown 1979). However, early/improved diagnosis and control of hypertension and diabetes are examples of diseases where stroke, mortality incidence or death from diabetes-related complications may be reduced or postponed to a later age through medical interventions. Earlier diagnosis of cervical cancer could be another example. Evidence from the Hypertension Detection and Follow-up Program suggests that a comprehensive hypertension treatment program can lead to an elimination of SES-related differences in mortality related to hypertension (Stamler et al. 1987).

There are many disease events that occur more frequently in lower SES people on which medical care can have very little substantial preventive impact. For example, the associations between SES and injuries (Kristiansen 1985; Sunderland 1984) and new occurrences of alcohol-related diseases (Coates et al. 1985; Edwards et al. 1978; Haberman and Baden 1974) and smoking-related diseases are clearly not alterable through medical treatment. SES differences in infant mortality do appear to be significantly influenced by access/utilization of medical care (Dott and Fort 1975; Grossman and Jacobowitz 1981; Kraus and Redford 1975; Papiernik et al. 1985; Taylor 1983; Wright 1975). For this outcome, mortality is clearly influenced by access to and quality of medical care. Starfield (1985) has exhaustively documented the efficacy of medical care in preventing infant mortality, low birthweight babies, and a variety of childhood diseases. However, SES differences in infant mortality have been reported in countries such as Sweden (Holme et al. 1981a) and Finland (Notkola et al. 1985; Salonen 1982) where equal access to prenatal/postnatal care for all SES groups is a matter of national health policy (Shin 1975).

In short, SES-related differences in access or utilization of preventive medical treatment may result in SES differences in survival from disease. Secondly, it may postpone the onset of some diseases or reduce the incidence of some diseases through the treatment of risk factors. If people of lower SES have differential access to medical care, their survival and age at mortality may indeed be affected. However, the fact that people of lower SES have higher incidence of many important diseases and injuries both in childhood and adulthood suggests that the SES link is unlikely to be explained *entirely* by lack of medical care access or poorer quality of medical care. It also seems unlikely that medical care could account for the SES gradient or for SES differences in health and injury outcomes not alterable by medical treatment. Nevertheless, our review of this issue does not rule out medical care as a possible and important intervention that would be useful in lessening the impact of SES on health.

Personal and Social Characteristics of Individuals

This approach to explaining the relationship between SES and health argues that the poor come to adopt and transmit through generations patterns of thought and action that place them at higher risk of poor health. There are a number of reasons for believing that such an approach cannot explain the SES-health link. It is hard to see, for example, exactly what patterns are consistently arrayed throughout SES strata in a way that could account for the gradients of health that have been observed. Furthermore, as pointed out, although high risk behaviors may be more prevalent in lower SES strata, they do not seem to account for the elevated disease rates in these groups.

Increasingly, references are made to the relationship between such concepts as control, efficacy, coherence, hardiness, coping style, and other related measures and health outcomes. Is it possible that these constructs provide a link between SES and health? There is some evidence that lower SES persons may perceive themselves as less in control of external events, and there is evidence that such beliefs are associated with poorer health (Rodin 1986). However, it is important to question whether these measures are psychological, reflecting characteristics of individuals, or whether instead they represent cognitive assessments of social process. In general, this latter hypothesis has not been well studied.

At a conceptual level, the observation that these perceptions of control and efficacy are differentially distributed by SES strata argues for viewing these characteristics as outcomes, reflecting differences in environment and experience at different levels of SES. Kohn and Schooler's (1974) classic study of the impact of job characteristics on an individual's personality and cognition is an example of such influences. In other words, the observation that beliefs and attitudes vary by SES strata should not be taken as convincing evidence that these beliefs and attitudes "explain" the SES-health link. Instead, they should prompt us to examine aspects of the lives of people in different SES strata that could lead to these different patterns of cognition and personality.

OTHER CONSIDERATIONS

Trends Over Time

Persistence or change over time of the SES-health association is of interest because examination of patterns of change may help to identify explanatory factors. Persistence over time also supports the notion that the SES-health association is not an artifact of a particular time period or data set.

Any attempt to characterize changes in SES differences in health over time should address several key questions:

- First, a descriptive matter: Have SES differences in mortality changed over time; and, if so, are there differences in the trends by cause of death?
- Can changes in exposure to behavioral or environmental risk factors account for these trends in SES differences?
- What roles do early selection or competing risk play in trends in SES differentials in mortality?

Several researchers have examined changes over time in the SES gradient of mortality. In general, SES differentials in all-cause mortality have remained stable or have possibly increased. Blaxter (1983) has reported that class differentials are widening even as overall mortality declines. Pamuck (1985) has reported in her analysis of mortality trends from 1921–1971 in England and Wales, that SES inequalities in health declined in the 1920s, increased in the 1950s and 1960s, and by the 1970s were greater than in the 1920s. Similarly, Fox et al. (1985), in their examination of SES mortality differentials, report that the SES differential in the Office of Population Censuses and Surveys (OPCS)

Longitudinal Study increased between 1971–1976 and 1976–1981 in England and Wales (Figure 22). Susser et al. (1985) have also reported a steepening differential in this association between 1931 and 1971. Wilkinson (1986) has also noted an increase in the all-cause differential between 1951–1971 (Figure 23). It should be noted that explanations for the observed changes primarily invoke shifts in lifestyle—especially in smoking, drinking, and diet—as the likely factors. However, Susser et al. (1985) and others have also noted that changes in environmental exposures and in the efficacy of medical care may contribute to SES-related mortality trends. For example, if occupational exposure to industrial pollution has increased and if those of lower SES are more highly exposed, such environmental changes could lead to increasing SES differences over time.

Relatively little research has been reported on trends in cause-specific mortality by SES. In general, the evidence supports an increasing SES mortality differential for major causes of death, consistent with the findings for all-cause mortality. For example, Yeracaris and Kim (1978) and Lerner and Stutz (1978) both report an increase in the SES-mortality differential between 1960 and 1970 for cancer and heart diseases.

When we examine cancer outcomes in more detail, SES differences in mortality appear to have persisted over time and increased. Lerner (1986), reporting on income differentials in cancer mortality separately for blacks and whites, found an SES differential for both races throughout the period between 1949 and 1971. In other words, low income whites and blacks had higher cancer mortality rates than high income whites and blacks when compared within race. This was true not only for all sites, but for many specific sites as well. The effect of income was especially strong for respiratory cancers. Similarly, Marmot et al. (1984) have reported that the SES differential in mortality from lung cancer increased between 1970–1972 and 1979–1983. Unfortunately, most data on cancer incidence and mortality are not reported by SES, but only by race. Data on race suggest that for lung, gastrointestinal, and reproductive cancers (excluding breast), incidence is higher among blacks and has increased.

Attempts to explain the SES-health association can benefit by examination of changes in trends. A particular example of the way that etiologic factors may be identified can be found in the possible reversal in the coronary heart disease (CHD)-SES association reported in three studies. Specifically, Marmot et al. (1978a) and Morgenstern (1980) have both reported that the association between SES and CHD reversed from a positive to a negative association between 1950 and 1960. Susser et al. (1985) have also reported a rise in age-specific CHD mortality between 1931 and 1971, with a similar reversal occurring about 1955 for men only. However, in this latter report, the picture for women is quite different: it shows no reversal in CHD, with low SES women remaining at higher risk throughout the 1931–1972 period. In fact the SES differential for women increased sharply after 1960. Other sources have reported that the SES gradient for CHD has persisted over time and may have increased in recent years.

Marmot et al. (1978a), Morgenstern (1980), and others (e.g., Pamuck 1985) have argued that the reversal in the CHD-SES-association may be explained by the diffusion of high risk behaviors to the lower classes at the same time that the upper classes were abandoning such behaviors. In the United States, however, the major reduction in prevalent risk behaviors *postdates* the reversal in CHD. The U.S. Surgeon General's report on smoking was not issued until 1964, and public consciousness and avoidance of these risk factors is relatively recent (U.S. Surgeon General 1985). Figure 24 shows the annual rate of decline in smoking prevalence by occupational class and birth cohort in the United States from 1950 to 1978 (Carstairs 1981). Birth cohort is presented in order to account for the rather substantial cohort differences in smoking. These data suggest that the greatest decline in smoking prevalence occurred between 1970 and 1978 and that the least change occurred between 1950 and 1960, the period during which the CHD-SES reversal may have occurred. Other data show that smoking prevalence increased for all classes until 1950 in the United States. In short, the greatest changes in high risk behavior did not begin until *after* the reversal in the CHD-SES association. Therefore, it would be temporally improbable for diffusion of high risk behavior to have accounted for this reversal.

In any event, the bulk of evidence on the association of smoking, cholesterol, and other risk factors and CHD–SES mortality suggests that these factors cannot fully explain SES-health differences. As we have mentioned previously, cholesterol, smoking, and other risk factors account for less than half of the CHD–SES association. While in some studies this lack of effect may be due to inadequate measurement of major risk factors, in several studies adequate measurement of these risk factors has not altered the observed association.

The role of selection and competing risk are important when examining SES-related trends in mortality. If the crossover reported by Marmot et al. cannot be accounted for by changes in smoking and diet, an alternative explanation may be found in SES differentials in competing risk. If higher SES groups not only have a general survival advantage but are also the first to receive the benefits of medical, behavioral, or environmental improvements, then conversely one may presume that the lower SES groups continue to get sick and die for a longer period from diseases that are on the decline in general.

If lower SES persons are dying younger, they are also probably dying at greater rates from causes characteristic of younger ages such as injuries, cirrhosis, and acute infectious diseases, since cardiovascular disease (CVD) and cancer are very much phenomena of old age. Thus trends in the SES-mortality link may be a product of both differential selection and competing risk. In other words, until 1960 the life expectancy of lower SES persons was such that they had less likelihood of living long enough to get CVD. The all-cause mortality-SES differential then could remain stable or increase while CVD mortality, once a disease of the privileged, became a disease more prevalent in lower SES groups. It must be said that Fox et al. (1985) did not find evidence for early selection in their analysis of recent trends (1971–1981), but they did not examine age-specific rates across different birth cohorts. However, no research has been done to examine SES and patterns of competing risk over time.

In short, trends in the SES-health association may be due to a number of factors that seem to be linked to behavioral changes, environmental changes, or changes in medical interventions. Changes in behavioral risk factors or changes in the social and physical environment, or both, may help to explain changes in the SES-health association. Appropriate examination of these changes will require comparisons of two or more cohorts of persons on whom SES, behavioral, environmental, and health data are collected over time. This approach will need to take account of the early selection and competing risk problems we have discussed.

SES and Minority Health

In the United States, minority status (particularly being black, Hispanic, or Native American) and SES are so closely linked that no examination of the relationship between SES and health is complete without a discussion of minority health. The question, simply put, is whether or not the association between SES and higher rates of disease simply reflects the higher percentage of minority persons in lower SES strata. Although little data are available to answer this important question, what is available suggests that the answer is no. For example, Figure 25 presents such an analysis for blacks and whites in the Alameda County Study (Haan and Kaplan 1985; Kaplan et al. 1986). Figure 25-A indicates the poorer mortality experience of blacks compared to whites. As can be seen, there is a substantial difference of approximately 30 percent in risk of death. Figure 25-B indicates what happens when black/white differences in income are taken into account. In these analyses, the difference between black and white mortality was substantially reduced and became statistically nonsignificant when income differences were taken into account. Adjustment for education reduced the black/white risk difference by 8 percent, but the association between race and mortality was still significant ($p = .02$). Thus, these analyses indicate that it is income, not being black, that is largely responsible for the observed mortality differentials.

This discussion has not attempted to address whether the poorer health seen in many minority groups is due exclusively to the lower SES predominant in these groups. It is possible that the simple measures of SES used in most analyses do not fully capture all the cultural and historical experiences that are relevant to the health experience of a given minority group. As Nickens points out in his comments in Chapter 7, these features may also interact differently with the lower socioeconomic status predominant in that group.

AN ALTERNATIVE APPROACH

In previous sections of this paper, we have outlined and discussed a variety of factors that may describe and/or account for the link between SES and health status. No factor or set of factors clearly emerges as a likely candidate. In this section, we attempt to summarize and discuss the associations between the social and physical environment and SES and health. This final approach differs from previous approaches because it is less well developed as a research area and because it is more controversial in its implications. In our discussion of the social and physical environment, we will separately discuss the community at large and the work environment since they comprise separate areas of research and have different implications for intervention.

Community Environment, SES, and Health

A number of studies (Brooks 1975; Dayal et al. 1982, 1984; Devesa and Diamond 1980, 1983; Harburg et al. 1973; Hathcock et al. 1982; Jenkins et al. 1977; Kasl and Harburg 1975; Kendrick 1980; Kraus and Redford 1975; Lawton and Nahemow 1979; Miller 1982; Taylor and Emery 1983) have examined the influence of the social and physical environment upon health. Somewhat less has been written about SES differentials in environmental exposures that might account for the SES-health link (Beresford 1981; Blair et al. 1980; Blot and Fraumeni 1976; Kuller et al. 1972; West 1977). For example, a number of epidemiological studies have used area characteristics to examine the influence of SES on health. Others have investigated the influences of SES-related differences in exposures to physical environmental hazards such as lead and air pollution. These studies have been criticized from at least two perspectives:

One, if there is an environment-health link, it is believed to be through the medium of individual behaviors (for example, smoking) that are induced by or influenced by environmental factors. These factors are thought to stress individuals to the point where they engage in high risk behaviors as a response to the stressors. However, the bulk of environmental studies lack data on individual characteristics or health status and rely instead upon the correlation between ecological measures of health and ecological measures of the social and/or physical environment.

Two, the measurement of the environment is ecological; that is, no direct link can be made between individual-level exposures or individual health status and the measures of the environment, leading thus to the so-called ecological fallacy. The statistical and inferential errors that may arise from trying to impute individual risk from ecological data have been pointed out by many.

An exhaustive review of these environmental studies is neither possible nor necessary for this discussion. The usual study design involves the use of socioenvironmental data derived from the Census, Housing Survey, Environmental Protection Agency air pollution monitoring stations, and other data bases that assess area characteristics. These data are linked to area mortality rates. For example, two well-known studies by Jenkins et al. (1977) linked elevated area rates of CHD mortality and cancer mortality to residence in lower SES neighborhoods. Similarly, Devesa and Diamond (1983) found elevated rates of lung cancer in lower SES neighborhoods. Neither of these studies was able to link individual characteristics or health status with the area measures.

These limitations have been addressed in research currently being carried out by Haan and Kaplan (1987, in preparation) in the Alameda County Study. Specifically, it has been possible to link area measures taken from the Census to individual-level measures taken from survey data on individuals, and to follow those individuals prospectively. In research by Haan et al. (1987, Figure 26), residence in a poverty area was significantly associated with subsequent nine-year all-cause mortality in Oakland, California. Current analyses of the same data have expanded to include all of Alameda County. More detailed measures of the social environment have been formulated based upon 1960 Census data and linked to data on individuals. At this time, four major factors have been identified that are consistently and persistently associated with all-cause, cardiovascular, and cancer mortality after adjustment for behavioral risk factors, race, income, education, social networks, baseline health status, political activity levels, depression, and personal uncertainty. These factors were identified through principal component analysis and represent clusters of variables that characterize the sociophysical environment of neighborhoods.

These analyses have supplied more information about the association between the social and physical environment and health. It appears that clusters of social and physical area characteristics collectively influence health status, whereas they do not do so when used as individual measures. Thus, for example, residence in a census tract simultaneously characterized by high proportions of men over 65, widowers, persons without cars, deteriorated housing, and housing without heat is associated with elevated all-cause and cardiovascular mortality, and with cancer incidence. Taken one at a time, these characteristics are not related to these outcomes. Taken together, they describe an ecological setting and are strong predictors of mortality. It seems clear from these findings and from research by others that socioenvironmental risk factors cluster and that they include measures of social network disruption, age of population, housing conditions, income, racial composition, and access to transportation. Ultimately, they are strongly associated with the health of individuals who live in their midst.

Research on SES and exposures to noxious physical environments is a long-standing tradition in public health, and investigations of poor sanitation and unsafe housing are common. More recent research has attempted to link air pollution exposure (Lave and Seskin 1977; Lloyd et al. 1985; Phillipp and Hughes 1985) and, in particular, exposure to environmental lead, with SES and health. For example, a recent study by Schwartz et al. (1985) found an association between blood lead levels and hypertension. Other analyses of leaded gasoline sales and hypertension have reported significant associations (Pirkle and Schwartz 1985). The supposition in these latter analyses has been that residential proximity to freeways (often a marker of low SES) is associated with increased exposure to environmental lead. In addition, some studies of soil lead levels have revealed that lower SES areas have higher levels of lead than suburban areas. Studies of elevated blood lead in children have found a threefold higher prevalence in children of lower SES (Mahaffey et al. 1982). The effect of lead is also potentiated by undernutrition and iron deficiency anemia, both of which occur commonly in children of lower SES. Residence in polluted areas tends to be strongly associated with other factors such as low income and poor housing.

Environmental pollution often covaries with sociodemographic factors such as area of residence and may indeed add to the overall burden of social and physical exposures encountered by persons of lower SES. However, no research has been done that examines the association between environmental pollution and health while adjusting for SES or in interaction with SES.

Work Environment, SES, and Health

Occupation is commonly used as a measure of SES. As with other measures of SES, little is understood about why occupation and health are linked. Research on this topic generally falls into the category of exposures to toxics on the job or into the category of psychosocial stress. It is clearly understood that persons of different SES have different kinds of jobs. In what ways job characteristics vary consistently by SES may be important in understanding the SES–health link. Much work examining psychosocial factors has already been done by researchers on job stress, health, and organizational environments. Little work has been done to examine the hypothesis that the physical environment of jobs could help to account for the SES–health link.

Considerable research has been conducted examining the association between job characteristics and health, particularly coronary heart disease. Although these findings are not always consistent, the bulk of evidence points to an association between CHD and jobs characterized by low variety and high demands accompanied by low control over pace and schedule. Haan (1985), Karasek et al. (1981), and Theorell and Rahe (1982) have all reported similar findings, taken mostly from prospective studies. For example, in a 10-year prospective study of ischemic heart disease in Finland, Haan found a strong association between education and income and job strain, and also found that job strain is a stronger predictor of CHD incidence than is education. Karasek et al. (1981) similarly reported that job strain accounted for more of the variance in a United States sample than did the Duncan SES scale (a commonly used measure of SES, composed of income, education, and occupation). The level of job strain to which an individual is exposed is not entirely independent of education. Job strain exposure may in fact be a consequence of education. In part, lifelong exposure to job strain may account for the association between education and health. Haan (1985) has found that in analyses that included adjustment for age, sex, six cardiovascular risk factors, and education, adjustment for job strain accounted for the association between education and ischemic heart disease. The same results were found for all-cause mortality. In general, it appears that the job strain model is promising as an explanatory factor that varies in a consistent manner across job categories, is strongly associated with more traditional measures of SES, and is associated with health. Furthermore, there is a gradient of health associated with job strain.

Although the physical work environment is often included in the measure of job strain discussed above, some researchers have suggested that exposures to noxious occupational physical or chemical agents could account for SES differences in health (Haan 1985). Although there is little research examining this supposition, it is not entirely implausible to think that persons in lower SES will be exposed to more hazardous agents on the job. However, the SES gradient in health cannot be accounted for by variations in such exposures since persons in the higher SES levels are not likely to be more exposed to physical or chemical agents than those in the highest SES. In addition, the unemployed, who are presumably not exposed at all, generally suffer the highest mortality and morbidity rates of all occupational groups. On the other hand, some evidence exists (Haan 1985) suggesting that workplace exposure to noise co-occurs with job strain and may interact with job strain to enhance the risk of coronary heart disease. This area deserves much more attention.

This discussion has attempted to sift through and summarize an expanding field of research on the sociophysical environmental causes of ill health, looking for a link between SES and health. Several findings seem to emerge from this examination:

1. Sociodemographic environmental factors may be associated with health status, and this association may not be due to the mediation of individual-level behavioral risk factors. These factors may be useful in accounting for the SES-health link.

2. Job strain is associated with the incidence of nonfatal and fatal coronary heart disease and with all-cause mortality and may provide additional explanatory material concerning the association between education and CHD and all-cause mortality.

3. There is a need for a general conceptual model to help organize thinking on this topic. The demands-control model developed for job strain research might be translated to wider settings such as the community and be used to examine the SES-health links in general. The central focus of the job strain model is that *control* over work pace, scheduling, and hours interacts with physical and psychosocial *demands* such that persons experiencing low control and high demands are at highest risk. Presumably, in a low control–high demands situation, individuals may be inhibited from mobilizing the personal and social resources they need to cope with and meet those demands. In addition, the availability of these resources may be an important factor in such responses. Although this approach is relatively well developed in the job stress literature, it has not been adapted or applied to the investigation of SES and health. We will expand upon this approach in our final section.

CONCLUSIONS

We have reviewed evidence in this paper and elsewhere that SES and health are associated, that the SES-health link is graded, and that this gradient exists in many industrialized countries. We have seen also that the SES differences in health have persisted over time and in fact have probably increased. Further, they are not likely to be primarily accounted for by behavioral risk factors, by medical care factors, by selection, by racial differences, or by personality differences. We have reviewed evidence that SES and health are linked by a variety of possible routes, including individual, social, and environmental, but no single factor or set of factors seems completely to account for this association. Clearly, what is needed is an approach to thinking about this problem that integrates and organizes what is known so that a coherent program of research and intervention can be designed.

Any attempt to provide a detailed discussion of such a theoretical approach is beyond the limits of this paper. However, we would like to summarize our thinking in this area. The job strain research discussed in the previous section may provide us with a new direction if it can be expanded and translated to a more general model. As noted, this research suggests that disease rates are higher when people are exposed to high levels of job demands coupled with few resources to cope with those demands. Extending this concept beyond the job circumstances, it is possible to argue that disease rates will be high when people live in high demands situations and where they have a smaller repertoire of resources. The fact that those in lower SES positions have a higher burden of demands is clear; that they have fewer resources for dealing with those demands seems clear as well.

It should be pointed out, however, that resources are not simply characteristics of individuals but are also, and perhaps predominantly, characteristics of the physical and social environment. Thus, while individuals in lower SES positions may have less training and experience in dealing with demands and in taking advantage of opportunities, they also are faced with a variety of important structural constraints that limit access to options and opportunities. A proper translation of the demands/resources model to the problem of SES and health, therefore, will require a far broader approach to risk factors than is generally utilized. As our research (Haan et al. 1987) has begun to demonstrate, community or area characteristics may be important determinants of the health of those who live in them.

One central disagreement among those researching SES and health seems to be whether different factors are responsible at different levels of SES for the link or whether a single "big factor" is responsible. It does seem that a consistent pattern of association exists between SES and health. There are also exceptions to the pattern, as noted by Harris in his discussion of breast cancer and malignant melanoma in Chapter 6. However, it is the practice of epidemiologists in investigations of disease to focus first on the commonalities of exposure for identification of an etiologic agent rather than on the exceptions. In fact, we have generally found that the various specific factors proposed as candidates for explaining the SES-health link frequently covary with one another and do form an underlying "big factor," statistically speaking. Since we have observed a consistency of effect, it is not unreasonable, and may in fact be enlightening, to search for commonalities across social classes that can "explain" the association. If, as some reviewers have commented, these commonalities are really a multiplicity of different factors, then some general model may be useful for organizing the pieces into a coherent picture. We have attempted to introduce one such possible model in our discussion of job strain and the demands–control concept. This model implies that different elements of the physical and social environment may *interact* with behavioral risk factors and may also, at the same time, *covary* with such factors.

This is not to say that interventions directed at specific factors may not be important. Rather, we would like to explore an approach to intervention that focuses on the social and physical environment. Such an approach could allow extension and generalization beyond single factors to the entire SES-health relationship.

Current research by Haan and Kaplan in this area suggests that the social and physical environment plays a significant role in the SES-health link. This approach may provide a model that incorporates and permits integration of the individual, interactive, and environmental levels at which the SES-health link is seen. The central focus in this approach would be the demands-resources model previously discussed. This model permits us to examine simultaneously the physical, economic, social, and psychological demands placed upon individuals by their environment while relating these same demands to the availability, quality, and nature of the resources that individuals can command in response to them. It also allows consideration of the characteristic ways in which individuals act upon their environment to obtain resources.

To explore this approach a program of research is needed that includes the following:

1. Conceptualization and measurement of physical and social environmental resources and demands which can be linked to individuals *over time*. Such measures should include the working, home, and neighborhood environment and should consider not only people's perceptions of their environment but also the objective circumstances within which people live.

2. Conceptualization and measurement of characteristic interactions *over time* between individuals and their environments. Again, such measures should include interactions among all three of the environments to which the individual is exposed.

3. Conceptualization and measurement of individual-level psychosocial, social, physical-biological, and behavioral resources and demands through self-report and observation.

The SES-health link is one of the most profound and pervasive observations ever made in public health. The reasons for this link are not clear. Previous efforts to explain it have left many questions unanswered. We believe that a focus on an approach that integrates environmental and individual levels, and centers on demands and resources at both levels, holds promise for clarifying and advancing understanding in this area.

REFERENCES

Antonovsky, A. 1967. Social class, life expectancy, and overall mortality. *Milbank Memorial Fund Quarterly* 45:31–73.
———, Berstein, J. 1977. Social class and infant mortality. *Social Sciences and Medicine* 11:453–70.
Arnesen, E., Forsdahl, A. 1985. The Tromso heart study: coronary risk factors and their association with living conditions during childhood. *Journal of Epidemiology and Community Health* 39:210–14.
Baker, S. P., O'Neill, B., Karpf, R. S. 1984. *The injury fact book.* Lexington, MA: Lexington Books.
Bakketeig, L. S., Hoffman, H. J., Oakley, A. R. 1984. Perinatal mortality. In Bracken, M. B., ed. *Perinatal epidemiology*, pp. 99–151. New York: Oxford University Press.
Beresford, S. A. 1981. The relationship between water quality and health in the London area. *International Journal of Epidemiology* 10:103–115.

Black Report. 1980. *Inequalities in health: report of a research working group.* Great Britain: Department of Health and Social Services.

Blair, A., Fraumeni, J. F., Mason, T. J. 1980. Geographic patterns of leukemia in the United States. *Journal of Chronic Diseases* 33:251–260.

Blane, D. 1985. An assessment of the Black Report's 'explanations of health inequalities.' *Sociology and Health Illness* 7:423–445.

Blaxter, M. 1983. Health Services as a defence against the consequences of poverty in industrialized societies. *Social Sciences in Medicine* 17:1139–1148.

Blot, W. J., Fraumeni, J. F., 1976. Geographic patterns of lung cancer: industrial correlations. *American Journal of Epidemiology* 103:539–550.

Brennen, M. E., Lancashire, R. 1978. Association of childhood mortality with housing status and unemployment. *Journal of Epidemiology and Community Health* 32:28–33.

Brooks, C. H. 1975. Path analysis of socioeconomic correlates of county infant mortality rates. *International Journal of Health Services* 5:499–514.

Carstairs, V. 1981. Multiple deprivation and health state. *Community Medicine* 3:4–13.

Chirikos, T. N., Horner, R. D. 1985. Economic status and survivorship in digestive system cancers. *Cancer* 56:210–217.

Coates, R. A., Corey, P. N., Ashley, M. J., Steele, C. A. 1985. Alcohol consumption and blood pressure: analysis of data from the Canada health survey. *Preventive Medicine* 14:1–14.

Comstock, G. W., Tonascia, J. A. 1978. Education and mortality in Washington County, Maryland. *Journal of Health and Social Behavior* 18:54–61.

Cunningham, L. S., Kelsey, J. L. 1984. Epidemiology of musculoskeletal impairments and associated disability. *American Journal of Public Health* 74:574–579.

Dayal, H. H., Chui, C. Y., Sharrar, R. et al. 1984. Ecologic correlates of cancer mortality patterns in an industrialized urban population. *Journal of the National Cancer Institute* 73:565–574.

Dayal, H. H., Polissar, L., Dahlberg, S. 1985. Race, socioeconomic status, and other prognostic factors for survival from prostate cancer. *Journal of the National Cancer Institute* 74:1001–1006.

Dayal, H. H., Power, R. N., Chui, C. 1982. Race and socioeconomic status in survival from breast cancer. *Journal of Chronic Diseases* 35:675–683.

Devesa, S. S., Diamond, E. L. 1980. Association of breast cancer and cervical cancer incidences with income and education among whites and blacks. *Journal of the National Cancer Institute* 65:515–528.

———. 1983. Socioeconomic and racial differences in lung cancer incidence. *American Journal of Epidemiology* 118:818–831.

Diehl, A. K., Rosenthal, M., Hazuda, H. P. et al. 1985. Socioeconomic status and the prevalence of clinical gallbladder disease. *Journal of Chronic Disease* 38:1019–1026.

Dobson, A. J., Gibberd, R. W., Leeder, S. R., O'Connell, D. L. 1985. Occupational differences in ischemic heart disease mortality and risk factors in Australia. *American Journal of Epidemiology* 122:283–290.

Dott, A. B., Fort, A. T. 1975. The effect of availability and utilization of prenatal care and hospital services on infant mortality rates. *American Journal of Obstetrics and Gynecology* 123:854–860.

Duncan, G. J. 1984. *Years of poverty/years of plenty.* Ann Arbor, MI: University of Michigan.

Dutton, D. B. 1985. Socioeconomic status and children's health. *Medical Care* 23:142–156.

Edwards, G., Kyle, E., Nicholls, P., Taylor, C. 1978. Alcoholism and correlates of mortality. *Journal of Studies in Alcohol* 39:1607–1617.

Ericson, A., Eriksson, M., Zetterstrom, R. 1979. Analysis of perinatal mortality rate in the Stockholm area. *Acta Paediatrica Scandinavica Supplement* 275:35–40.

Fisher, S. 1978. Relationship of mortality to socioeconomic status and some other factors in Sydney in 1971. *Journal of Epidemiology and Community Health* 32:41–46.

Forsdahl, A. 1977. Are poor living conditions in childhood and adolescence an important risk factor for arteriosclerotic heart disease? *British Journal of Preventive and Social Medicine* 31:91–95.

Fox, A. J., Goldblatt, P. O., Jones, D. R. 1985. Social class mortality differentials: artefact, selection or life circumstance. *Journal of Epidemiology and Community Health* 39:1–8.

Frerichs, R. R., et al. 1984. *Cardiovascular disease in Los Angeles.* Los Angeles: American Heart Association, Greater Los Angeles Affiliate.

Gortmaker, S. L. 1979. The effects of prenatal care upon the health of the newborn. *American Journal of Public Health* 69:653–660.

Grossman, M., Jacobowitz, S. 1981. Variations in infant mortality rates among counties of the United States: the roles of public policies and programs. *Demography* 18:695–713.

Haan, M. N. 1985. *Organizations and ischemic heart disease: an epidemiologic study of employees in a Finnish metal fabrication company.* Doctoral dissertation. Berkeley, CA: University of California.

————, Kaplan, G. A. 1985. The contribution of socioeconomic position to minority health. In Heckler, M., ed. *Report of the secretary's task force on black and minority health. Vol. II. Crosscutting issues in minority health*, pp. 69–103. Washington, D.C.: Department of Health and Human Services.

Haan, M., Kaplan, G. A., Camacho, T. 1987. Poverty and health: prospective evidence from the Alameda County Study. *American Journal of Epidemiology* 125(6):989–998.

Haberman, P. W., Baden, M. M. 1974. Alcoholism and violent death. *Quarterly Journal of Studies on Alcohol* 35:221–231.

Hadley, J., Osei, A. 1982. Does income affect mortality? An analysis of the effects of different types of income on age/sex/race-specific mortality rates in the United States. *Medical Care* 20(9):901–914.

Haglund, J. A. 1985. Geographical and socioeconomic distribution of high blood pressure and borderline high blood pressure in a Swedish rural county. *Scandinavian Journal of Social Medicine* 13:53–66.

Hakama, M., Hakulinen, T., Pukkala, E., Saxen, E., Teppo, L. 1982. Risk indicators of breast and cervical cancer on ecologic and individual levels. *American Journal of Epidemiology* 116:990–1000.

Harburg, E., Erfurt, J. C., Chape, C. et al. 1973. Socioecological stressor areas and black-white blood pressure: Detroit. *Journal of Chronic Diseases* 26:595–611.

Hathcock, A. L., Greenberg, R. A., Dakan, W. A. 1982. An analysis of lung cancer on a microgeographical level. *Social Science and Medicine* 16:1235–1238.

Holme, I., Helgeland, A., Hjermann, I., Leren, P. 1981a. The Oslo study: social indicators, risk factors and mortality. In Bostrum, H., and Ljungstedt, N., eds. *Medical aspects of mortality statistics.* Stockholm: Almquist Wiksell.

Holme, I., Helgeland, A., Hjermann, I., Leren, P., Lund-Larsen, P. G. 1981 b. Physical activity at work and at leisure in relation to coronary risk factors and social class. *Acta Medicina in Scandinavica* 209:277–283.

Illsley, R. 1955. Social class selection and class differences in relation to stillbirths and infant deaths. *British Medical Journal* (Dec 24):1520–1524.

Institute of Medicine. 1985. *The prevention of low birth weight.* Washington, D.C.: National Academy Press.

Jenkins, C. D. 1983. Social environment and cancer mortality in men. *New England Journal of Medicine* 308:395–398.

———, Tuthill, R. W., Tannenbaum, S. I., Kirby, C. R. 1977. Zones of excess mortality in Massachusetts. *New England Journal of Medicine* 296:1354–1356.

Kaplan, G. A., 1985. Psychosocial aspects of chronic illness: direct and indirect associations with ischemic heart disease mortality. In Kaplan, R. M., and Criqui, M., eds., pp. 237–269. *Behavioral epidemiology and diseases prevention.* New York: Plenum Press.

———, Haan, M. N. Sept. 1986. *Socioeconomic position and health: prospective evidence from the Alameda County Study.* Presented at 114th Annual Meeting of the American Public Health Association, Las Vegas.

Kaplan, G. A., Haan, M. N., Syme, S. L., Miszcynski, M. 1987. Socioeconomic position and health. Invited paper, Carter Center Conference on "Closing the Gap." Supplement to *American Journal of Preventative Medicine* 1987:3(5).

Karasek, R., Baker, D., Marxer, F., Ahlbom, A., Theorell, T. 1981. Job decision latitude, job demands, and cardiovascular disease: a prospective study of Swedish men. *American Journal of Public Health* 71:694–705.

Kasl, S. V., Harburg, E. 1975. Mental health and the urban environment: some doubts and second thoughts. *Journal of Health and Social Behavior* 16:268–282.

Kendrick, B. L. 1980. A spatial environmental and socioeconomic appraisal of cancer in New Zealand. *Social Science and Medicine* 14d:205–214.

Kitagawa, E. M., Hauser, P. M. 1973. *Differential mortality in the United States: a study in socioeconomic epidemiology.* Cambridge, MA: Harvard University Press.

Kohn, M., Schooler, C. 1974. Job conditions and personality: a longitudinal assessment of their reciprocal effects. *American Journal of Sociology* 6:1257–1286.

Koskenvuo, M., Sarna, S., Kaprio, J., Lonnqvist, J. 1979. Cause-specific mortality by marital status and social class in Finland during 1969–1971. *Social Science and Medicine* 13a:691–697.

Kraus, J., Redford, R. J. 1975. Some ecological correlates of perinatal mortality in a metropolis. *Medical Journal of Australia* 2:16–18.

Kristiansen, C. M. 1985. Seat belt legislation and seat belt use: effects on differences related to sex, social class, and smoking. *Accident Analysis and Prevention* 17:75–78.

Kuller, L. H., Seltser, R. 1967. Cerebrovascular disease mortality in Maryland. *American Journal of Epidemiology* 86:442–450.

Kuller, L. H., Cooper, M., Perper, J., Fisher, R. 1973. Myocardial infarction and sudden death in an urban community. *Bulletin of the New York Academy of Medicine* 49(6):532–543.

Lapidus, L., Bengtsson, C. 1986. Socioeconomic factors and physical activity in relation to cardiovascular disease and death: a 12-year follow-up of participants in a population study of women in Gothenburg, Sweden. *British Heart Journal* 55:295–301.

Lave, L. B., Seskin, E. P. 1977. *Air pollution and human health.* Baltimore: The Johns Hopkins University Press for Resources for the Future.

Lawton, P. M., Nahemow, L. 1979. Social areas and the well-being of tenants in housing for the elderly. *Multivariate Behavioral Research* 14:463–484.

Lerner, M. 1986. Cancer mortality differentials in Baltimore, 1959–1961 to 1979–1981. In *Cancer in the economically disadvantaged*. New York: American Cancer Society.

———, Stutz, R. N. 1978. Mortality by socioeconomic status, 1959–1961 and 1969–1971. *Maryland State Medical Journal* (Dec):35–43.

Leren, P., Helgeland, A., Hjermann, I., Holme, I. 1983. The Oslo study: CHD risk factors, socioeconomic influences and intervention. *American Heart Journal* 106:1200–1206.

Lines, D. R. 1977. An Auckland high school health survey. *Australia and New Zealand Journal of Medicine* 7:143–147.

Lipworth, L., Abelin, T., Connelly, R. R. 1970. Socioeconomic factors in the prognosis of cancer patients. *Journal of Chronic Diseases* 23:105–116.

Lloyd, O. L., Smith, G., Lloyd, M. M., Holland, Y., Gailey, F. 1985. Raised mortality from lung cancer and high sex ratios of birth associated with industrial pollution. *British Journal of Industrial Medicine* 42:475–480.

Mack, T. M., Paganini-Hill, A. 1981. Epidemiology of pancreas cancer in Los Angeles. *Cancer* 47:1474–1483.

Mahaffey, K. R., Annest, J. L., Roberts, J., Murphy, R. S. 1982. National estimates of blood lead levels: United States 1976–1980: association with selected demographic and socioeconomic factors. *New England Journal of Medicine* 307:573–579.

Mare, R. D. 1982. Socioeconomic effects on child mortality in the United States. *American Journal of Public Health* 72:539–547.

Markides, K. S., Barnes, D. 1977. A methodological note on the relationship between infant mortality and socioeconomic status with evidence from San Antonio, Texas. *Social Biology* 24:38–44.

Marmot, M. G. 1986. Social inequalities in mortality: the social environment. In Wilkinson, R. G., ed. *Class and health—research and longitudinal data*, pp. 1–20. London: Tavistock Publications.

———, Adelstein, A. M., Robinson, N., Rose, G. A. 1978a.

Changing social-class distribution of heart disease. *British Medical Journal* 2:1109–1112.

Marmot, M. G., Rose, G., Shipley, M., Hamilton, P. J. S. 1978b. Employment grade and coronary heart disease in British civil servants. *Journal of Epidemiology and Community Health* 32:244–249.

Marmot, M. G., Shipley, M. J., Rose, G. 1984. Inequalities in death-specific explanations of a general pattern. *Lancet* (May 5):1003–1006.

McCormick, M. C. 1985. The contribution of low birth weight to infant mortality and childhood morbidity. *New England Journal of Medicine* 312:82–90.

McKeown, T. 1979. *The role of medicine: dream, mirage, or nemesis?* Princeton, NJ: Princeton University Press.

McWhirter, W. R., Smith, H., McWhirter, K. M. 1983. Social class as a prognostic variable in acute lymphoblastic leukemia. *Medical Journal of Australia* 2:319–321.

Medalie, J. H., Papier, C., Herman, J. B. et al. 1974. Diabetes mellitus among 10,000 adult men. I. Five-year incidence and associated variables. *Israel Journal of Medical Sciences* 10:681–697.

Metropolitan Life Insurance Company. 1977. Socioeconomic mortality differentials by leading causes of death. *Metropolitan Life Insurance Company Statistical Bulletin* 58:5–8.

Miller, A. B. 1982. Risk factors from geographic epidemiology for gastrointestinal cancer. *Cancer* 50:2533–2540.

Morgan, M., Chinn, S. 1983. ACORN group, social class, and child health. *Journal of Epidemiology and Community Health* 37:196–203.

Morgenstern, H. 1980. The changing association between social status and coronary heart disease in a rural population. *Social Science and Medicine* 14a:191–201.

Morris, J. N. 1979. Social inequalities undiminished. *Lancet* 87–90.

Moser, K. A., Fox, A. J., Jones, D. R. 1984. Unemployment and mortality in OPCS longitudinal study. *Lancet* 2:1324–1330.

Murrells, T. J., Catford, J. C., Smith, T. M. F., Machin, D. 1985. The use of logit models to investigate social and biological factors in infant mortality. II: Stillbirths. *Statistics in Medicine* 4:189–200.

Nagi, M. H., Stockwell, E. G. 1973. Socioeconomic differentials in mortality by cause of death. *Health Services Reports* 88:449–456.

National Academy of Sciences. 1985. *Institute of medicine prevention of low birth weight.* Washington, D.C.: National Academy Press.

National Center for Health Statistics. 1986. *Current estimates from the National Health Interview Survey: United States, 1983. Series 10, No. 154.* Hyattsville, MD.: Department of Health and Human Services.

———. 1985. *Health characteristics according to family and personal income. Series 10, No. 147.* Hyattsville, MD.: Department of Health and Human Services.

———. 1986. *Types of injuries and impairments due to injuries. Series 10, No. 159.* Hyattsville, MD.: Department of Health and Human Services.

———. 1986. *Disability days: United States, 1983. Series 10, No. 158.* Hyattsville, MD.: Department of Health and Human Services.

———. 1972–73. *Vital and Health Statistics. Series 10, No. 94 and No. 109.* Hyattsville, MD.: Department of Health and Human Services.

Nayha, S. 1977. Social group and mortality in Finland. *British Journal of Preventive and Social Medicine* 31:231–237.

Notkola, V., Punsar, S., Karvonen, M. J., Haapakoski, J. 1985. Socioeconomic conditions in childhood and mortality and morbidity caused by coronary heart disease in adulthood in rural Finland. *Social Science and Medicine* 21:517–523.

Pamuck, E. R. 1985. Social class inequality in mortality from 1921 to 1972 in England and Wales. *Population Studies* 29:17–31.

Papiernik, E., Maine, D., Rush, D., Richard, A. 1985. Prenatal care and the prevention of preterm delivery. *International Journal of Gynaecology and Obstetrics* 23:427–433.

Pearce, N. E., Davis, P. B., Smith, A. H., Foster, F. H. 1983a.

Mortality and social class in New Zealand I: overall male mortality. *New Zealand Medical Journal* 96:281–285.

———. 1983b. Mortality and social class in New Zealand II: male mortality by major disease groupings. *New Zealand Medical Journal* 96:711–716.

———. 1985. Social class, ethnic group, and male mortality in New Zealand, 1974–1978. *Journal of Epidemiology and Community Health* 39:9–14.

Phillipp, R., Hughes, A. 1985. Population sampling for studies of long-term residential exposure to air-borne lead: migration problems identified from electoral registrations. *Public Health London* 9:302–306.

Pirkle, J. L., Schwartz, J., et al. 1985. The relationship between blood lead levels and blood pressure and its cardiovascular risk implications. *American Journal of Epidemiology* 121:246–258.

Rantakallio, P. 1979. Social background of mothers who smoke during pregnancy and influence of these factors on the offspring. *Social Science and Medicine* 13a:421–429.

Rodin, J. 1986. Aging and health: effects of the sense of control. *Science* 233:1271–1276.

Rose, G., Marmot, M. G. 1981. Social class and coronary heart disease. *British Heart Journal* 45:13–19.

Rush, D., Cassano, P. 1983. Relationship of cigarette smoking and social class to birth weight and perinatal mortality among all births in Britain, 5–11 April 1970. *Journal of Epidemiology and Community Health* 37:249–255.

Salonen, J. T. 1982. Socioeconomic status and risk of cancer, cerebral stroke, and death due to coronary heart disease and any disease: a longitudinal study in eastern Finland. *Journal of Epidemiology and Community Health* 36:294–297.

Savage, D., Lindenbaum, J., Van Ryzin, J., Struening, E., Garrett, T. J. 1984. Race, poverty, and survival in multiple myeloma. *Cancer* 54:3085–3094.

Schwartz, J. 1985. *The relationship between blood lead levels and blood pressure.* Washington, D.C.: EPA.

Shin, E. H. 1975. Economic and social correlates of infant mortality: a cross-sectional and longitudinal analysis of 63 selected countries. *Social Biology* 22:315–325.

Simpson, S. P. 1984. Causal analysis of infant deaths in Hawaii. *American Journal of Epidemiology* 119:1024–1029.

Smith, J. P., Day, T. G. 1979. Review of ovarian cancer at the University of Texas Systems Cancer Center, M. D. Anderson hospital and tumor institute. *American Journal of Obstetrics and Gynecology* 136:984–993.

Spiers, P. S., Schlesselman, J. J., Wright, S. G. 1974. Sudden infant death syndrome in the United States: a study of geographic and other variables. *American Journal of Epidemiology* 100:380–389.

Stamler, R., Hardy, R. J., Payne, G. H., et al. 1987. Education level and five-year all-cause mortality in the hypertension detection and follow-up program. *Hypertension* 9:641–646.

Starfield, B. 1982. Family income, ill health and medical care of U.S. children. *Journal of Public Health Policy* 3:244–259.

———. 1985. *The effectiveness of medical care: validating clinical wisdom.* Baltimore: The Johns Hopkins University Press.

———, Budetti, P. P. 1985. Child health status and risk factors. *Health Services Research* 19(6):817–886.

Steinhorn, S. C., Myers, M. H., Hankey, B. F., Pelham, V. F. 1986. Factors associated with survival differences between black women and white women with cancer of the uterine corpus. *American Journal of Epidemiology* 124:85–93.

Stern, J. 1983. Social mobility and the interpretation of social class mortality differentials. *Journal of Social Policy* 12:27–49.

Sunderland, R. 1984. Dying young in traffic. *Archives of Disease in Childhood* 59:754–757.

Susser, M., Watson, W., Hopper, K. 1985. *Sociology in medicine.* New York: Oxford University Press.

Syme, S. L., Berkman, L. F. 1976. Social class, susceptibility, and sickness. *American Journal of Epidemiology* 104:1–8.

Taylor, E. M., Emery, J. L. 1983. Family and community factors associated with infant deaths that might be preventable. *British Medical Journal* 287:871–874.

Theorell, T., Rahe, R. H. 1972. Behavior and life satisfactions characteristic of Swedish subjects with myocardial infarction. *Journal of Chronic Diseases* 25:139–147.

Townsend, P., Davidson, N., eds. 1982. *Inequalities in health: the Black Report*. Harmondsworth, England: Penguin Books.

U.S. Surgeon General. 1985. The health consequences of smoking: cancer and chronic lung disease in the workplace, a report of the Surgeon General. Rockville, MD: Department of Health and Human Services.

van den Berg, B.J., Oechsli, F.W. 1984. Prematurity. In Bracken, M.B., ed. *Perinatal epidemiology*, pp. 69–85. New York: Oxford University Press.

Wadsworth, M.E.J. 1986. Serious illness in childhood and its association with later-life achievement. In Wilkinson, R.G., ed. *Class and health—research and longitudinal data*, pp. 50–74. London: Tavistock Publications.

Wegner, E.L., Kolonel, L.N., Nomura, A.M.Y., Lee, J. 1982. Racial and socioeconomic status differences in survival of colorectal cancer patients in Hawaii. *Cancer* 49:2208–2216.

West, R.R. 1977. Geographical variation in mortality from ischaemic heart disease in England and Wales. *British Journal of Preventative and Social Medicine* 31:245–250.

Wilkinson, R.G. 1986. Socioeconomic differences in mortality: interpreting the data on their size and trends. In Wilkinson, R.G., ed. *Class and health—research and longitudinal data*, pp. 1–20. London: Tavistock Publications.

World Health Organization. 1985. *A WHO report on social and biological effect of perinatal mortality*. Budapest, Hungary: WHO.

Wright, N.H. 1975. Family planning and infant mortality rate decline in the United States. *American Journal of Epidemiology* 101:182–187.

Yeracaris, C.A., Kim, J.H. 1978. Socioeconomic differentials in selected causes of death. *American Journal of Public Health* 68:342–351.

Chartbook

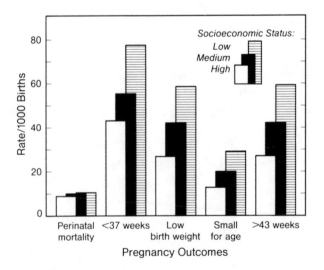

FIGURE I. Pregnancy Outcomes and Socioeconomic Status, Sweden, 1976–1977. *Source: adapted from Ericson, et al. (1984).*

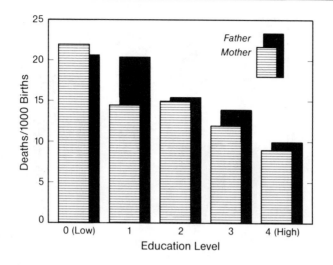

FIGURE 2. Perinatal Death Rates by Parental Education for Six States in 1973, United States. *Source: adapted from World Health Organization (1985).*

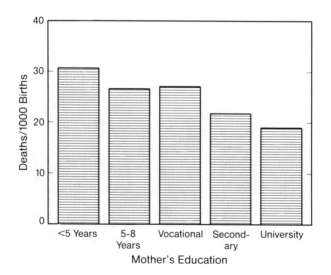

FIGURE 3. Perinatal Mortality and Mother's Education in Finland. *Source: adapted from Rantakallio (1979).*

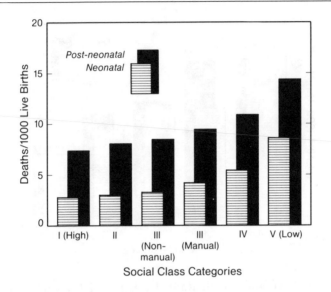

FIGURE 4. Infant Mortality Rates, by Social Class of Patients, England and Wales, 1975–1976. *Source: adapted from Morris (1979).*

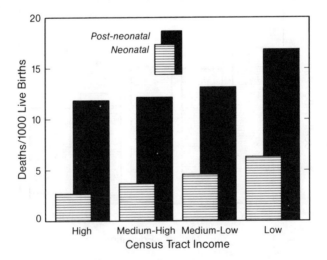

FIGURE 5. Neonatal and Post-Neonatal Mortality Rates by Income of Census Tract of Residence, San Antonio, Texas, 1970–1974. *Source: adapted from Markides and Barnes (1977).*

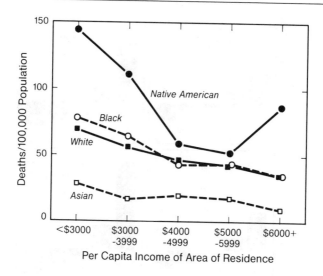

FIGURE 6. Death Rates from Unintentional Injury by Per Capita Income of Area of Residence and Race, United States, 1977–1979. *Source: adapted from Baker, et al. (1984).*

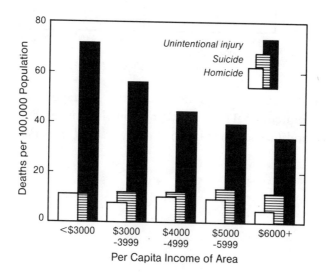

FIGURE 7. Death Rates from Unintentional Injury, Suicide, and Homicide by Per Capita Income of Area of Residence, United States, 1977–1979. *Source: adapted from Baker, et al. (1984).*

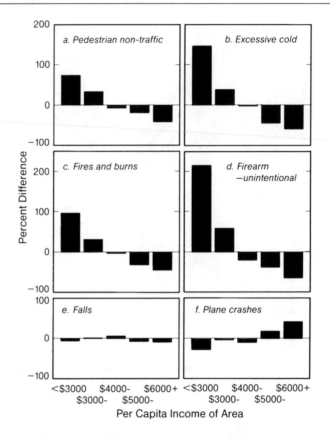

FIGURE 8. Percent Difference from the Average Death Rates from Unintentional Injury by Per Capita Income of Area of Residence and Cause, 1977–1979. *Source: adapted from Baker, et al. (1984).*

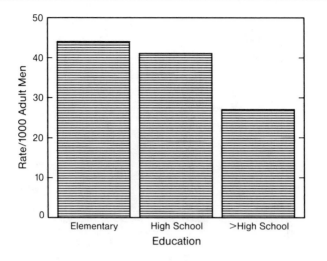

FIGURE 9. Education and 9-Year Incidence of Diabetes Mellitus in Adult Men. *Source: adapted from Medalie, et al. (1974).*

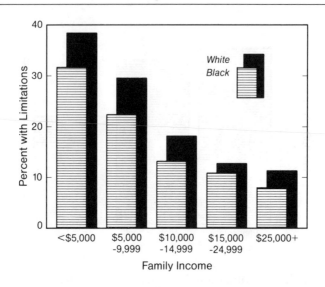

FIGURE 10. Family Income, Race and Activity Limitations due to Chronic Conditions, United States, 1979–1980. *Source: adapted from National Center for Health Statistics (1985).*

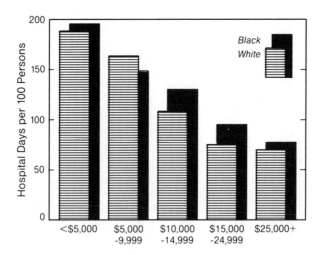

FIGURE 11. Family Income, Race and Short-Stay Hospital Days, United States, 1979–1980. *Source: adapted from National Center for Health Statistics (1985).*

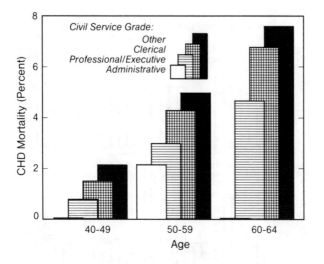

FIGURE 12. Coronary Heart Disease Mortality Rates in 7½ Years by Civil Service Grade and Age for British Civil Servants. *Source: adapted from Marmot, et al. (1978).*

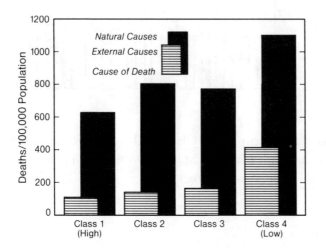

FIGURE 13. Social Class and Mortality by Natural and External Causes in Finland, 1969–1971. *Source: adapted from Koskenvuo, et al. (1979).*

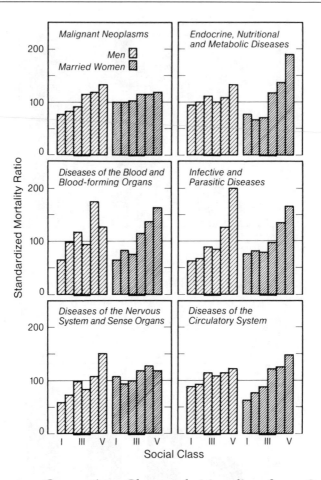

FIGURE 14. Occupation Class and Mortality from Several Causes in Adult Men and Married Women by Husband's Occupational Grade. *Source: Susser (1985).*

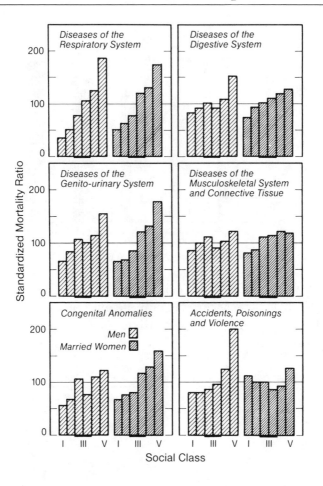

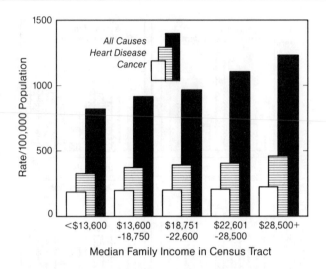

FIGURE 15. Mortality from All Causes, Heart Disease, and Cancer, for Males, by Median Family Income of Census Tract of Residence, Los Angeles, 1979–1981. *Source: adapted from Frerichs, et al. (1984).*

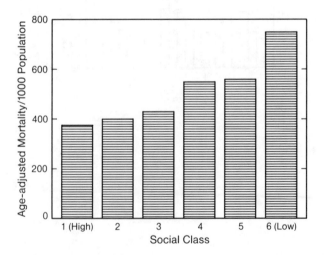

FIGURE 16. Mortality from All Causes for New Zealand Males by Social Class. *Source: adapted from Pearce, et al. (1983a).*

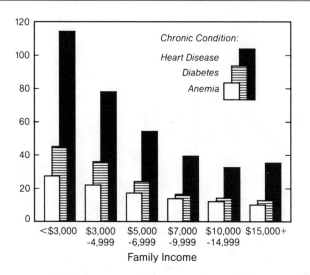

FIGURE 17. Annual Income and the Prevalence of Selected Chronic Diseases, United States, 1972–1973. *Source: adapted from National Center for Health Statistics (1972, 1973).*

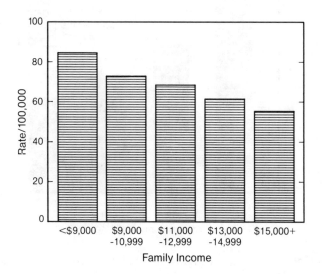

FIGURE 18. Lung Cancer Incidence and Family Income, Third National Cancer Study, 1969–1971. *Source: adapted from Devesa and Diamond (1980).*

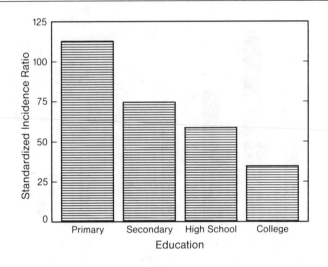

FIGURE 19. Cervical Cancer Incidence and Education in Finland, 1971–1975. *Source: adapted from Hakama, et al. (1982).*

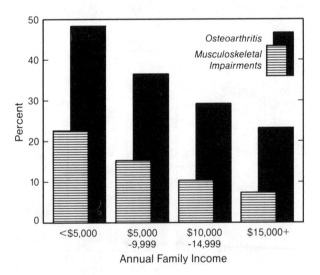

FIGURE 20. Prevalence of Musculoskeletal Impairments and Osteoarthritis by Annual Family Income, National Health and Nutrition Examination Study, 1971–1975. *Source: adapted from Cunningham and Kelsey (1984).*

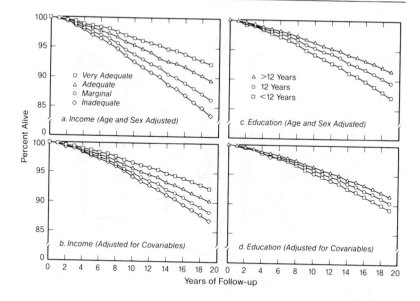

FIGURE 21. Age and Sex-Adjusted 19-year Mortality by Education and Income, with and without Adjustment for Race, Smoking, Alcohol Consumption, Leisure-time Physical Activity, Relative Weight, Sleep Habits, and Prevalence of Chronic Conditions (Hypertension, Heart Trouble, Cancer, Diabetes), Alameda County Study. *Source: adapted from Kaplan, et al. (1986).*

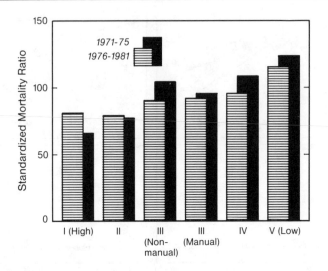

FIGURE 22. Social class and Mortality from All Causes, England and Wales, 1971–1975 and 1976–1981. *Source: adapted from Fox, et al. (1985).*

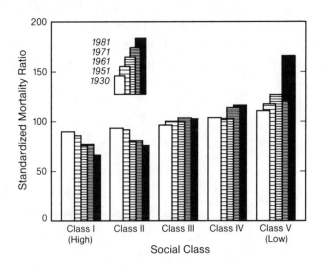

FIGURE 23. Trends in Mortality from All Causes by Social Class, England and Wales, 1931–1981. *Source: adapted from Wilkinson (1986).*

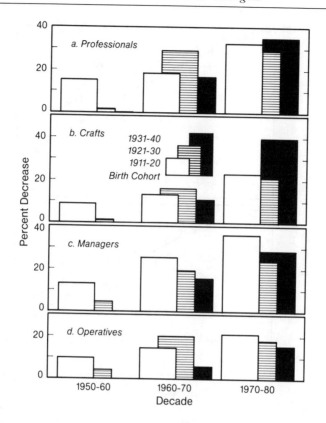

FIGURE 24. Changes in Smoking Rates by Birth Cohort, Year, and Occupation Class. *Source: adapted from Carstairs (1981).*

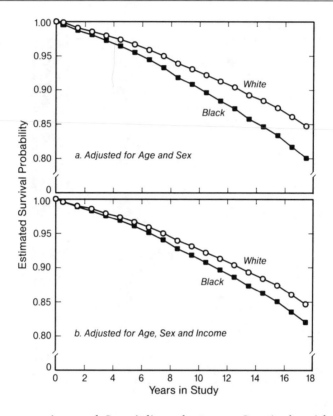

FIGURE 25. Age and Sex-Adjusted 18-year Survival, with and without Adjustment for Income, for Blacks and Whites, Alameda County Study. *Source: adapted from Haan and Kaplan (1985).*

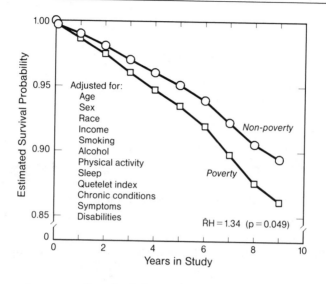

FIGURE 26. 9-year Survival from All Causes by Poverty Area Residence with Adjustment for Risk Factors, Alameda County Study. *Source: adapted from Haan, et al. (1987).*

Comments on Chapter 4

Mark R. Cullen

This paper approaches the observed SES health link by first elucidating the pervasive nature of the association, spanning almost all social classes, gradients, ages, historic time periods, and countries. Then the "usual" theories are tested for their ability to explain the whole association. Since none can, some alternative concepts are sought.

While I am considerably sympathetic with the central concepts in their emerging theory—hinted at but not developed—I think the arguments against the more traditional possibilities are not entirely satisfactory. In particular, I believe it is fallacious to assume, given the multifactoral nature of the outcomes, that to be an adequate explanation for a portion of the association a factor must account for the pervasiveness of the association over age, time, nation, etc. For example, the roles of lifestyle factors cannot be overlooked because they explain only 50 percent of the association, nor can differences in access to health care because the association persists in Sweden (perhaps more a comment about Sweden!), nor should occupational hazards because differences also exist among the higher classes and have persisted after OSHA (perhaps more a comment about OSHA!).

In fact, the underlying presumption of these authors seems to be that some "big factor" lurks behind many of these epiphenomena and can better explain the observed robust association between SES and health. I suspect, to the contrary, that the global association is made up of multiple interacting components whose sum (because of the untested interactions) exceeds its measurable parts. Furthermore, given the inherently remediable aspects of some contributory variables and the likelihood of multiple effects because of interactions, I would surely favor direct control of established causes with appropriate longitudinal follow-up as one of the best methodologic approaches to the residuals not explained in the simple models.

Lincoln Moses

We have here a very interesting and apparently comprehensive literature review.

A cautionary note may be in order about how strongly we may invoke the notion of trend in the problem. For example, early in the paper, we read, "This observation is important because whatever single or multiple factors are responsible for the SES health association should take this gradient into consideration." The cautionary note is this: SES, (or "education" or "income" by themselves) is measured rather approximately, and the distinction between one ordered class and another might, in principle at least, correspond not to a *different intensity* of some quality among people in the two classes, but rather to different *frequency of occurrence* of some type of person (some unrecognized analogue of readers of Henry James). Another small thought: In one section we find an SES-lung cancer gradient *after* adjustment for pack-years of smoking! This suggests to me that the manner of smoking of cigarettes among high and low SES Alameda women should be studied; it's possible that butt length, filter, or inhaling behaviors could be explanatory.

I find the dismissal of personal and social characteristics as explaining the SES health relationship to be somewhat less convincing than the other caveats. True, a sense of control may be thought of as an outcome of SES, but it also may be a possible intermediate agent in behaviors linked to disease. I do not find this thought in that section. How to distinguish the following two possibilities might be an important agenda item for future endeavors:

(a) Environment acts directly on the individual's attitudes and disease-resisting capabilities.

(b) Environment acts on the individual's attitudes and resources, thus leading to less successful disease-resisting behaviors.

I find the job strain hypothesis attractive, and like even better its generalization to strain in three environments (home, job, neighborhood).

The three-point approach to a research program that ends the paper seems to call for comprehensive global formulations; it may be more profitable to seek out some especially powerful special cases to examine.

5. Socioeconomic Status and Health: A Personal Research Perspective

Michael Grossman and Theodore J. Joyce

INTRODUCTION

We have been engaged in research in health economics at the National Bureau of Economic Research (NBER) for more than twenty-five years. The household production function model of consumer behavior, developed by Becker (1965) and Lancaster (1966), has served as the point of departure for much of our research. According to traditional demand theory, each consumer has a utility or preference function that allows him or her to rank alternative combinations of goods and services purchased in the market. Consumers are assumed to select that combination that maximizes their utility function subject to an income or resource constraint: namely, outlays on goods and services cannot exceed income. While this theory provides a satisfactory explanation of the demand for many goods and services, students of medical economics have long recognized that what consumers demand when they purchase medical services are not these services per se but rather "good health." This rather obvious point explains why health economists beginning with Grossman (1972a, 1972b) have adopted the household production function model of consumer behavior.

The household production function model draws a sharp distinction between fundamental objects of choice—called commodities—that enter the utility function and market goods and services. Consumers produce commodities with inputs of market goods and services and their own time. For example, they

use sporting equipment and their own time to produce recreation, traveling time and transportation services to produce visits,
and part of their Sundays and church services to produce "peace
of mind." The concept of a household production function is
perfectly analogous to the concept of a firm production function. Each relates a specific output to a set of inputs.[1] Since goods
and services are inputs into the production of commodities, the
demand for these goods and services is a derived demand for a
factor of production. That is, the demands for medical care and
other health inputs are derived from the basic demand for health.

In Grossman's (1972a, 1972b) model, health—defined broadly
to include longevity and illness-free days in a given year—is
both demanded and produced by consumers. Health is a choice
variable because it produces satisfaction (utility) and because it
determines income or wealth levels. The health production
function relates an óutput of health to such choice variables or
health inputs as medical care utilization, diet, exercise, cigarette
smoking, and alcohol consumption. In addition, the production
function is affected by the efficiency or productivity of a given
consumer—the amount of health obtained from a given amount
of health inputs—as reflected by his or her personal characteristics. Examples include age, race, sex, years of formal schooling
completed, and the endowed or initial level of health.

Maximization of the utility function subject to health production and resource constraints generates demand functions for
health and for endogenous health inputs. These demand functions depend on income, prices, efficiency in production, tastes,
and health endowments. Taste variables influence the choice of
different health levels by consumers with identical incomes,
prices, efficiency, and endowments. For example, some consumers may have a strong preference for cigarettes despite the
health hazards.

The distinction between health and medical care, which is
embedded in the multivariate production function, is a useful
point of departure for a discussion of research on the effects of
socioeconomic status in general and years of formal schooling
completed in particular on health status, because it emphasizes a
variety of mechanisms that govern health outcomes. In the remainder of this paper, we focus on research on the impact of

schooling on health, partly because schooling is a causal determinant of the two other components of socioeconomic status—income and occupation. Furthermore, a number of studies in the United States suggest that schooling is a more important correlate of health than occupation or income, particularly when one controls for reverse causality from poor health to low income (for example, Auster, Leveson, and Sarachek 1969; Grossman 1972b; Silver 1972; Grossman and Benham 1974; Grossman 1975 and the references he cites; Newhouse and Friedlander 1980; Edwards and Grossman 1981, 1982, 1983; Grossman and Jacobowitz 1981; Shakotko, Edwards, and Grossman 1981; Corman and Grossman 1985). This finding emerges whether health levels are measured by mortality rates, morbidity rates, self-evaluation of health status or by physiological indicators of health, and whether the units of observation are individuals or groups. Our research summary is selective rather than comprehensive. Indeed, it draws exclusively on our own studies and those that are closely related to them.

CONCEPTUAL FOUNDATION

In a broad sense, the observed positive correlation between health and schooling may be explained in one of three ways. The first argues that there is a causal relationship that runs from increases in schooling to increases in health. The second holds that the direction of causality runs from better health to more schooling. The third argues that no causal relationship is implied by the correlation; instead, differences in one or more "third variables," such as physical and mental ability and parental characteristics, affect both health and schooling in the same direction.

It should be noted that these three explanations are not mutually exclusive and can be used to rationalize any observed correlation between two variables. But from a public policy point of view, it is important to distinguish among them and to obtain quantitative estimates of their relative magnitudes. A stated goal of public policy in the United States is to improve the level of health of the population or of certain groups in the population. Given this goal and given the high correlation between health and schooling, it might appear that one method of implementation would be to increase government outlays on schooling. In fact, Auster, Leveson, and Sarachek (1969) suggest that the rate of return on increases in health via higher schooling outlays far exceeds the rate of return on increases in health via higher medical care outlays. This argument assumes that the correlation between health and schooling reflects only the effect of schooling on health. If, however, the causality ran the other way or if the third-variable hypothesis were relevant, then increased outlays on schooling would not accomplish the goal of improved health.

Causality from schooling to health results when more educated persons are more efficient producers of their health. This efficiency effect can take two forms: Productive efficiency and allocative efficiency. Productive efficiency pertains to a situation in which the more educated obtain a larger health output from given amounts of endogenous (choice) inputs (Grossman 1972a, 1972b). Allocative efficiency pertains to a situation in which schooling increases information about the true effects of the inputs on health (Rosenzweig and Schultz 1981, 1982a; Edwards and Grossman 1983). For example, the more educated may have more knowledge about the harmful effects of cigarette smoking or about what constitutes an appropriate diet. Allocative efficiency will improve health to the extent that it leads to the selection of a better input mix.

With regard to the competing explanations of the health-schooling correlation, the direction of causality may run from better health to more schooling because healthier students may be more efficient producers of additions to the stock of knowledge (or human capital) via formal schooling and because current and past health are likely to be positively related. Evidence in favor of this proposition is presented by Edwards and Grossman (1979); Shakotko, Edwards, and Grossman (1981); Perri (1984); and Wolfe (1985).

The "third variable" explanation is particularly relevant if one thinks that a large unexplained variation in health remains after controlling for socioeconomic status. To borrow from research results in the related field of investment in human capital and the determination of earnings (for example, Mincer 1974), it is clear that the percentage of the variation in health explained by schooling is much smaller than the percentage of the variation in earnings explained by schooling. Yet it also is intuitive that health and illness have larger random components than earnings. Thus, we need to worry about third variables only to the extent that they are correlated with schooling.

ADULT HEALTH

Grossman (1975) subjected the alternative explanations of the observed positive correlation between schooling and health to empirical testing and concluded that schooling has a significant and large causal impact on the current self-rated health of middle-aged white male adults in the NBER-Thorndike sample.[2] The estimated schooling effect in Grossman's study controls for health in high school, parents' schooling, scores on physical and mental tests taken by the men when they were in their early twenties, current hourly wage rates, property income, and job satisfaction. His finding is particularly notable because all the men graduated from high school. Hence it suggests that the favorable impact of schooling on health persists even at high levels of schooling. Grossman's decomposition analysis of the schooling effect reveals that a substantial fraction of this effect operates via the impact of schooling on wife's schooling, job satisfaction, and weight difference (the absolute value of actual weight minus ideal weight for a given height). Indeed, these three channels of influence account for nearly 40 percent of the total impact of schooling on health.

Grossman's analysis of the mortality experience of the Thorndike sample between 1955 and 1969 confirms the important role of schooling in health outcomes. This analysis is restricted to men who reported positive full-time salaries in 1955. To further reduce the magnitude of a possible relationship from survival to full-time salary, he estimated survival functions for men whose 1955 full-time salary exceeded one half the median full-time salary of $6,000 and for men whose salary exceeded the median salary.

In the fitted logit functions, schooling has a positive and statistically significant effect on the probability of survival. Indeed schooling is the only variable whose logit coefficient differs from zero in a statistical sense. Other regressors include earnings and job satisfaction in 1955 and the physical and mental test scores. The schooling effect is independent of the level of median salary in 1955 and suggests that in the vicinity of the adjusted death rate, a one-year increase in schooling lowers the probability of death by .4 percentage point. These results must be interpreted with some caution because the men in the Thorndike sample were only in their thirties in 1955, and relatively few variables were available for that year.

The importance of schooling as a determinant of self-rated health status and disability of persons in the preretirement years is reinforced in recent studies by Leigh (1983); Lairson, Lorimor, and Slater (1984); Kemna (1986); Wagstaff (1986); and Desai (1987). Leigh (1983) employs data from the University of Michigan's Quality of Employment Surveys of 1973 and 1977 and considers persons 16 years of age and older who worked for pay for 20 or more hours per week in these two national surveys. He shows that most of the statistically significant positive effect of schooling on health can be explained by decisions with regard to cigarette smoking, exercise, and the choice of less hazardous occupations by the more educated. This finding provides support for the allocative efficiency hypothesis.

Lairson, Lorimor, and Slater (1984) estimate separate demand for health equations for white and black males aged 45 through 59 in the 1966 National Longitudinal Survey. Schooling has a statistically significant positive coefficient in the regression for the self-rated health of white males, but the corresponding coefficient is practically zero for black males. Wife's schooling, however, has a positive and significant effect for blacks but not for whites. Given the high correlation between own schooling and wife's schooling and given that the black sample is only two fifths as large as the white sample, these results do not necessarily imply that a black male's education is an unimportant determinant of his health.

Kemna (1987) reports significant schooling coefficients in self-rated health equations estimated from the 1980 National Health Interview Survey. His findings are notable because he controls for the initial level of health with a dichotomous variable that indicates activity limitation due to chronic conditions. Unlike

Leigh, Kemna reports a large schooling effect with occupational hazards held constant. His measures, which are based on objective indicators from the Dictionary of Occupational Titles, are more refined than the self-reported variable used by Leigh. Moreover, Kemna utilizes information on both the respondent's current job and longest job, while Leigh lacks this information.

Wagstaff (1986) uses the 1976 Danish Welfare Survey to estimate a sophisticated multiple indicator version of Grossman's (1972a, 1972b) health model by maximum likelihood methods. He performs a principal components analysis of 19 indicators of nonchronic health problems to obtain four health indicators that reflect physical mobility, mental health, respiratory health, and presence of pain. He then treats these four variables as indicators of the unobserved stock of health capital. In those versions of his estimated model that are not clouded by multicollinearity, an increase in schooling leads to an increase in the stock of health.

In a study limited to low income men in the 1974 National Health Interview Survey, Desai (1987) finds significant positive impacts of schooling on their self-rated health and significant negative impacts on their work-loss days due to illness. Her results control for such factors as the number of chronic conditions (a measure of the initial level of health), the use of preventive medical care, and housing crowding. Together with Grossman's (1975) results for high income men, they suggest that beneficial impacts of schooling on health are observed at all levels of income.

The importance of schooling as a determinant of the self-rated health of older white males and of the mortality experience of white males of all ages is underscored by recent studies by Rosen and Taubman (1982) and Taubman and Rosen (1982). The first study is based on the 1973 Exact Match Sample, which was obtained by matching persons in the March 1973 Current Population Survey with their Social Security records and then tracing their mortality experience through 1977. Rosen and Taubman estimate separate mortality regressions for white males aged 25 through 64 in 1973 and for white males aged 65 and over in that year. For both groups mortality is negatively related to education, with marital status, earnings in 1973, and health status in that year held constant. Rosen and Taubman conclude: ". . . the effect of education does not flow solely or primarily through income effects, does not reflect a combination of differential marriage patterns and the health benefits of having a wife, and . . . those who are disabled or not working because of ill health are not found disproportionately in any one education group" (p. 269).

Taubman and Rosen (1982) use the 1969, 1971, and 1973 Retirement History Survey to study the self-rated health and survival experience of white males who were between the ages of 58 and 63 in the initial year of the survey. With health in 1969, income, and marital status held constant, health levels in 1971 and 1973 and changes over time are strongly related to years of formal schooling completed. There also is evidence that own schooling is a more important predictor of health than wife's schooling for married men.

Fuchs (1982) has challenged the conclusion that schooling has a substantial causal impact on health. He argues that the relationship may be due to an omitted third factor: namely, differences in time preference among individuals. That is, persons who are more future oriented (have a higher degree of time preference for the future) attend school for longer periods of time and make larger investments in their health. Fuchs attempted to measure time preference in a telephone survey by asking respondents questions in which they chose between a sum of money now and a larger sum in the future. He included an index of time preference in a multiple regression in which health status is the dependent variable and schooling is one of the independent variables. Fuchs is not able to demonstrate that the schooling effect is due to time preference. The latter variable has a positive regression coefficient, but it is not statistically significant. When time preference and schooling are entered simultaneously, the latter dominates the former. These results must be regarded as preliminary because they are based on one small sample of adults in Long Island and on exploratory measures of time preference.

Farrell and Fuchs (1982) explored the time preference hypothesis in the context of cigarette smoking using inteviews conducted in 1979 by the Stanford Heart Disease Prevention Program in four small agricultural cities in California. They examined smoking behavior of white non-Hispanics who were not students at the time of the survey, had completed 12 to 18 years of schooling, and were at least 24 years old. The presence of retrospective information on cigarette smoking at ages 17 and 24 allowed them to relate smoking at these two ages to years of formal schooling completed by 1979 for cohorts who reached age 17 before and after the widespread diffusion of information concerning the harmful effects of cigarette smoking on health. Farrell and Fuchs found that the negative relationship between schooling and smoking, which rises in absolute value for co-horts born after 1953, does not increase between the ages of 17 and 24. Since the individuals were all in the same school grade at age 17, the additional schooling obtained between that age and age 24 cannot be the cause of differential smoking behavior at age 24. Based on these results, Farrell and Fuchs reject the hy-pothesis that schooling is a causal factor in smoking behavior in favor of the view that a third variable causes both. Since the strong negative relationship between schooling and smoking developed only after the spread of information concerning the harmful effects of smoking, they argue that the same mechanism may generate the schooling-health relationship.

Farrell and Fuchs indicate two potential third variables that may generate the schooling-smoking relationship: mental abil-ity and time preference for the future. Grossman (1983) reports a negative relationship between smoking and high school achieve-ment test scores, and it is well known that these test results are important predictors of the probability of college attendance. Farrell and Fuchs downplay this explanation because, if the schooling-smoking relationship were due to superior mental ability, it should fall over time as knowledge about the harmful effects of smoking rises. Their analysis by cohort does not pro-vide evidence of a reduction over time. Note, however, that this result is based on a comparison of schooling coefficients for two cohorts: one who reached age 17 between 1953 and 1963 and the second who reached age 17 between 1964 and 1972. Since the first Surgeon General's Report on Smoking and Health was not published until 1964, neither of the cohorts reached age 17 after the process of information diffusion was completed.

Farrell and Fuchs conclude that their results are consistent with the time preference hypothesis but are careful to acknowledge that it cannot be tested with their data. In interpreting their findings, one should also keep in mind that they pertain to the residents of four small agricultural cities in California. Thus, they may not be generalizable to the population of the United States as a whole. Moreover, Farrell and Fuchs fail to uncover a negative effect of parents' schooling on smoking at age 17 even when own schooling is omitted from the set of regressors. Yet it is well known that parents' schooling is a significant predictor of teenage smoking in national data (for example, Lewit, Coate, and Grossman 1981).

Leigh (1985) presents evidence that supports Fuchs's (1982) finding that the positive relationship between schooling and health cannot be explained by time preference. Using the Panel Study of Income Dynamics, a nationally representative panel survey conducted by the University of Michigan's Survey Research Center annually since 1968, Leigh measured health inversely with a dichotomous variable that identified persons who became disabled (developed conditions that limited the amount or kind of work they could do) in 1971 or 1972. The independent variables in logit equations that explain the probability of becoming disabled pertained to the year prior to the onset of the disability. Schooling had a negative and statistically significant logit coefficient. When a risk preference index, which is highly correlated with a time preference index (Leigh 1986), was introduced into the equation, the schooling coefficient declined by only 10 percent and remained statistically significant (personal communication with Leigh).

Berger and Leigh (1986) have developed an extremely useful methodology for disentangling the schooling effect from the time preference effect. Their methodology amounts to treating schooling as an endogenous variable in the health equation and estimating the equation by a variant of two-stage least squares.[3] If the instrumental variables used to predict schooling in the first stage are uncorrelated with time preference, this technique yields an unbiased estimate of the schooling coefficient. Since the framework generates a recursive model with correlated errors, exogenous variables that are unique to the health equation are not used to predict schooling.

Berger and Leigh apply their methodology to two data sets:

the first National Health and Nutrition Examination Survey (NHANES I) and the National Longitudinal Survey of Young Men (NLS). In NHANES I, health was measured by blood pressure, and separate equations were obtained for persons aged 20 through 40 and over age 40 in the period 1971 through 1975. The schooling equation was identified by ancestry and by average real per capita income and average real per capita expenditures on education in the state in which an individual resided from the year of birth to age 6. These variables entered the schooling equation but were excluded from the health equation. In the NLS, health was measured by a dichotomous variable that identified men who in 1976 reported that health limited or prevented them from working and alternatively by a dichotomous variable that identified the presence of a functional health limitation. The men in the sample were between the ages of 24 and 34 in 1976, had left school by that year, and reported no health limitations in 1966 (the first year of the survey). The schooling equation was identified by IQ, Knowledge of Work test scores, and parents' schooling.

In the NLS, the schooling coefficient rises in absolute value when predicted schooling replaces actual schooling, and health is measured by work limitation. When health is measured by functional limitation, the two-stage least squares schooling coefficient is approximately equal to the ordinary least squares coefficient, although the latter is estimated with more precision. For persons aged 20 through 40 in NHANES I, schooling has a larger impact on blood pressure in absolute value in the two-stage regressions. For persons over age 40, however, the predicted value of schooling has a positive and insignificant regression coefficient. Except for the last finding, these results are inconsistent with the time preference hypothesis and consistent with the hypothesis that schooling causes health.

In his penetrating analysis of the availability effect in the market for physicians' services, Pauly (1980) argues that the more educated should be less susceptible to demand manipulation by physicians because they have more information. His demand functions for physician visits estimated with the 1970 National Health Interview Survey contain empirical evidence in favor of this proposition. In particular, positive and significant coefficients of physicians per capita in the primary sampling unit of residence are observed only for persons in households in which heads are not high school graduates. One would have to go a long way in order to explain these results in terms of time preference.

CHILDHOOD AND ADOLESCENT HEALTH

Evidence that schooling causes health is contained in research by Edwards, Grossman, and Shakotko on the determinants of child and adolescent health (Edwards and Grossman 1981, 1982, 1983; Shakotko, Edwards, and Grossman 1981). They studied child and adolescent health in the context of the nature-nurture controversy. Their research used data from Cycle II of the U.S. Health Examination Survey (children aged 6 through 11 years in the period 1963 through 1965), Cycle III of the Health Examination Survey (adolescents aged 12 through 17 years in the period 1966 through 1970), and the panel of individuals (one third of the full Cycle III sample) who were examined in both cycles.

Edwards, Grossman, and Shakotko found that the home environment in general and mother's schooling in particular play an extremely important role in the determination of child and adolescent health. It is not surprising to find that children's home environment has a positive impact on their health with no other variables held constant. Moreover, it is difficult to sort out the effect of nature from that of nurture because it is difficult to measure a child's genetic endowment and because genetic differences may induce environmental changes. Nevertheless, Edwards, Grossman, and Shakotko have accumulated a number of suggestive pieces of evidence on the true importance of the home environment. With birth weight, mother's age at birth, congenital abnormalities, and other proxies for genetic endowment, and with family income held constant, parents' schooling has positive and statistically significant effects on many measures of health in childhood and adolescence. For example, children and teenagers of more educated mothers have better oral health, are less likely to be obese, and less likely to have anemia than children of less educated mothers. Father's schooling plays a much less important role in the determination of oral health, obesity, and anemia than mother's schooling. The latter findings are important because equal effects would be expected if the schooling variables were simply proxies for unmeasured genetic endowments. On the other hand, if the effect of schooling is primarily environmental, one would expect the impact of mother's schooling to be larger because she is the family member most involved with children's health care.

Several additional pieces of evidence underscore the robustness of the above finding. When oral health is examined in a longitudinal context, mother's schooling dominates father's schooling in the determination of the periodontal index in adolescence, with the periodontal index in childhood held constant. Similar comments apply to the effect of mother's schooling on school absence due to illness in adolescence (with school absence due to illness in childhood held constant) and to the effect of mother's schooling on obesity in adolescence (with obesity in childhood held constant).

Research by Wilcox-Gök (1983) calls into question some of the above interpretations. She studied the determinants of child health in a sample of natural and adopted sibling pairs. The children in her sample were between the ages of 5 and 14 in 1978 and were all members of the Medical Care Group of Washington University (a prepaid, comprehensive medical care plan) in St. Louis, Missouri. Health was measured by the number of days a child had missed from usual activities due to illness or injury in a five-month period as reported by parents. The results for natural siblings reveal that the proportion of the variation in health explained by unmeasured sources of common family background is much greater than the proportion explained by measured variables. Moreover, the correlation between natural siblings' health is significantly higher than for sibling pairs in which one child was adopted (was not the natural child of at least one parent). These results point to the importance of genetic endowment.

Clearly, Wilcox-Gök's findings are not generalizable to the population of the United States. Not only are they specific to the residents of one city, but the families in the sample had a higher mean income and a larger number of children (the prepaid group practice offered special family membership rates) than the typical U.S. family. In addition, one parental-reported health indicator is employed in contrast to the variety of measures, many of which come from physical examinations, used by Edwards, Grossman, and Shakotko.

INFANT HEALTH

Since 1980, Grossman and his associates (Grossman and Jacobowitz 1981; Corman and Grossman 1985; Joyce and Grossman 1986; Corman, Joyce, and Grossman 1987; Joyce 1987a, 1987b) as well as other economists (Rosenzweig and Schultz 1981, 1982, 1983a, 1983b, 1988; Harris 1982) have devoted a considerable amount of attention to infant health in the United States. In part this is because birth outcomes are objectively measured by birthweight and survival to age 1 and because the infant death rate is approximately equal to the mortality rate of persons between the ages of 55 and 64 and much greater than age-specific death rates of persons between the ages of 1 and 54. Moreover, data bases have become available or have been constructed that contain information on the use of a variety of infant health inputs such as prenatal care, neonatal intensive care, nutrition, maternal cigarette and alcohol consumption, abortion, and contraception.

These data bases have facilitated attempts to fit infant health production functions in which the inputs are treated as endogenous or choice variables and such simultaneous equations estimation methods as two-stage least squares are employed. In particular, women with poor genetically determined birth outcomes, or their physicians, have incentives to offset these unfavorable prospects by selecting a different mix of inputs than other women. Consequently, ordinary least squares estimates of the parameters of the production function may be biased and inconsistent because the inputs are likely to be correlated with the disturbance term, which reflects the infant's unobserved biological endowment. Put differently, the observed correlation between an infant health outcome and an input reflects causality not only from an increase in input use to a better outcome but also from a reduction in the level of health to an increase in input use.

A number of the studies mentioned contain complete estimates of the components of models of the production of and demand for infant health. Not only are production functions fitted, but health output and input demand equations also are obtained. The demand functions constitute the reduced form of the model because only exogenous variables appear on their right-hand sides. The infant health demand function results when the input demand functions are substituted into the production function. This generates an equation in which birthweight or infant survival depends on a vector of input prices, whose direct and indirect cost components are negatively related to input availability, socioeconomic characteristics that reflect command over resources, and productive and allocative efficiency.

Estimation of the reduced form is particularly useful in assessing the importance of mother's schooling in infant health outcomes. Corman and Grossman (1985) fitted this equation using large counties of the United States (counties with a population of at least 50,000 persons in 1970) as the units of observation and a three-year average of the neonatal mortality rate centered on 1977 as the dependent variable. Separate regressions were obtained for whites and blacks. The independent variables were as follows: the race-specific percentage of women with family income less than 200 percent of the poverty level; the race-specific percentage of women aged 15 to 49 with at least a high school education; the number of hospitals with neonatal intensive care units per thousand women aged 15 to 44; the number of abortion providers per thousand women aged 15 to 44; the number of organized family planning clinics per thousand women aged 15 to 44 with family income less than 200 percent of the poverty level; the sum of the number of maternal and infant care projects and community health centers per thousand women aged 15 to 44 with family income less than 200 percent of the poverty level; the percentage of eligible pregnant women served by the Special Supplemental Food Program for Women, Infants, and Children (the WIC program); categorical variables pertaining to Medicaid coverage of prenatal care for first-time pregnancies and to the likelihood of obtaining Medicaid financing of newborn care; and the average annual Medicaid payment per adult recipient in the Aid to Families with Dependent Children (AFDC) program.

To examine the relative contributions of schooling, poverty, and public program measures to the recent U.S. neonatal mortality experience, Corman and Grossman applied the estimated regression coefficients to trends in the exogenous variables between 1964 and 1977. The extrapolations start in 1964 because that year marked the beginning of the acceleration in the downward trend in neonatal mortality. They end in 1977 because the regressions pertained to that year. In the period at issue the white neonatal mortality rate declined by 7.5 deaths per thousand live births, from 16.2 to 8.7. The black neonatal mortality rate declined by 11.5 deaths per thousand live births, from 27.6 to 16.1. The statistical analysis "explains" approximately 28 percent of the white decline on average and 33 percent of the black decline on average.

The increase in white female schooling made the largest contribution to the decline in white neonatal mortality. The reduction due to schooling amounts to approximately .5 death per thousand live births. The increase in black female schooling ranked second to the increase in abortion availability as a contributing factor to the reduction in black neonatal mortality. The estimated abortion effect amounts to a decline of about 1 death per thousand live births, while the schooling trend produces a decline of about .7 death per thousand live births.

Rosenzweig and Schultz (1981, 1982, 1983a, 1983b, 1988) examined birthweight and infant survival outcomes in the 1967–69 and 1980 National Natality Followback Surveys (NNFS). They estimated production functions in the context of a model in which mother's age at birth, birth interval, prenatal care, and mother's cigarette smoking are endogenous inputs. Rosenzweig and Schultz stress the allocative efficiency, as opposed to the productive efficiency, role of mother's schooling in the production process. To be specific, they argue that an increase in mother's schooling may improve the household's information about the true nature of the production function. Given such a model, schooling is a relevant regressor in the reduced form demand functions for the health inputs and outputs, but it is not a relevant regressor in the structural production functions. The same conclusion emerges from a model in which schooling influences the parents' references for healthy offspring.

Rosenzweig and Schultz (1981) tested the implication of the

allocative model by estimating birthweight production functions by two-stage least squares with and without mother's schooling. They found that schooling has a positive and statistically significant effect on birthweight (a continuous variable), but the inclusion of the schooling variable increases the sum of squared errors. (This is possible only in the context of an estimation method other than ordinary least squares.) Rosenzweig and Schultz conclude that they cannot reject the hypothesis that schooling should be omitted from the production function. This exclusion restriction was adopted but not tested in structural production functions obtained by Corman, Joyce, and Grossman (1987) and by Joyce (1987a, 1987b) with the county data base used in the Corman-Grossman study.

The conclusion that mother's schooling does not belong in the infant health production function should be interpreted with caution because the use of two-stage least squares rather than ordinary least squares frequently involves a tradeoff between a reduction in simultaneous equations bias and increases in specification or omitted variables bias and multicollinearity. Specification bias becomes a problem because certain variables must be omitted from the production function to satisfy identification restrictions. The degree of multicollinearity in the data rises because the predicted values of the inputs tend to be more highly correlated than the actual values.

Even if the hypothesis that mother's schooling should be omitted from the infant health production function is accepted, Rosenzweig and Schultz (1988) present evidence of the importance of schooling in birth outcomes. Their estimated input demand functions reveal that more educated mothers are much less likely to smoke cigarettes or to delay the initiation of prenatal care. These same mothers are much more likely to have a smaller number of previous births, to deliver when they are older, to receive an X ray while pregnant, and to deliver by caesarean section. Moreover, Joyce's (1987b) county-level abortion demand functions reveal that an increase in the fraction of black women aged 15 through 49 with at least a high school education leads to an increase in the abortion rate. Similarly, Leibowitz, Eisen, and Chow (1986) report that unmarried pregnant teenagers in a California sample were more likely to have an abortion if they were high school graduates as opposed to dropouts and if they had higher self-reported grade point averages.

Harris (1982) found a significant productive efficiency effect of mother's schooling for black birth outcomes in Massachusetts in 1974–75, and Joyce and Grossman (1986) indicate a similar finding for black birth outcomes in New York City in 1983. Neither study employed two-stage least squares estimation. Instead, they controlled for the unobserved health endowment by making specific assumptions about the nature of the correlation between the disturbance term in the production function and the corresponding term in the demand function for prenatal care. Harris's result pertains to gestation, while Joyce and Grossman's pertains to birthweight. The latter authors report that black women who completed at least one year of college gave birth to infants who weighed 85 grams more than the infants of women who completed at least 9 but no more than 12 years of schooling. This amounts to a 3 percent increase relative to a mean of 3,131 grams for this group.

IMPLICATIONS

The studies summarized in this paper contain the following implications for future research and public policy:

1. The demand for health model provides an attractive framework to examine differences in health between whites and minorities. With a few exceptions, most of the studies discussed deal with the health of whites or persons of all races. Thus they do not consider the extent to which the relationship between health and schooling differs by race. Research in this area will be most useful if it is based on national data in which minorities are oversampled and relatively complete information on health inputs are available. Of course, there is a fairly massive literature on racial differences in health, but this literature has not in general capitalized on all the insights provided by the demand for health model.

2. To date, the proposition that schooling causes health has withstood the challenge posed by the time preference hypothesis. This does not necessarily mean that more schooling leads to

better health via the mechanism of productive or allocative efficiency, because schooling may cause tastes to differ. But it does mean that the positive correlation between schooling and health cannot be attributed to an exogenous third variable, at least on the basis of the existing evidence.

At the same time, we applaud efforts to study the relationship between health and schooling in more detail, and we agree with Fuchs's (1982) contention that the mechanisms through which schooling affects health have not been fully identified. We also must acknowledge that the persistence of a negative relationship between schooling and cigarette smoking in very recent data points to the potential importance of time preference in health outcomes. Clearly more research on the time preference hypothesis with national data sets and in the context of the methodology proposed by Berger and Leigh (1986) is warranted. If these data are sufficiently rich to identify health production functions, the productive efficiency hypothesis can be tested against the allocative efficiency hypothesis using the procedure proposed by Rosenzweig and Schultz (1981).

3. Cigarette smoking, excessive alcohol use, and the consumption of illicit drugs have demonstrated adverse health effects. Recent theoretical work by Becker and Murphy (1988) suggests that these addictive behaviors can be understood in the context of a rational economic model of decision making over the life cycle. Becker and Murphy show that the demand for addictive goods such as cigarettes and alcohol should be inversely related not only to the current price of the good but also to its past and future prices. Past prices are relevant because they affect the current stock of the addictive good (an endogenous variable), and an increase in the current stock due to a reduction in the past price raises current consumption. The future price is relevant because a reduction in it raises future consumption, which lowers the "shadow price" of current consumption. This model should be pursued to see whether it contains implications concerning differential price effects and other differential responses according to years of formal schooling completed.

4. If schooling is the most important socioeconomic determinant of health, policies to improve the health of minorities and other low income groups by means of income transfers and sub-

sidized medical care may not have the desired payoffs. This policy implication is subject to the modification that, in the long run, income transfers might raise health by narrowing schooling differentials. But the studies summarized here suggest that public programs to improve health will not have dramatic effects unless they change efficiency in household production or tastes. These behavioral changes may be both difficult and costly to achieve, particularly if the mechanisms through which schooling operates are not firmly established.

NOTES

1. More precisely, a firm production function relates the firm's output to such inputs as labor, capital, and raw materials. Similarly, a household production function relates the household's output of a specific commodity to such inputs as the own time (labor) of various family members and goods and services purchased in the market.

2. In 1955, Robert L. Thorndike and Elizabeth Hagan collected information on earnings, schooling, and occupation for a sample of 9,700 men drawn from a population of 75,000 white males who volunteered for, and were accepted as candidates for, Aviation Cadet status in the Army Air Force in the last half of 1943. Candidates were given 17 specific tests that measured 5 basic types of ability: general intelligence, numerical ability, visual perception, psychomotor control, and mechanical ability. In 1969 and again in 1971, the National Bureau of Economic Research mailed questionnaires to the members of the Thorndike-Hagan 1955 sample.

3. Any multiple regression equation contains a disturbance term that summarizes unmeasured determinants of the dependent variable. To obtain unbiased estimates of the effects of the observed explanatory variables (the regressors) on the dependent variable, the regressors must be uncorrelated with the disturbance term. When this condition is satisfied, ordinary least squares is the appropriate estimation technique. When it is not, such instrumental variable estimation techniques as two-stage least squares must be employed. In the study by Berger and Leigh (1986), time preference,

which is the disturbance term in the health equation, is correlated with schooling, which is one of the explanatory variables. Therefore, in the first stage of two-stage least squares estimation, schooling is regressed on a set of variables that are uncorrelated with time preference by assumption. In the second stage of this procedure, the value of schooling predicted from the first stage, rather than the actual value of schooling, is employed as a regressor in the estimation of the health equation.

REFERENCES

Auster, R., Leveson, I., Sarachek, D. 1969. The production of health: an exploratory study. *Journal of Human Resources* 4:411–436.
Becker, G. S. A theory of the allocation of time. 1965. *Economic Journal* 75:493–517.
———, Murphy, K. M. Sept. 1988. A theory of rational addiction. *Journal of Political Economy* 96:675–700.
Berger, M. C., Leigh, J. P. Dec. 1986. Schooling, self-selection, and health. Presented at a session sponsored by the Econometric Society at the annual meetings of the Allied Social Science Associations in New Orleans, LA.
Corman, H., Grossman, M. 1985. Determinants of neonatal mortality rates in the United States: a reduced form model. *Journal of Health Economics* 4:213–236.
Corman, H., Joyce, T. J., Grossman, M. 1987. Birth outcome production functions in the U.S. *Journal of Human Resources* 22:339–60.
Desai, S. 1987. The estimation of the health production function for low-income working men. *Medical Care* 25:604–615.
Edwards, L. N., Grossman, M. 1979. The relationship between children's health and intellectual development. In Mushkin, S. J., Dunlop, D. W., eds. *Health: what is it worth*. Elmsford, NY: Pergamon Press.
———, 1981. Children's health and the family. In Scheffler, R. M., ed. *Advances in health economics and health services research*, Vol. II. Greenwich, CT: JAI Press.
———. 1982. Income and race differences in children's health in the mid-1960's. *Medical Care* 20:915–930.

————. 1983. Adolescent health, family background, and preventive medical care. In Salkever, D. S., Sirageldin, I., Sorkin, A., eds. *Research in human capital and development*, Vol. III. Greenwich, CT: JAI Press.

Farrell, P., Fuchs, V. R. 1982. Schooling and health: the cigarette connection. *Journal of Health Economics* 1:217–230.

Fuchs, V. R. 1982. Time preference and health: an exploratory study. In Fuchs, V. R., ed. *Economic aspects of health*. Chicago: University of Chicago Press for the National Bureau of Economic Research.

Grossman, M. 1972a. On the concept of health capital and the demand for health. *Journal of Political Economy* 80:223–255.

————. 1972b. *The demand for health: a theoretical and empirical investigation*. New York: Columbia University Press for the National Bureau of Economic Research.

————. 1975. The correlation between health and schooling. In Terleckyj, N. E., ed. *Household production and consumption*. Studies in Income and Wealth, Vol. 40, Conference on Research in Income and Wealth. New York: Columbia University Press for the National Bureau of Economic Research.

————. Dec. 1983. Economic and other factors in youth smoking. Final report, Grant Number SES-8014959, National Science Foundation.

————, Benham, L. 1974. Health, hours, and wages. In Perlman, M., ed. *The economics of health and medical care*. Proceedings of a conference held by the International Economics Association at Tokyo. New York: Wiley.

Grossman, M., Jacobowitz, S. 1981. Variations in infant mortality rates among counties of the United States: the roles of public policies and programs. *Demography* 18:695–713.

Harris, J. E. 1982. Prenatal medical care and infant mortality. In Fuchs, V. R., ed. *Economic aspects of health*. Chicago: University of Chicago Press for The National Bureau of Economic Research.

Joyce, T. J. 1987a. The demand for health inputs and their impact on the black neonatal mortality rate in the U.S. *Social Science and Medicine* 24:911–918.

————. 1987b. The impact of induced abortion on black and

white birth outcomes in the United States. *Demography* 24:229–244.

————, Grossman, M. Dec. 1986. The impact of induced abortion on birth weight among racial and ethnic groups in New York City. Paper presented at a session sponsored by the American Economic Association and the Health Economics Research Organization at the annual meetings of the Allied Social Science Associations in New Orleans, LA.

Kemna, H. J. M. I. 1987. Working conditions and the relationship between schooling and health. *Journal of Health Economics* 6:189–210.

Lancaster, K. J. 1966. A new approach to consumer theory. *Journal of Political Economy* 74:132–157.

Lairson, D., Lorimor, R., Slater, C. 1984. Estimates of the demand for health: males in the pre-retirement years. *Social Science and Medicine* 19:741–747.

Leibowitz, A., Eisen, M., Chow, W. K. 1986. An economic model of teenage pregnancy decision-making. *Demography* 23:67–77.

Leigh, J. P. 1986. Accounting for tastes: correlates of risk and time preferences. *Journal of Post Keynesian Economics* 9:17–31.

————. 1983. Direct and indirect effects of education on health. *Social Science and Medicine* 17:227–234.

————. 1985. An empirical analysis of self-reported, work-limiting disability. *Medical Care* 23:310–319.

Lewit, E. M., Coate, D., Grossman, M. 1981. The effects of government regulation on teenage smoking. *Journal of Law and Economics* 24:545–69.

Mincer, J. 1974. *Schooling, experience, and earnings.* New York: Columbia University Press for the National Bureau of Economic Research.

Newhouse, J. P., Friedlander, L. J. 1980. The relationship between medical resources and measures of health: some additional evidence. *Journal of Human Resources* 15:200–18.

Pauly, M. V. 1980. *Doctors and their workshops: economic models of physician behavior.* Chicago: University of Chicago Press for the National Bureau of Economic Research.

Perri, T. J. 1984. Health status and schooling decisions of young men. *Economics of Education Review* 3:207–213.

Rosen, S., Taubman, P. 1982. Some socioeconomic determinants of mortality. In van der Gaag, J., Neenan, W. B., Tsukahara, T., Jr., eds. *Economics of health care.* New York: Praeger Publishers.

Rosenzweig, M. R., Schultz, T. P. 1982. The behavior of mothers as inputs to child health: the determinants of birth weight, gestation, and rate of fetal growth. In Fuchs, V. R., ed. *Economic aspects of health.* Chicago: University of Chicago Press for the National Bureau of Economic Research.

————. 1983a. Consumer demand and household production: the relationship between fertility and child mortality. *American Economic Review* 73:38–42.

————. 1981. Education and household production of child health. *Proceedings of the American statistical association, social statistics section.* Washington, D.C.: American Statistical Association.

————. 1983b. Estimating a household production function: heterogeneity, the demand for health inputs, and their effects on birth weight. *Journal of Political Economy* 91:723–746.

————. 1988. The stability of household production technology: a replication. *Journal of Human Resources* 23:535–549.

Shakotko, R. A., Edwards, L. N., Grossman, M. 1981. An exploration of the dynamic relationship between health and cognitive development in adolescence. In van der Gaag, J., Perlman, M., eds. *Contributions to economic analysis: health, economics, and health economics.* Amsterdam: North-Holland Publishing Company.

Silver, M. 1972. An econometric analysis of spatial variations in mortality rates by race and sex. In Fuchs, V. R., ed. *Essays in the economics of health and medical care.* New York: National Bureau of Economic Research.

Taubman, P., Rosen, S. 1982. Healthiness, education, and marital status. In Fuchs, V. R., ed. *Economic aspects of health.* Chicago: University of Chicago Press for the National Bureau of Economic Research.

Wagstaff, A. 1986. The demand for health: some new empirical evidence. *Journal of Health Economics* 5:195–233.

Wilcox-Gök, V. L. 1983. The determination of child health: an application of sibling and adoption data. *The Review of Economics and Statistics* 65:266–273.

Wolfe, B. L. 1985. The influence of health on school outcomes: a multivariate approach. *Medical Care* 23:1127–1138.

Comments on Chapter 5

Mark R. Cullen

This paper focuses on a narrower and more testable framework for approaching the relationship between SES and health. It concludes, weighing diverse but relevant data sets, that educational level explains, in a causal way, a significant portion of that relationship.

As a pragmatist, perhaps more eager to reduce the gaps than understand them in a theoretical sense, I found this review most engaging. Considerable and appropriate attention is given to countervailing opinion and its supportive data, particularly the theory that education is merely a surrogate for the underlying association with health. The framework of Fuchs, which identifies the personality characteristic "time preference" as the possible underlying factor, is fairly and openly discussed, with available data for and against the hypothesis presented. Grossman and Joyce conclude that present data do not, overall, support Fuchs's idea but that more research is necessary to rule it in or out; I agree. (See also Fuchs's comments about the background papers in chapter 7.)

Overall, in view of the very clear ramifications this paper has for other background papers, I was disappointed that more serious debate about strategies for investment in education as an approach to the SES gradient did not emerge at the conference. For while it may be true that more education causes better health, given the present social and class structure, the impact of *change* in educational patterns on health remains less clear and indeed it is this relationship which would form the foundation for sound public (or private!) policy.

6. Social and Economic Causes of Cancer

Jeffrey E. Harris

INTRODUCTION

People of lower socioeconomic status are more likely to contract and die from cancer. This finding has been consistently observed no matter how socioeconomic status (SES) is defined—by income, educational attainment, occupation, housing tenure, census tract of residence, race, ethnicity, or by public versus private hospital care.[1]

In this essay I ask: How could an individual's socioeconomic status be a "cause" of his or her cancer? To answer such a question, I shall view the development of cancer as a protracted process that takes place in multiple stages in an individual over many years. The rates of transition between stages, I shall suggest, may be affected not only by conventional carcinogens such as chemicals, viruses, and radiation, but also by social and economic conditions.

In essence, my idea is to expand the narrow definition of carcinogen beyond those identifiable physicochemical agents that we usually regard as causing cancer. In doing so, I do not intend to downplay the role of the established carcinogens. In fact, I shall suggest that social and economic conditions may interact synergistically with such identifiable agents.

Among the individual, identifiable agents are the so-called occupational carcinogens. These agents—such as chromium, dichloromethyl ether, nickel, vinyl chloride, and radon daughters—have been termed occupational carcinogens because people are exposed to them primarily as workers on the job. Many of these jobs—copper smelters, shipyard workers, roofers, asphalters, miners, and leather workers—might be filled by workers from the lower socioeconomic strata; but this is not what I mean by a socioeconomic "cause" of cancer. Instead, my focus is on occupational and other social-economic conditions for which specific agents have not been identified. For example, I shall be concerned about the possible relationship between cancer, immune defenses, and unemployment (Arnetz et al. 1987) which, after all, is also an occupational category.

Likewise, persons of lower socioeconomic status may reside in places that are more exposed to pollution through the air, water, and other media. I do not analyze whether exposure to specific chemicals, such as polyaromatic hydrocarbons in air or polychlorinated biphenyls (PBCs) in water, is higher in poor neighborhoods.

Among the most important indentifiable carcinogens is cigarette smoke, which causes specific cancers among persons in all socioeconomic groups. I do not determine what proportions of such cancers among persons of lower SES might be attributed to their cigarette smoking, either alone or in combination with other exposures such as asbestos in the workplace or alcoholic beverages. For smoking-sensitive neoplasms, such as cancers of the lung and esophagus, attempts to identify an independent contribution of SES have yielded ambiguous findings at best (Brown, Selvin, and Winkelstein 1975; Devesa and Diamond 1983; Fox and Adelstein 1978; Pottern et al. 1981; Williams and Horm 1977). Socioeconomic gradients in incidence and survival have been observed, however, for cancers that are not known to be sensitive to cigarette use.

Instead, I focus specifically on interactions between cigarette smoking and the less well-delineated features of lower socioeconomic status. One notable example is the potential interaction between cigarette smoking and certain viral infections in the genesis of cancers of the uterine cervix (Brinton et al. 1986; Holly et al. 1986; Winkelstein et al. 1984), liver (Austin et al. 1986; Trichopoulos et al. 1987), and oral cavity (Schantz et al. 1986; Shillitoe et al. 1982). More careful attention, I shall suggest, needs to be given to the relationship between socioeconomic characteristics and certain viral infections, as well as the potential interactions between such viral infections and specific agents in the development of cancer (Rous and Kidd 1936, 1938; Schrier et al. 1983; Winkelstein et al. 1984).

[Black persons in the United States have higher incidence and mortality rates from many cancers (Henschke et al. 1973); they also are more likely to be economically disadvantaged. Although much of the excess of cancer among black persons may be a consequence of their lower socioeconomic position,]I do not resolve whether any of the excess is somehow intrinsic to being black (American Cancer Society 1986; Berg, Ross, and Latourette 1977; Devesa and Diamond 1983; Lerner 1986). Being black is clearly protective for certain skin cancers. A number of known genetic conditions that predispose to cancer occur predominantly among white persons (Swift et al. 1987; Schimke 1978). What matters in this essay is the acquired, not the inherited.

Finally, morbidity and mortality from cancer can surely impair productivity, cut short education, divert family resources, and reduce wealth. I acknowledge such issues of reverse causality (Bartel and Taubman 1979; Duleep 1985; Farrell and Fuchs 1982; Fox, Goldblatt, and Jones 1985; Luft 1975, 1978; Parsons 1977; Reynolds 1980; Wilkinson 1986), and discuss them no further.

In the three sections that follow, I analyze social and economic influences on three specific cancers—the breast and the uterine cervix in women, and melanoma of the skin in whites. These cancers display very different, contrasting relationships to SES. For breast and cervical cancer, moreover, there is little current evidence to incriminate occupational carcinogens. For melanoma, white-collar workers appear to have the highest incidence; moreover, with one exception (Bahn et al. 1976), I know of no identifiable carcinogenic agents associated with the disease.

Having considered some illustrative cases in detail, I turn in the fourth section to cancer in general. In particular, I examine current knowledge of human cancer as a multistep process, and begin to identify how social and economic conditions might impinge upon each step.

The remaining sections analyze two specific mechanisms in detail. The fifth section considers the potential effects of social and economic stresses on the body's immune defenses to tumor development. The sixth section investigates the role of social and economic factors in the timing and content of medical care for cancer. In the last section an agenda for future research is outlined.

1. BREAST CANCER: EARLY DETECTION AND REPRODUCTIVE HISTORY

I begin with breast cancer—a specific and important exception to the general rule that people of higher SES have less cancer. In fact, women in the upper socioeconomic strata have a *higher* incidence of breast cancer than women in lower socioeconomic groups (Cohart 1955a; Dorn and Cutler 1959; Hakama et al. 1982; Hirayama, Waterhouse, and Fraumeni 1980; Kitagawa and Hauser 1973; Williams and Horm 1977).

While upper class women may contract more breast cancer than lower class women, this does not mean that upper and lower class women get the same kinds of breast cancers. For example, at the time of diagnosis, upper SES women tend to show a higher proportion of localized breast cancers that have not metastasized to the lymph nodes or to other body organs. (Axtell, Asire, and Myers 1977; Axtell and Myers 1978; Berg, Ross, and Latourette 1977; Dayal, Power, and Chiu 1982; Linden 1969; Lipworth, Abelin, and Connelly 1970). It is not obvious, however, whether such localized cancers can alone account for the higher incidence among upper class women.[2] Nor is it clear whether socioeconomic differentials in incidence or staging of breast cancer have changed since the advent of mammography in 1956 (Egan 1962; Habbema et al. 1986; Shapiro 1977) or since the enactment of Medicare and Medicaid legislation in the United States in 1966.[3]

Cancer Survival

Once their breast cancers are identified, however, women of higher socioeconomic status have longer disease-free intervals and more favorable survival. The improved survival is not solely the result of more localized tumors in upper class women. It is observed even when the comparison is restricted to cases of the same clinical staging, or to cases of the same age.[4] There are likewise insufficient data to ascertain whether socioeconomic differences in survival have changed since the advent of adjuvant chemotherapy in the mid-1970s (Ries, Pollack, and Young 1983). The most reliable evidence comes from death rates, which show the combined effect of changes in both incidence and survival. The overall age-adjusted death rate from breast cancer among white women was 22.4 per 100,000 in 1960, 23.4 per 100,000 in 1970, and 22.8 per 100,000 in 1980; among black women, the corresponding death rates were 21.3, 21.5, and 23.3 per 100,000 (U.S. Department of Health and Human Services 1985). These black-white differentials, however, are poor proxies for socioeconomic differences.

Why the Higher Incidence Rates in Upper Socioeconomic Status Women?

One is tempted to explain the gradients in incidence and survival as entirely the consequence of improved cancer detection and better treatment. Thus, women in the upper social and economic strata are more likely to identify and seek care for early symptoms of cancer. Having identified such symptoms, they have better access to diagnostic and therapeutic medical services. Having obtained such services, they are better equipped to adhere to medical instructions. Having received care, their overall standard of living makes treatment more effective. As I discuss in Section Six there is reasonably good empirical support for most of these assertions. But they may not tell the whole story.

The observation that breast cancer patients in the higher SES groups have more localized tumors and better survival rates is applicable to many other malignancies. (Axtell and Myers 1978; Berg, Ross, and Latourette 1977; Cohart 1955a, 1955b; Dayal and Chiu 1982; Dayal, Power, and Chiu 1982; Linden 1969; Lipworth, Abelin, and Connelly 1970; Nomura et al. 1981; Pendergrass, Hoover, and Godwin 1975; Ries, Pollack, and Young 1983; Wegner et al. 1982; Young, Ries, and Pollack 1984). But the higher incidence of breast tumors in upper class women needs explaining. To make a cogent case for improved detection as the sole explanation for the higher incidence, we would need to postulate that the additional cancer cases detected in such women are in fact much less virulent forms of the disease. In that case, the incidence data would overstate the excess of genuinely malignant cancer among upper class women. Instead, through self-examination, doctor checkups and mammography, gross and microscopic lesions are discovered that would otherwise remain quiescent and thus go unidentified during life. But is there any biological basis for such a speculation?

The Receptor Story

It has been suggested that many breast lesions that are histologically cancerous to the pathologist under the microscope are actually clinically benign (Fox 1979). Indeed, there is increasing evidence that histologically similar breast tumors may be highly heterogeneous. One important source of heterogeneity is the presence or absence of "hormone receptors" on breast cancer cells. These receptors are only identifiable by means other than the pathologist's microscope. The presence in the cancer specimen of one particular receptor, called a "cytosolic estrogen receptor," appears to predict a lower level of malignancy, as well as a favorable response to certain types of therapy.[5]

Among postmenopausal breast cancer cases (and probably premenopausal cases), a higher proportion of white women's tumors in fact display such cytosolic estrogen receptors (Beverly et al. 1987; Mohla et al. 1982; Pegoraro et al. 1986). While the higher proportion is arguably the result of genetic differences between races, environmental factors could be important. No study of estrogen receptors among breast cancer patients has focused specifically on measures of socioeconomic status. But if environmental conditions do affect the presence or absence of estrogen receptors, the question is how?

Pregnancy History and Cancer

Women of lower socioeconomic position become pregnant for the first time at earlier ages than do women in higher strata.

Epidemiologic analyses indicate that a lower age at first full-term birth protects against subsequent breast cancer (Mac-Mahon et al. 1970). The effect is quantitatively significant. Women who have their first full-term pregnancy before the age of 22 have about one third the risk for breast cancer of those whose first pregnancy is after age 30.

Early first pregnancy appears to reduce the number of estrogen receptors in normal breast tissue. In a recent study, breast cancer patients whose tumors were rich in estrogen receptors were found more likely to have late first pregnancies (Mc-Tiernan et al. 1986). Early first pregnancy among women of lower socioeconomic status thus appears to eliminate those mammary cells that might ultimately yield less malignant forms of disease. If so, then differences in pregnancy history among women of varying social background could explain their observed differences in cancer incidence and survival.[6]

Early and Late Influences on Cancer

We thus have two explanations for the observed differences in breast cancer incidence and survival among women of different social status: reproductive history, especially the timing of the first full pregnancy; and access to cancer detection and treatment. These two explanations reflect events at quite distant points in the life cycle. Menarche and first pregnancy are early life events. They precede by many years the development of a clinical breast cancer in an afflicted person. Detection and cancer care are, in comparative terms, later life events.

This critical distinction—between factors that influence the early genesis of cancer and those that affect its later progression and morbidity—is of considerable importance and will be discussed in more detail in Section Four. Later-stage influences on cancer should reflect contemporary and more recent social and economic conditions, whereas early-stage influences should reflect socioeconomic conditions prevalent in the more distant past. The median age of breast cancer diagnosis is about 57 years (Axtell, Asire, and Myers 1977), so that the median year of birth of women now incurring breast cancer is about 1930, and the median year of menarche is about 1943. For this cohort, socioeconomic differences in the timing of first birth during 1945–1965 could be critical.

Many economists have described how education, one indicator of socioeconomic position, may permit an individual to "produce" his or her own health more "efficiently" (Grossman 1975). Others have noted that to some degree, education and health are "produced jointly" (Farrell and Fuchs 1982). The fact that more educated women are more likely to identify and seek treatment of early breast lesions may be an example of the former phenomenon. The fact that women with less education start families at earlier ages may illustrate the latter. The economic distinction between education as an input to health and education as produced jointly with health corresponds, in a rough way, to the biological distinction between late-stage and early-stage facilitators of carcinogenesis.[7]

2. Cervical Cancer: Pap Smears, Promiscuity, and Cigarettes

In contrast to breast cancer, the incidence of invasive cancer of the uterine cervix is elevated among women of lower socioeconomic status (Clemmesen and Nielsen 1951; Cohart 1955a; Hakama et al. 1982; Williams and Horm 1977). Like breast cancer, however, newly diagnosed cervical cancers in women of lower social status are less likely to be localized. Moreover, they carry a poorer prognosis (Axtell, Asire, and Myers 1977; Lipworth et al. 1970). While breast cancers vary considerably in their histopathology, over 85 percent of invasive cervical cancers are of the squamous cell type. The overall incidence and mortality from cervical cancer have been declining in the United States since at least 1950. The death rate from cervical cancer has been declining notably faster in whites than in blacks.

The influence of socioeconomic status on morbidity and mortality from cervical cancer may entail three different mechanisms: the use of pap smears; individual sexual practices; and cigarette smoking.

Pap Smears

Regular pap smears can detect early cervical cancer and, through appropriate treatment, reduce morbidity from the disease. Women in lower SES groups undergo pap tests less frequently (Kegeles et al. 1965; U.S. Department of Health and Human Services 1983). There is little doubt that increasing use of pap smears has been important in the decline of cervical cancer.

Sex and Viruses

Individual sexual practices, gauged mostly by the number of different sexual partners, have been found to be an important determinant of cancer of the cervix (Terris and Oalman 1960; Wynder et al. 1954). The cancer, in fact, is rare among virgins. The most compelling explanation of this finding is that sexual contact transmits certain viruses, primarily human papilloma virus and herpes simplex virus-2 (*Lancet* editorial 1987). The herpes viruses and certain other viruses have been increasingly implicated in the genesis of cancer in humans, particularly squamous cell carcinomas (Austin et al. 1986; Bréchot et al. 1982, 1985; de Villiers et al. 1985; Schantz et al., 1986; Shillitoe et al. 1982; Smith et al. 1976; Trichopoulos et al. 1987; Winkelstein et al. 1984; zur Hausen 1982).

Cigarette Smoking

Until recently, the epidemiological evidence on cigarette smoking in relation to cervical cancer was considered inconsistent. Within the past five years, however, there is increasing evidence of a potential role of cigarette smoking in the genesis of cervical cancer (Brinton et al. 1986; Winkelstein et al. 1984). While carcinogenic components of cigarette smoke are initially absorbed through the lungs, they have a wide bodily distribution outside the lung.[8] In fact, there is preliminary evidence for mutagenic compounds in the cervical mucus of cigarette smokers (Holly et al. 1986).

Synergistic Interactions

These three causal influences—pap smears, viral infection, and cigarette smoking—need not act independently. In fact, there is good reason to think they would act synergistically in the development of cancer.

Viral infection can result in the insertion of foreign DNA into the genetic material of the infected cell. This is one way that viruses are thought to cause cancer in humans and other animals. Moreover, it has long been known that viruses could enhance the carcinogenic effects of tars (Rous and Kidd 1936, 1938). Viruses can also turn on and turn off the cellular markers that permit the body's immune system to recognize and attack growing tumors (Schrier et al. 1983; Tanaka et al. 1985). Still other agents can depress the ability of the natural killer cells in the immune system to attack the viruses themselves. When the body's system of cellular immunity is depressed—for example by cigarette smoking—the humoral system takes over and increased antibodies to the virus are detected (Smith et al. 1976).

The notion of a biological synergism between viruses and cigarette smoking in the genesis of cancer is actually a special case of a much wider class of potential interactions between physicochemical agents and social and economic conditions. After all, there is little reason not to think of the failure to obtain pap smears as a social condition that interacts with the physicochemical agents. For many women, viral infection of the cervix through sexual contact and carcinogen absorption through cigarette smoking may have figured in the genesis of cervical cancer. Still, such women might not have exhibited clinically overt cancer had the lesion been identified at the preneoplastic or early neoplastic stages.[9]

3. MALIGNANT MELANOMA AND THE CONSUMPTION
OF LEISURE

We start with two observations. First, sunlight exposure appears to have a role in the genesis of malignant melanoma of the skin. Second, the incidence of melanoma, at least in developed countries, appears to be directly related to socioeconomic status (Lee and Strickland 1980; Vågerö and Persson 1984). While there is substantial evidence to support the first proposition,[10] the socio-economic gradient in melanoma deserves more careful scrutiny.

In an analysis of melanoma cases in the United States, college education and high income were positively associated with its incidence (Williams and Horm 1977). In an Australian study, skilled and semiskilled outdoor workers had lower rates than clerks and salesman, who in turn had lower rates than the managerial and professional occupations. Women showed the same gradient in melanoma incidence when classified according to their husbands' occupations (Lee and Strickland 1980). In New Zealand, there was likewise a socioeconomic gradient in melanoma incidence, with production-transport workers having the lowest rates. Melanoma incidence appeared to have little relation to outdoor/indoor work exposure (Cooke, Skegg, and Fraser 1984). A Swedish study revealed a similar occupational gradient in melanoma incidence, but only for the covered parts of the body (Vågarö, Ringbäck, and Kiviranta 1986).

Some investigators have concluded from such data that there is a genuine effect of SES on melanoma incidence, independent of an effect of sunlight exposure. Others suggest that such effects are still somehow mediated by differential ultraviolet light exposure among various socioeconomic groups. For example, indoor, undiffused fluorescent lighting may contribute to melanoma in white-collar workers (Beral and Robinson 1981).

Recreational Tanning versus Work-Related Sun Exposure

The dose-response relationships between melanoma incidence and sunlight exposure are no doubt more complex than for other skin-sensitive cancers. The critical question is whether intermittent recreational tanning, as opposed to prolonged work-related sun exposure, may have a different effect on skin melanocytes.

Some studies have suggested that melanoma incidence is related to cumulative sun exposure, both occupational and recreational (Holman and Armstrong 1984; MacKie and Aitchison 1982). But one large case-control analysis found that intermittent episodes of sunburn do pose a higher risk (Elwood et al. 1985). If so, then the hypothesis most consistent with the evidence is that outdoor work produces a protective tan on sun-exposed parts of the body. Further, the occupational gradient in melanoma incidence for the covered parts of the body would be an effect of intermittent, recreational tanning among upper socioeconomic groups. The fact that melanoma is found at much younger ages than other sunlight-sensitive skin cancers (McGovern 1977) may reflect a higher prevalence of recreational tanning among young persons.

I shall not dwell here on the evidence concerning recreational tanning among various social groups (Vågerö, Ringbäck, and Kiviranta 1986). The critical point is that the socioeconomic gradient in melanoma incidence may depend not only on work-related exposures, but also on the way in which leisure time is consumed. Analysis of the amount and content of leisure time may in fact have general application in the study of socioeconomic influences upon health. Consider, for example, the finding that certain types of leisure-time exercise, as opposed to work-related exertion, may be protective against coronary heart disease (Chave et al. 1978; Karvonen 1982).

4. The Multistep Nature of Cancer

I have hinted at "early stage" and "late stage" events in the genesis of breast cancer. I have also noted that viruses, cigarette smoking, and medical intervention can affect different stages in the development of cervical cancer. The dosing schedule of ultraviolet light that most predisposes to malignant melanoma, I have suggested, is the intermittent, high-intensity exposure characteristic of leisure-time suntanning among persons of higher socioeconomic position. I now seek a more general framework for tying some of these ideas together.

The development of human cancer is a protracted, multistep process that evolves over years, if not decades, during an individual's lifetime. It is widely recognized that specific chemical and physical agents in the environment can affect the multiple stages of tumor evolution. My main point here is that social and economic conditions can likewise impinge upon various specific steps in the oncogenic process.

The concept of the multistep origin of cancer is often applied solely to the process by which a single cell develops into a biologically distinct tumor. Here I employ the notion more generally to include the entire sequence of tumor generation, growth, detection, clinical progression, morbid evolution and, where applicable, recovery or death.

There is compelling evidence that at least the early stages of cancer development entail one or more alterations in the genetic apparatus of individual cells. The concept of "carcinogenic" or "cancer-causing" is sometimes applied solely to agents or host characteristics that influence such alterations in cell genes. Here I refer also to those characteristics of the human host that may influence the rate of growth of the abnormal tumor cells, their differential survival advantage over normal cells, their metastatic spread to other tissues, or their susceptibility to medical interventions. Among such host characteristics are a person's occupation, diet, sexual behavior, allocation of work and leisure time, exposure to infectious agents, psychological stresses, as well as the timing and content of medical care.

The Early Stages of Cancer

Most if not all human cancers appear to begin with some damaging alteration in the genetic material of a single cell. Although such genetic alterations may not offer a full explanation of cancer, they are central to its genesis.[11]

There are several routes by which such genetic changes can be effected: by ultraviolet light from the sun, by ionizing radiation, by certain viruses, and by certain chemicals. In patients with primary cancer of the liver, for example, the DNA from hepatitis B virus has been found integrated within the normal genetic sequence of liver cells (Bréchot et al. 1982). In the case of chemical carcinogenesis, the damage to DNA is not necessarily caused by the chemical in the original form that it enters the body. Instead, it is very often a metabolite of the entering chemical, produced in specific organs, that is capable of reacting directly or forming an "adduct" with DNA and with other large molecules.[12] In fact, the specificity of certain carcinogenic chemicals to certain animal species and to certain human organs may be governed largely by variations in species and organ metabolism (Miller 1980).

Oncogenes

The alterations in DNA that initiate the cancerous process appear to be specific to certain genes, called "proto-oncogenes," which are critical in the regulation of cell growth and differentiation (Balmain 1985; Bishop 1987; Weinberg 1982). Many different and complex types of damage to the genetic material of cells can apparently turn a proto-oncogene into an abnormally expressed "oncogene."[13] Many such oncogenes have been discovered in human and other animal tumors. In fact, experimental models now exist in which specific carcinogenic chemicals produce specific mutations in specific proto-oncogenes, consistently yielding the same type of cancer (Bishop 1987).

It remains uncertain whether the expression of a single oncogene can alone be sufficient to initiate cancer development in humans. In some experimental settings, two cooperating oncogenes are required for the conversion to a "transformed," neoplastic cell (Land, Parada, and Weinberg 1983). Such a finding is consistent with the notion, mentioned in the previous section, that very different genotoxic agents can interact in the production of malignant change. The finding of multiple oncogenes in many naturally occurring human tumors may also reflect the combined effects of various carcinogenic agents, encountered over a lifetime.

The likelihood that such compound genetic alterations will occur and be perpetuated appears to depend upon the rate at which cells are dividing (Borek and Sachs 1968). The rate of cell division may in turn be enhanced by nonspecific injuries to an organ. The idea is that nonspecific injuries stimulate tissue repair, which entails cell division. For example, in experimental studies, the effect of certain carcinogenic chemicals on liver cells is markedly enhanced by prior surgical injury of the liver (Kitagawa et al. 1980; Pitot 1982).

Although specific environmental agents may thus initiate the cancer process through genetic damage, the magnitude of their carcinogenic effects can depend upon other, possibly nonspecific characteristics of the human host. In principle, any nonspecific exposure or behavior that alters metabolism (e.g., alcohol's effect on liver microsomes) could in turn induce those critical enzymes which convert specific chemical carcinogens into their active metabolites. In principle, nonspecific forms of tissue injury, again through nonspecific toxic exposures or environmental conditions, could accelerate cell division at susceptible sites and thus enhance the genotoxic effects of more specific agents. Thus, a number of nonspecific irritants or inflammatory processes in the lung could enhance the carcinogenic effect of cigarette smoking (Skillrud et al. 1986). Such mechanisms could underlie the synergistic effect of asbestos exposure and cigarette smoking on the production of lung cancer. Moreover, the genotoxic actions of one agent could in principle potentiate the carcinogenic effects of another. (Certain chromosomal aberrations induced by BaP are enhanced in asbestos-exposed smokers [Kelsey, Christiani, and Little 1986].)

Cancer Promotion and Progression

The genetic alterations that characterize the initial stages of cancer yield an irreversibly modified, "transformed" cell. The existence of a transformed cell, however, may be a necessary but not a sufficient condition for the development of a biologically distinct cancer. In some identified experimental instances, the expression of an oncogene creates only a "precancerous" or "initiated" cell (Bishop 1987). Genuine malignant potential does not obtain until additional changes ensue.

There are two forceful arguments for the importance of such additional changes. First, there is a long-standing literature on the existence of precancerous lesions in humans, ranging from the identification of leukoplakia as a precancerous lesion of the oral cavity (Judd and New 1923) to the clinical diagnosis of early forms of cancer by cytological smears (Auerbach et al. 1957; Papanicolaou and Traut 1943; Papanicolaou and Koprowska 1951).

Second, in a long line of animal experimentation, mostly through the application of such chemicals as tars to rodent and rabbit skin, investigators recognized how more benign-appearing papillomas and epitheliomas could later turn into

more malignant carcinomas; they further recognized that sufficiently small doses of such tars could produce a preneoplastic
state in which no tumors were apparent (Rous and Kidd 1941).
Such experiments have been standardized into what is now
called the "initiation-promotion" model (Pitot 1982).

The Initiation-Promotion Model

In the initiation-promotion model, a single application of an
initiating chemical is followed by repeated applications of a
promoting chemical. While the initiating agent alters the cells'
genetic material irreversibly, the process of promotion is
reversible.[14] Although the precise mechanisms of promotion are
not fully elucidated, it appears that pure promoters do not initiate the early genetic changes of cancer. Instead, they may stimulate the growth of initiated cells, thereby rendering them more
susceptible to further genetic change.[15]

Many investigators regard promoters as widespread in the human environment. Alcoholic beverages have been described as
promoting oral, liver, and esophageal cancer; asbestos as promoting lung cancer; saccharin as promoting bladder cancer; and
synthetic estrogens as promoting adenomas of the liver (Pitot
1982).[16] Cigarette smoke is thought to contain both initiating and
promoting agents.

Whether or not the experimental initiation-promotion model
suffices to characterize the natural history of human cancer,
there remains little doubt that the early genetic changes in precancerous cells are part of a multicomponent, protracted sequence of events, in which the emerging cancer acquires selective advantages over other normal cells, resists attack by the
cellular immune system, becomes capable of proliferation and
invasion of adjacent tissue, and ultimately metastasizes to distant
organs. A more general term to describe such a sequence is cancer "progression."

Socioeconomic Influences on Cancer Progression

I suggest here that a number of nonspecific socioeconomic influences impinge upon cancer development during the progres-

sion phases. Two classes of socioeconomic influences will receive special attention.

First, I focus sharply on what many authors have generally termed the "stress" of poor social and economic conditions, and the ways in which such stress may affect "host susceptibility" (Cassel 1976; Haan and Kaplan 1985; Haan, Kaplan, and Camacho 1986; Marmot et al. 1987; Syme and Berkman 1976). I shall attempt to put in perspective what we currently know about the potential role of various types of social and economic stress on bodily immune defenses in cancer progression. Although there is a substantial experimental and clinical basis for a role of stress in cancer progression, we have very little idea, I suggest, as to its quantitative importance, particularly in explaining socioeconomic gradients in cancer morbidity and mortality.

Second, I examine the interaction between socioeconomic status, medical care, and cancer progression. Although there has been considerable work on the determinants of seeking medical care, little has been done on the content of such care or on the manner in which social and economic factors may influence the effectiveness of cancer treatment.

5. Immunity, Cancer, and Stress

There are numerous biological mechanisms by which the immune defensive system of the body could affect the genesis and progression of cancer.

First, the immune system conducts surveillance against viruses that may be oncogenic.[17] Second, in combination with certain mechanical defenses, the immune system influences the clearance of certain chemical complexes from the body.[18] Third, the immune system appears to have a role in recognizing and attacking newly transformed cancer cells. This is the most important and least settled area of inquiry.

Roughly speaking, the immune system is designed to detect and neutralize "foreign" or "antigenic" material. The system of surveillance against antigens is highly regulated. Antibodies against the antigen are produced by B lymphocytes; the B lymphocytes are in turn stimulated by "helper" T lymphocytes; the helper T lymphocytes are in turn regulated by "suppressor" T lymphocytes. Certain "killer" T lymphocytes and other immune system cells also attack the target material, producing a number of substances that execute the attack. The killer T lymphocytes are in turn regulated by "suppressor" T lymphocytes. The overall state of the human immune response depends on the counterbalancing effects of these regulatory cells (Nossal 1987).

Accordingly, an external insult that disrupts T lymphocyte function need not result in depression of the immune response. An insult to the regulatory T cells could actually enhance the immune response (Herberman and Ortaldo 1981; Reinherz and Schlossmen 1980). Many acquired diseases of the immune system show both kinds of defects. The process of aging is accompanied by progressive involution of the thymus gland, resulting in nonspecific deterioration of the entire T lymphocyte system ("immunosenescence"). While depressed aspects of the immune response in the aged could facilitate the initial establishment of tumor, the enhanced aspects could slow tumor growth. Such complex feedback effects have been invoked to explain why cancers occur more frequently but grow more slowly in older persons (Ershler 1986).

There is extensive experimental evidence that the immune system does indeed recognize some tumors.[19] Although some human cancers likewise express antigens that could be recognized by the immune system, nevertheless a great many others—at least at the stage of cancer in which they are studied—do not appear to be "immunogenic." That is, the immune system no longer recognizes them as foreign (Ershler 1986). Such a finding, however, does not necessarily imply that the immune response was irrelevant; instead, such tumors, though initially immunogenic, may have undergone further genetic changes that removed the immunogenicity. On the other hand, there also are experimental models in which the immune response appears to stimulate rather than attack tumors.[20]

A final difficulty is that the cancer, once established, can itself produce an immune deficiency syndrome. Accordingly, measurement of immune deficiencies among cancer patients need not imply that the deficiency facilitated the development of cancer. Just as some cancers produce hormones and other substances that cause wasting, hot flashes, and other bizarre syndromes, so they can produce substances that upset the immune system.

Stress and the Immune System

It is well established that stress can impair the immune defense system. Although the mechanism probably involves the brain's mediating influence on the endocrine system, the details are sketchy (Borysenko and Borysenko 1982; Stein, Schiavi, and Camerino 1976; Solomon, Amkraut, and Kasper 1974). Stress can result in the production of certain steroid hormones that in turn cause at least temporary regression in the thymus gland.

There is both experimental and clinical evidence for the immunosuppressive effects of stress. In one experimental model, for example, daily exposure of mice to a "shock avoidance task" resulted in increased susceptibility to herpes simplex virus (Rasmussen et al. 1957; Rasmussen 1969). Among the stressors that appear to affect the immune response in humans are space travel, sleep deprivation, physical trauma, imprisonment, loneliness, the stress of an academic examination, the death of a family member and other bereavements, psychiatric symptoms of anxiety and depression, marital disruption, and unemployment.[21]

It remains unclear whether such diverse environmental stresses have any characteristics in common. One possible feature—variously termed "avoidability" or "escapability" in the experimental literature—may correspond to what is termed "coping style" in clinical investigations (Laudenslager et al. 1983; Locke et al. 1984; Pavlidis and Chirigos 1980; Sklar and Anisman 1979). Another is the prolonged, repetitive character of the stress. Immune impairment was not detectable until nine months of continuous unemployment in a cohort of women (Arnetz et al. 1987). Marital disruption over extended periods likewise produced immune impairment (Kiecolt-Glaser et al. 1987).

Stress and Tumor Development

Stress can enhance the progression of pre-existing tumors in a number of experimental systems (Andervont 1944; Marchant 1967; Riley 1975; Sklar and Anisman 1979; Sklar, Bruto, and

Anisman 1981). Although common features of such models are difficult to discern, considerations of escapable versus inescapable stress, and of acute versus chronic stress have been raised. In some models, isolation of experimental animals enhances tumors; in others, it inhibits them.

If the immune system can in principle influence tumor development, and if stress can affect the immune system in both the laboratory and the clinic, and if stress promotes oncogenesis in some experimental models, then can we not conclude that stress contributes to cancer in humans? Yes, but that is not the problem. The more difficult questions are these: Even if stress can facilitate cancer progression, is the effect quantitatively important in humans? Can't we be more specific about the relevant characteristics of stress in humans? Do these characteristics have any bearing on the stresses frequently identified with certain social and economic environments? At this juncture, the epidemiologic and clinical evidence on stress and cancer has not afforded clear answers to these questions.

Psychological Stress and Cancer

There is an enormous, long-standing clinical literature on psychological stress and cancer.[22] Much of this literature makes the mistake of attempting to define a typical "cancer personality" (Sontag 1977). A number of papers have attempted to assess, mostly retrospectively, what psychological characteristics of newly diagnosed cancer patients appeared to improve survival. Although there is a general theme that patients with certain coping styles did better—especially those who expressed anger and other feelings, as opposed to those who suppressed affect—more careful studies suggest that such effects on survival may be small at best (Angell 1985; Casselith et al. 1985).

Epidemiology

Unfortunately, epidemiological investigations of stress and cancer have been sparse. Studies of cancer in relation to bereavement have provided mixed, circumstantial evidence (Ernster et al. 1979; Jones, Goldblatt, and Leon 1984). In one prospective study, however, psychological depression was predictive of the

17-year risk of cancer, even when an attempt was made to control for the potentially confounding effects of cigarette smoking, occupation, age, and alcoholic beverage consumption (Shekelle et al. 1981).

Studies of the stresses associated with lower socioeconomic status have pointed to marital disruption, low social mobility, job dissatisfaction, unemployment, social disorganization, "status inconsistency," and other factors. To the extent that such stresses are unavoidable and chronic, they appear to mimic those stresses that facilitate cancer under more controlled conditions. To the extent that such stresses might be repetitively experienced over long periods but still reversible, they might act in ways similar to other oncogenic promoters. Despite the significant body of evidence that such stresses matter to some degree, we remain far from being able to determine to what degree.

6. MEDICAL CARE: QUANTITY, TIMING, AND CONTENT

Substantial differences in the use of medical services among socioeconomic groups are well documented and of long standing (Sydenstricker 1929). In the period before the introduction of widespread private and public health insurance in the United States, poorer persons generally had fewer doctor visits and hospitalizations.

Equalization of Health Care?

Beginning in about 1950, however, and especially after the enactment of Medicare and Medicaid in 1966, the income-related gradients in physician visits, surgical rates, and hospital days per capita narrowed markedly in the United States (Bice et al. 1973; Bombardier et al. 1977; Freeborn et al. 1977; Newacheck et al. 1980; U.S. Department of Health and Human Services 1985; Wilson and White 1977). By 1980, with the noted exception of dental services, the income gradients for many medical services were either eliminated or actually reversed. We have some evidence, moreover, that the increased health insurance caused—not just arrived coincidentally with—the growth of medical care use by the poor (Shapiro et al. 1986).

Still, there is a reasonable basis for disputing the apparent trend toward equalization in medical care use among social classes. The comparisons generally involve crude rates; they do not always withstand attempts to take account of age or health status (Davis, Gold, and Makuc 1981; Kleinman, Gold, and Makuc 1981). Moreover, data on overall contact rates do not address differences in the content of medical care. They do not tell us whether there is still a disproportionate use of hospital clinics and emergency rooms among black persons and the poor. They do not tell us who does and does not have a regular source of care (Dutton 1986).

The growth of health insurance had a clearly documented, nonspecific effect on the demand for medical care. However, there is surprisingly little evidence that such subsidies actually enhanced the use of medical services that are specific to cancer diagnosis and treatment.

Consider cancer detection. Income differentials in the use of pap smears and self-examination for breast lumps appear to persist (U.S. Department of Health and Human Services 1985). Similar evidence on hemoccult tests for blood in the detection of colon cancer or on mammographic screening for breast cancer appears lacking.

Consider early seeking of medical treatment. While the proportion of localized breast cancers among newly diagnosed elderly cases increased after the enactment of Medicare (Friedman 1974), such a finding may have little to do with increased insurance among the elderly. In one study of Massachusetts breast cancer cases (Friedman, Parker, and Lipworth 1973), there was no relationship between the extent of insurance coverage and the clinical stage of the initial lesion.

Recent results from the RAND Health Insurance Experiment suggest that copayment affects the decision to seek care only for minor ailments—not for such serious symptoms as exertional chest pain, loss of consciousness, significant involuntary weight loss, or nonmenstrual bleeding unrelated to nosebleeds or minor trauma (Shapiro et al. 1986). In this study, subjects were selected to overrepresent black and lower income persons. It was striking that the proportion of subjects seeking a physician for any particular serious symptom was only on the order of 20 percent.

What was once an enormous, burgeoning literature on the determinants of delay in cancer treatment[23] appears to have gone out of fashion after the advent of Medicare and Medicaid. Yet evidence on persistent differences in the proportions of localized cancers among white and black patients at least suggests that delay remains a serious problem.

The literature on delay in cancer was part of a much larger inquiry: why people seek medical care; whether they follow the medical advice they have received; what are their values and beliefs concerning the efficacy of treatment or the degree of personal control over health; how decisions to seek care are influenced by mass communications and lay referral networks.[24] Except for studies of patient compliance, which deal primarily with conformance to outpatient medication regimens, this literature appears to offer little insight into potential differences in the content of care among persons of varying social and economic position.

The Content of Medical Care

I have already documented significant socioeconomic gradients in cancer survival, even when patients with the same clinical staging have been compared. (See also Dayal and Chiu 1982; Nomura et al. 1981; Pendergrass, Hoover, and Godwin 1975; Wegner et al. 1982.) These differences persist when reasonable adjustments are made for differences in noncancer death rates. While clinical staging imperfectly reveals tumor virulence, we cannot dismiss the possibility that the content of cancer care differs meaningfully among persons of varying social positions.

Socioeconomic Status and the Doctor-Patient Relationship

The literature on delay in the diagnosis and treatment of cancer, especially in the 1920s and 1930s, was especially concerned with the distinction between physician versus patient "culpability" for delay. In the parlance of analysis of variance, we might now term these "patient-specific effects" and "physician-specific effects." The former category reflects concerns, which have been repeatedly voiced in the literature, that patients do not comply with prescribed regimens, or that other unspecified characteristics of the host environment influence the efficacy of cancer treatment. The latter category reflects differences in quality of care.

Adherence to our statistical terminology requires that we also consider "patient-doctor interaction effects." There has been some sporadic interest in the social distance between the upper class doctor and the lower class patient (McKinlay 1975; Stoeckle 1987). Still, we do not know whether recent changes in the demographic mix of graduating physicians could indeed have affected the content of care among minorities and others in lower social strata.

7. A RESEARCH AGENDA

- Can documented differences in reproductive history among women of various socioeconomic groups explain quantitatively the observed differences in breast cancer incidence? Can they explain the differences in severity of cancer at the time of initial diagnosis?

  Although there is a substantial literature on the economic and social determinants of marriage and fertility (Montgomery and Trussell 1986), much work remains to be done on the timing of the first birth. Historically there have been marked differentials by income, education, and race in the age of first full-term pregnancy; but these patterns may have radically changed with the advent of oral contraceptives in the 1960s and the continued influx of women of all social strata into the labor force. Although economists and demographers have attempted to fashion mathematical models of the timing of first birth and subsequent birth intervals (Heckman, Hotz, and Walker 1985), these have been mostly descriptive. We really do not have a clear theoretical model of birth timing.

  Although epidemiological studies have examined the quantitative relationship between reproductive history and breast cancer, they have been performed without attention to the determinants of reproductive history. We know that timing of the first birth influences breast cancer incidence. From separate studies, we know that income, education, and race also influence breast cancer incidence and survival. We need to study these determinants of cancer together.

- How do specific sexual practices vary across social strata? Have differences in such indices as the number of different sexual partners annually diverged over time? How will such trends impinge upon future cervical cancer rates?

Even in the relatively short interval between initial writing and revision of this paper, the public concern about the sexual transmission of human immunodeficiency virus (HIV) has risen dramatically. There is serious concern that the virus is spreading by heterosexual means, particularly among persons of lower socioeconomic status. Yet our understanding of the problem is hampered seriously by a general lack of information on sexual practices among various social and economic groups. And the difficulty applies just as well to studies of the relationship between sexually transmitted viruses and cancer.

- Can we amass detailed information on the use of cervical pap smears by various social groups, assessing recent trends?

Despite numerous studies on the use of medical care among various social and economic groups, we need to focus more sharply on preventive measures. We need to know more clearly whether insurance coverage or nonprice factors are critical in the use of pap smears, mammography, stool blood analyses, and the like.

- How do leisure-time sun-tanning practices vary among socioeconomic groups in the United States? Do the results accord with current evidence on melanoma incidence?

In Section Three, I did not directly confront the question of the empirical relation between social status and leisure-time tanning. While there is indeed some evidence that upper income people have more frequent high-intensity bursts of sun exposure, this empirical regularity needs more careful study. Even if there was a socioeconomic gradient in the past, it may now be changing. The issue is not trivial. While basal cell epithemiola (the most prevalent form of sun-related skin cancer) is usually not fatal, malignant melanoma is.

- If nonspecific chemical and physical toxins can accelerate initiation of cancer, and if we suspect that such toxins are more prevalent in poorer environments, then how do we identify such agents?

  This is an extraordinarily difficult research question. For if nonspecific insults did matter, then studies to identify isolated chemical spills, water contamination, occupational exposures, and the like would identify only a small fraction of the cancer that might be related to lower SES. One possible approach is to examine those localities with a persistently elevated incidence of certain cancers. Do the residents in such places have lower incomes and education? How often can the elevated cancer incidence be attributed to specific, identifiable carcinogens? Except for a few case studies, we seem to be a long way from this end.

- Could molecular epidemiologic studies, based upon measurements of adducts to macromolecules, permit us to say more about differences in early stage carcinogenesis among varying social groups?

  This is indeed a promising area for further research. But first we have to widen the array of agents that can be detected in such molecular studies. Once this biological research is further advanced, we will want to know how adduct levels relate to income, education, occupation, sexual behavior, and other characteristics.

- What epidemiologic studies are needed to delineate the quantitative effect of social and economic stresses on cancer progression?

  At this writing, I can identify only one prospective cohort analysis to assess the predictive value of psychological depression on subsequent cancer incidence (Shekelle et al. 1981). But depression, as measured by standard questionnaires, may be a poor indicator of social and environmental stress. Without additional long-term cohort studies, the role of stress in human cancer will remain speculative.

- What field studies are needed to assess differences in the content of cancer treatment among various socioeconomic groups?

  Even after the advent of Medicare and Medicaid, we are

still not in a position to assess the content of cancer treatment among various educational and income groups. We need to know much more about the content of such care. Do poorer patients receive curative chemotherapy or adjuvant chemotherapy? Is chemotherapy or radiation treatment terminated earlier? Do patients in different social strata tolerate the side effects of such treatments to different degrees? How much do doctors explain to their patients about cancer? How does the message vary with doctor and patient? Is the phenomenon of doctor-patient mismatch important? Has the growing supply of minority physicians affected the care and treatment of cancer among minorities?

Much of the required research will require a detailed analysis of the actual course of cancer care among cohorts with different socioeconomic characteristics. In this case, we will be asking not whether poorer people have lower cancer survival rates, but why they fare so poorly. Much of the favorable clinical data on various cancer treatment regimens come from controlled studies of defined protocols in selected populations. We don't really know whether these protocols are actually followed in nonstudy populations. If they are not, we don't know why not.

Notes

1. See the following references: American Cancer Society 1986; Axtell, Asire, and Myers 1977; Berg, Ross, and Latourette 1977; Brown, Selvin, and Winkelstein 1975; Buell, Dunn, and Breslow 1960; Clemmesen and Nielsen 1951; Cohart 1954, 1955a, 1955b; Dayal et al. 1984; Devesa and Diamond 1983; Dorn 1944; Dorn and Cutler 1959; Graham, Levine, and Lilienfeld 1961; Haan and Kaplan 1985; Hakama et al. 1982; Henschke et al. 1973; Jenkins 1983; Kitagawa and Hauser 1973; Knight and Dublin 1917; Kogevinas 1987; Lombard and Doering 1929; Marmot and McDowall 1986; Marmot, Kogevinas, and Elston 1987; Salonen 1982; Seidman 1970; Williams and Horm 1977; Yeracaris and Kim 1978.

2. The most reliable data are on black-white differences. Based upon results from the 1969–71 Third National Cancer Sur-

vey (Cutler and Young 1975) and the Cancer Surveillance,
Epidemiology and End Results (SEER) Program (Axtell,
Asire, and Myers 1977), I compute that white women have
annual incidence rates of 36 localized cancers and 39 nonlo-
calized cancers per 100,000 persons. The corresponding
black incidence rates are 19 localized cancers and 39 nonlo-
calized cancers per 100,000. While these data suggest that all
of the black-white incidence differential reflects localized
disease, they may not accurately reflect differences due to
socioeconomic status.

3. According to the SEER data, among newly diagnosed
   white cases, the proportion of localized tumors increased
   from 41 percent in 1950–54 to 48 percent in 1970–73.
   Among newly diagnosed black cases, the corresponding
   proportions were 29 percent in 1950–54 and 33 percent in
   1970–73. Whether the SEER data accurately reflect the incidence or case-mix of breast cancers, however, remains
   unclear (Doll and Peto 1981).

4. See Axtell, Asire, and Myers 1977; Axtell and Myers 1978;
   Berg, Ross, and Latourette 1977; Cohart 1955a; Dayal et al.
   1982; Linden 1969; Lewison, Montague, and Kuller 1966;
   Lipworth, Abelin, and Connelly 1970; Ries, Pollack, and
   Young 1983; Young, Ries, and Pollack 1984. From the
   1960–73 SEER data (Axtell, Asire, and Myers 1975; Axtell
   and Myers 1978), I compute that the higher proportion of
   clinically localized tumors accounts for only about half of
   the survival advantage of white over black patients.

5. Whether the presence or absence of such estrogen receptors
   is a consistent feature of a particular tumor over its lifetime
   is still unknown. The fact that there are fewer such receptors
   in samples taken from metastatic sites of breast cancers suggests tumors may lose their estrogen receptors as they become more malignant (Mohla et al. 1982).

6. There may be other mechanisms whereby early first full-
   term pregnancy reduces breast cancer risk. A woman's first
   delivery appears to produce a long-term reduction in the secretion of the pituitary hormone prolactin (Kwa et al. 1981;
   Musey et al. 1987). In animal experiments described in Section Four, prolactin promotes the growth of breast cancers

that have been initiated by other agents (Manni, Trujillo, and Pearson 1977; Pitot 1982). Elevated prolactin levels predict subsequent breast cancer in postmenopausal women (Kwa et al. 1981).

The timing of the first delivery is not the only relevant feature of reproductive history. Early onset of menstruation and later onset of menopause, which are both more prevalent in women of higher SES, are also predictive of higher breast cancer risk. Estrogens and prolactin both increase the mitotic activity of breast epithelium. Such mitotic activity is particularly enhanced during normal menstrual cycles, whereas it is reduced after menopause. Early menarche and late menopause may therefore promote the development of breast cancer by increasing the number of normal menstrual cycles and thus the total lifetime exposure of breast tissue to estrogens and prolactin. Given that there is a permanent reduction of prolactin following the first pregnancy, the number of normal menstrual cycles prior to the first pregnancy may be especially critical in the development of mammary cancers (Pike et al. 1983).

7. Although I concentrate on reproductive history and access to care, nutrition also needs to be considered. Various aspects of nutrition—fat, fiber, and caloric intake, the consumption of such specific constituents as minerals and fish oils, and total body weight—have been repeatedly cited as influencing cancer in general and breast cancer in particular (Benson, Lev, and Grand 1956; Bonser and Wainman 1940; Carroll et al. 1986; Dunning, Curtis, and Maun 1949; Graham et al. 1982; Graham 1986; Kreyberg 1938; Maisin and François 1928; Tannenbaum 1940, 1942; Tannenbaum and Silverstone 1953; Willett and MacMahon 1984; Willett et al. 1987; Wynder, Rose, and Cohen 1986). Although the experimental evidence on the role of fat intake has been particularly impressive, the epidemiological evidence nevertheless remains in a state of flux. One difficult problem has been the accurate measurement of intake of dietary fat and specific dietary constituents in individual human subjects, especially over extended time periods. There are indeed so-

cioeconomic gradients in diet and body weight. The issue
here is whether such gradients could be quantitatively significant in explaining socioeconomic differences in breast
cancer incidence and survival.

8. For example, cigarette smoking can cause bladder cancer;
    and in fact the bladder carcinogen 4-aminobiphenyl can be
    detected in the blood of cigarette smokers (Bryant et al.
    1987), while mutagenic compounds can be detected in
    smokers' urine.

9. Excision of suspicious lesions that have been identified by
    cervical cytology is not the only way to stop the progres-
    sion of an early cancer. Elective hysterectomy (as might be
    performed for uterine fibroids) is another means. To this
    end, we need to investigate whether elective hysterectomies
    are more prevalent among women in upper socioeconomic
    groups.

10. See Lancaster and Nelson 1957; McGovern 1952. Black per-
    sons and other pigmented races have a much lower inci-
    dence of the disease, with the exception of melanomas in
    less pigmented parts of the body, such as the sole of the foot
    and the mucosa of the oral cavity (McGovern 1977). In
    white persons, melanoma occurs predominantly on the
    sun-exposed parts, though the bodily distribution of tu-
    mors is not as consistent as that for other sun-sensitive skin
    cancers, e.g., basal cell cancers of the skin of the face and
    neck in white persons (McGovern 1952). Moreover, there is
    a general gradient of melanoma incidence in relation to lat-
    itude of residence, though the gradient is not limited to me-
    lanomas at sun-exposed body sites (Lancaster and Nelson
    1957). Patients with the inherited disease xeroderma pig-
    mentosum, who cannot repair ultraviolet light-induced
    damage to the DNA in their skin cells (Robbins et al. 1974),
    have a much higher risk of melanoma as well as other skin
    cancers.

11. See Bishop 1987; Sager 1986. Through individual point
    mutations or large rearrangements in chromosomes, an er-
    ror occurs in the replication of DNA, a highly faithful pro-
    cess that precedes the division of each parent cell into a new
    generation of cells. If the cell fails to repair the error in

DNA or repairs it improperly, and if the error is compatible with continued cell life, then the damaging alteration is inherited by future generations of cells within the body.

12. See Miller and Miller 1952. For example, the chemical carcinogen benzo(a)pyrene (BaP), identified in the 1930s (Cook et al. 1932, 1933), is metabolized to various "diol epoxides" that adduct with DNA (Brookes and Lawley 1964). Such adducts can be detected among coke-oven workers exposed to BaP in the work atmosphere (Haugen et al. 1986). Likewise, the chemical 4-aminobiphenyl, a cause of bladder cancer to which certain occupations and cigarette smokers are exposed, is metabolized first to a "hydroxylamine" and ultimately to a form that can interact with the DNA in bladder cells. Measurement of the amount of the hydroxylamine of 4-aminobiphenyl that is bound to hemoglobin in human blood has been proposed as a precise method of gauging the carcinogen's exposure in cigarette smokers (Bryant et al. 1987).

13. For example, chromosomal breaks and rearrangements may shift proto-oncogenes away from their normal locations in the gene sequence, where the previously silent genes are then abnormally expressed (Rowley 1984; Sager 1986).

14. The experiment produces cancer only if the initiator is applied first, and only if the promoter is applied subsequently in frequent, repetitive doses. Thus, BaP serves as an initiator in experimental liver cancer, while phenobarbital and PCBs serve as promoters (see Pitot 1982).

15. In some experiments in mouse skin, it appears that an initiating agent can cause a point mutation in a single proto-oncogene, yielding benign papillomas. The promoting agent then acts to enhance the expression of the abnormal oncogene, leading to malignant skin tumors.

16. As mentioned in note 6, prolactin, a human pituitary hormone whose secretion appears to be depressed by first pregnancies, is a promoter of breast cancer in animal experiments. Also, many gross aspects of nutrition, including fat, fiber, and caloric intake, appear to have promotional effects. See note 7.

17. As mentioned in Section 2, the cellular immune system could be important in preventing the herpes virus infections linked to cancers of the cervix and upper aerodigestive tract (Schantz et al. 1986).

18. Among such complexes are the "particulates" formed from the burning of cigarette smoke and fuels, such as the coke-oven emissions mentioned in Section 4 (see note 12). While the carbonaceous core of such particulates may be chemically inert, the entire particle may contain reactive, potentially carcinogenic agents. The fate of the reactive compounds on such particulates may depend critically on the manner by which inhaled particles are cleared by the lung. Thus, clinicians have repeatedly observed how patients with lung cancer also have noncancerous chronic obstructive lung disease. It has now been suggested that the concomitant, noncancerous lung disease actually sets up the lung for the subsequent development of cancer by impairing the clearance mechanism for carcinogenic particulates (Skillrud et al. 1986).

19. A particular mouse tumor, for example, can be made cancerous by one virus and rendered inactive by a cousin virus. The latter virus activates the cellular machinery to express an antigen that is in turn recognized by the immune system (Schrier et al. 1983; Tanaka et al. 1985).

20. In at least some of these cases, T suppressor cells are turned on, thus inhibiting the killer cells that attack the tumor. In others, the immune response disrupts natural tissue barriers, allowing the tumor to spread.

21. See Arnetz et al. 1987; Jacobs and Charles 1980; Glaser et al. 1985; Kiecolt-Glaser et al. 1984, 1987; Locke et al. 1984; Shekelle et al. 1981. Such immune impairments have been measured by diminution in killer T cell activity, ability to respond to standard skin tests for cellular immunity, impaired responsiveness of B lymphocytes to various chemical challenges, increased antibodies to EB virus (a particular herpes virus that causes mononucleosis), and DNA repair in certain lymphocytes (Kiecolt-Glaser et al. 1985).

22. See Angell 1985; Casselith et al. 1985; Derogatis et al. 1979; Evans 1926; Greer et al. 1979; Jacobs and Charles 1980; Les-

han and Worthington 1956; Pettingale, Greer, and Tee Deh 1977; West, Blumberg, and Ellis 1952.

23. See Bates 1948; Cobb et al. 1954; Goldsen, Gerhardt, and Handy 1957; Kutner, Makover, and Oppenheim 1958; Leach and Robbins 1947; Pack and Gallo 1938; Robbins et al. 1950; Robbins, Macdonald, and Pack 1953.

24. See Becker et al. 1972, 1974; Becker and Maiman 1975; Blackwell 1973; Caldwell 1970; Cowles et al. 1963; Deasy 1956; Finnerty et al. 1973; Gordis, Markowitz, and Lilienfeld 1969; Gray, Kesler, and Moody 1966; Janz and Becker 1984; Kegeles et al. 1965; Macdonald et al. 1963; Pill and Stott 1982; Rodin 1986; Rosenstock et al. 1959; Rosenstock 1966; Sackett 1978; Svarstad 1986; Watts 1966.

REFERENCES

American Cancer Society. 1986. *Cancer in the economically disadvantaged. A special report.* Subcommittee on Cancer in the Economically Disadvantaged. New York: American Cancer Society.

Andervont, H. B. 1944. Influence of environment on mammary cancer in mice. *Journal of the National Cancer Institute* 4:579–581.

Angell, M. 1985. Disease as a reflection of the psyche. *New England Journal of Medicine* 312:1570–1572.

Arnetz, B. B., Wasserman, J., Petrini, B., et al. 1987. Immune function in unemployed women. *Psychosomatic Medicine* 49:3–12.

Auerbach, O., Gere, J. B., Pawlowski, J. M., et al. 1957. Carcinoma-in-situ and early invasive carcinoma occurring in the tracheobroncheal trees in cases of bronchial carcinoma. *Journal of Thoracic Surgery* 34:298–309.

Austin, H., Delzell, E., Grufferman, S., et al. 1986. A case control study of hepatocellular carcinoma and the hepatitis B virus, cigarette smoking, and alcohol consumption. *Cancer Research* 46:962–966.

Axtell, L. M., Asire, A. J., Myers, M. H., eds. 1976. *Cancer patient survival.* Report No. 5. Department of Health, Education and Welfare Publication (NIH) 77-992. Washington, D.C.: G.P.O.

Axtell, L. M., Myers, M. H. 1978. Contrasts in survival of black and white cancer patients, 1960–1973. *Journal of the National Cancer Institute* 60:1209–1215.

Bacon, C. L., Renneker, R., Cutler, M. 1952. A psychosomatic survey of cancer of the breast. *Psychosomatic Medicine* 14:453–460.

Bahn, A. K., Rosenwaike, I., Herrmann, N., Grover, P., et al. 1976. Melanoma after exposure to PCBs. *New England Journal of Medicine* 295:450.

Balmain, A. 1985. Transforming *ras* oncogenes and multistage carcinogenesis. *British Journal of Cancer* 51:1–7.

Bartel, A., Taubman, P. 1979. Health and labor market success: the role of various diseases. *Review of Economics and Statistics* 61:1–8.

Bates, F. E., Ariel, I. M. 1948. Delay in treatment of cancer. *Illinois Medical Journal* 94(6):361–365.

Becker, M. H., Drachman, R. H., Kirscht, J. P. 1972. Predicting mothers' compliance with pediatric medical regimens. *Journal of Pediatrics* 81:843–854.

———. 1974. A new approach to explaining sick-role behavior in low-income populations. *American Journal of Public Health* 64:205–216.

Becker, M. H., Maiman, L. A. 1975. Sociobehavioral determinants of compliance with health and medical recommendations. *Medical Care* 13:10–24.

Benson, J., Lev, M., Grand, C. G. 1956. Enhancement of mammary fibroadenomas in the female rat by a high fat diet. *Cancer Research* 16:135–137.

Beral, V., Robinson, N. 1981. The relationship of malignant melanoma, basal, and squamous skin cancers to indoor and outdoor work. *British Journal of Cancer* 44:886–891.

Berg, J. W., Ross, R., Latourette, H. B. 1977. Economic status and survival of cancer patients. *Cancer* 39:467–477.

Beverly, L. N., Flanders, W. D., Go, R. C. P., Soong, S-J. 1987. A comparison of estrogen and progesterone receptors in black and white breast cancer patients. *American Journal of Public Health* 77:351–353.

Bice, T. W., Rabin, D., Starfield, B., White, K. 1973. Economic class and use of physician services. *Medical Care* 11:287.

Bishop, J. M. 1987. The molecular genetics of cancer. *Science* 235:306–311.

Blackwell, B. 1973. Drug therapy: patient compliance. *New England Journal of Medicine* 289:249–252.

Bombardier, C., Fuchs, V. R., Lillard, L. A., Warner, K. E. 1977. Socioeconomic factors affecting the utilization of surgical operations. *New England Journal of Medicine* 297:699–705.

Bonser, G. M., Wainman, L. M. 1940. Effect of a diet supplemented by fresh liver on induced skin tumors in inbred mice. *Journal of Pathology and Bacteriology* 50:548–550.

Borek, C., Sachs, L. 1968. The number of cell generations required to fix the transformed state in x-ray induced transformation. *Proceedings of the National Academy of Sciences* 59:83–85.

Borysenko, M., Borysenko, J. 1982. Stress, behavior, and immunity: animal models and mediating mechanisms. *General Hospital Psychiatry* 4:59–67.

Boutwell, R. K. 1974. The function and mechanism of promoters of carcinogenesis. *Critical Reviews in Toxicology* 2:419–443.

Bréchot, C., Degos, F., Lugassy, C., et al. 1985. Hepatitis B virus DNA in patients with chronic liver disease and negative tests for hepatitis B surface antigen. *New England Journal of Medicine* 312:270–276.

Bréchot, C., Nalpas, B., Courouce, A. M., et al. 1982. Evidence that hepatitis B virus has a role in liver-cell carcinoma in alcoholic liver disease. *New England Journal of Medicine* 306:1384–1387.

Brinton, L. A., Schairer, C., Haenszel, W., et al. 1986. Cigarette smoking and invasive cervical cancer. *Journal of the American Medical Association* 255:3265–3269.

Brookes, P., Lawley, P. D. 1964. Evidence for the binding of polynuclear aromatic hydrocarbons to the nucleic acids of mouse skin: relation between carcinogenic power of hydrocarbons and their binding to DNA. *Nature* 202:781–784.

Brown, S. M., Selvin, S., Winkelstein, W. 1975. The association of economic status with the occurrence of lung cancer. *Cancer* 36:1903–1911.

Bryant, M. S., Skipper, P. L., Tannenbaum, S. R., MacLure, M. 1987. Hemoglobin adducts of 4-aminobiphenyl in smokers and nonsmokers. *Cancer Research* 47:602–608.

Buell, P., Dunn, J. E., Jr., Breslow, L. 1960. The occupational-social class risks of cancer mortality in men. *Journal of Chronic Diseases* 12:600–621.

Caldwell, J. R., Cobb, S., Dowling, M. D., De Jongh, D. 1970. The dropout problem in antihypertensive treatment. *Journal of Chronic Diseases* 22:579–592.

Carroll, K. K., Braden, L. M., Bell, J. A., Kalamegham, R. 1986. Fat and cancer. *Cancer* 58:1818–1825.

Cassel, J. 1976. The contribution of the social environment to host resistance. *American Journal of Epidemiology* 104:107–123.

Cassileth, B. R., Lusk, E. J., et al. 1985. Psychosocial correlates of survival in advanced malignant disease? *New England Journal of Medicine* 312:1551–1555.

Chave, S. P. W., Morris, J. N., Moss, S., Semmence, A. M. 1978. Vigorous exercise in leisure time and the death rate: a study of male civil servants. *Journal of Epidemiology and Community Health* 32:239–243.

Cleaver, J. E. 1980. DNA damage, repair systems, and human hypersensitive diseases. *Journal of Environmental Pathology and Toxicology* 3:453–468.

Clemmesen, J., Nielsen, A. 1951. The social distribution of cancer in Copenhagen, 1943 to 1947. *British Journal of Cancer* 5:159–171.

Cobb, B., Clark, R. L., McGuire, C., Howe, C. D. 1954. Patient-responsible delay of treatment in cancer. *Cancer* 7:920–925.

Cohart, E. M. 1954. Socioeconomic distribution of stomach cancer in New Haven. *Cancer* 7:455–461.

———. 1955a. Socioeconomic distribution of cancer of the female sex organs in New Haven. *Cancer* 8:34–41.

———. 1955b. Socioeconomic distribution of cancer of the lung in New Haven. *Cancer* 8:1126–1129.

Cook, J. W., Hieger, I., Kennaway, et al. 1932. The production of cancer by pure hydrocarbons. Part I. *Proceedings of the Royal Society of London, Series B* 111:455–484.

Cook, J. W., Hewett, C. L., Hieger, I. 1933. The isolation of a cancer-producing hydrocarbon from coal tar. Parts I, II, and III. *Journal of the Chemical Society* 1:395–405.

Cooke, K. R., Skegg, D. C. G., Fraser, J. 1984. Socioeconomic status, indoor and outdoor work, and malignant melanoma. *International Journal of Cancer* 34:57–62.

Cowles, W., Polgar, S., Simmons, L., Switzer, J. 1963. Health and communication in a negro census tract. *Social Problems* 10:228–236.

Cutler, S. J., Young, J. L., Jr. 1975. *Third national cancer survey: incidence data. National Cancer Institute Monograph 41.* Department of Health, Education and Welfare Pub. No. (NIH) 75-787. Washington, D.C.: G.P.O.

Davis, K., Gold, M., Makuc, D. 1981. Access to health care for the poor: does the gap remain? *Annual Review of Public Health* 2:159–182.

Dayal, H. H., Chiu, C. Y. 1982. Factors associated with racial differences in survival for prostatic carcinoma. *Journal of Chronic Diseases* 35:553–560.

Dayal, H. H., Chiu, C. Y., Sharrar, S., et al. 1984. Ecologic correlates of cancer mortality patterns in an industrialized urban population. *Journal of the National Cancer Institute* 73:565–574.

Dayal, H. H., Power, R. N., Chiu C. Y. 1982. Race and socioeconomic status in survival from breast cancer. *Journal of Chronic Diseases* 35:675–683.

Deasy, L. C. 1956. Socioeconomic status and participation in the poliomyelitis vaccine trial. *American Sociological Review* 21:185–191.

Derogatis, L. R., Abeloff, M. D., Melisaratos, N. 1979. Psychological coping mechanisms and survival time in metastatic breast cancer. *Journal of the American Medical Association* 242:1504–1508.

Devesa, S. S., Diamond, E. L. 1983. Socioeconomic and racial differences in lung cancer incidence. *American Journal of Epidemiology* 118:818–831.

de Villiers, E. M., Weidauer, H., Otto, H., et al. 1985. Papillomavirus DNA in human tongue carcinomas. *International Journal of Cancer* 36:575–578.

Doll, R., Peto, R. 1981. The causes of cancer: quantitative estimates of avoidable risks of cancer in the United States today. *Journal of the National Cancer Institute* 66:1197–1308.

Dorn, H. F. 1944. Illness from cancer in the United States. *Public Health Reports* 59:33–48, 65–67, 95–115.

———, Cutler, S. J. 1959. Morbidity from cancer in the United States. II. *Public Health Monograph* No. 56, pp. 88–106. Washington, D.C.: G.P.O.

Duleep, H. 1985. *Poverty and inequality in mortality.* Unpublished Ph.D. dissertation. Cambridge: Massachusetts Institute of Technology.

Dunning, W. F., Curtis, M. R., Maun, M. E. 1949. The effect of dietary fat and carbohydrate on diethylstilbestrol-induced mammary cancer in rats. *Cancer Research* 9:354–361.

Dutton, D. B. 1986. Social class, health, and illness. In Aiken, L. H., Mechanic, D., eds. *Applications of social science to clinical medicine and health policy,* pp. 31–62. New Brunswick, N.J.: Rutgers University Press.

Egan, R. L. 1962. Fifty-three cases of carcinoma of the breast, occult until mammography. *American Journal of Roentgenology, Radium Therapy, and Nuclear Medicine* 88:1095–1101.

Elder, R., Acheson, R. M. 1970. New Haven survey of joint diseases. XIV. Social class and behavior in response to symptoms of osteoarthritis. *Milbank Memorial Fund Quarterly* 48:495–502.

Elwood, J. M., Gallagher, R. P., Hill, G. B., Pearson, J. 1985. Cutaneous melanoma in relation to intermittent and constant sun exposure—the Western Canada Melanoma Study. *International Journal of Cancer* 35:427–433.

Ernster, V. L., Sacks, S., Selvin, S., Petrakis, N. L. 1979. Cancer incidence by marital status: U.S. third national cancer survey. *Journal of the National Cancer Institute* 63:587–595.

Ershler, W. B. 1986. Why tumors grow more slowly in old people. *Journal of the National Cancer Institute* 77:837–839.

Evans, E. 1926. *A psychological study of cancer.* New York: Dodd, Mead.

Farrell, P., Fuchs, V. R. 1982. Schooling and health. The cigarette connection. *Journal of Health Economics* 1:217–230.

Feldman, A. R., Kessler, L., Myers, M. H., Naughton, M. D.

1986. The prevalance of cancer. Estimates based on the Connecticut Tumor Registry. *New England Journal of Medicine* 315:1394–1397.

Finnerty, F. A., Jr., Mattie, E. C., Finnerty, F. A. III, 1973. Hypertension in the inner city. I. Analysis of clinic dropouts. *Circulation* 47:73–75.

Fox, A. J., Adelstein, A. M. 1978. Occupational mortality: work or way of life? *Journal of Epidemiology and Community Health* 32:73–78.

Fox, A. J., Goldblatt, P. O., Jones, D. R. 1985. Social class mortality differentials: artefact, selection, or life circumstances? *Journal of Epidemiology and Community Health* 39:1–8.

Fox, M. S. 1979. On the diagnosis and treatment of breast cancer. *Journal of the American Medical Association* 241:489–494.

Freeborn, D. K., Pope, C. R., Davis, M.A., Mullooly, J. P. 1977. Health status, socioeconomic status, and utilization of outpatient services for members of a prepaid group practice. *Medical Care* 15:115–128.

Friedman, B. 1974. A test of alternative demand-shift responses to the Medicare program. In Perlman, M., ed. *The economics of health and medical care*. New York: Wiley.

———, Parker, P., Lipworth, L. 1973. The influence of Medicaid and private health insurance on the early diagnosis of breast cancer. *Medical Care* 11:485–490.

Galloway, D. A. McDougall, J. K. 1983. The oncogenic potential of herpes simplex viruses: evidence for a "hit-and-run" mechanism. *Nature* 302:21–24.

Glaser, R., Kiecolt-Glaser, J. K., Speicher, C. E., Holliday, J. E. 1985. Stress, loneliness, and changes in herpesvirus latency. *Journal of Behavioral Medicine* 8:249–260.

Goldsen, R. K., Gerhardt, P. R., Handy, V. H. 1957. Some factors related to patient delay in seeking diagnosis for cancer symptoms. *Cancer* 10:1–7.

Gordis, L., Markowitz, M., Lilienfeld, A. M. 1969. Why patients don't follow medical advice: a study of children on long-term antistreptococcal prophylaxis. *Journal of Pediatrics* 75:957–968.

Graham, S. 1986. Hypotheses regarding caloric intake in cancer development. *Cancer* 58:1814–1817.

————, Levin, M., Lilienfeld, A. M. 1960. The socioeconomic distribution of cancer of various sites in Buffalo, New York, 1948–1952. *Cancer* 13:180–191.

Graham, S., Marshall, J., Mettlin, C., et al. 1982. Diet in the epidemiology of breast cancer. *American Journal of Epidemiology* 116:68–75.

Gray, A. M. 1982. Inequalities in health. The Black Report: a summary and comment. *International Journal of Health Services* 12:349–380.

Gray, R. M., Kesler, J. P., Moody, P. M. 1966. The effects of social class and friends' expectations on oral polio vaccination participation. *American Journal of Public Health* 56:2028–2032.

Greer, S., Morris, T., Pettingale, K. W. 1979. Psychological response to breast cancer: effect on outcome. *Lancet* 2:785–787.

Grossman, M. 1975. The correlation between health and schooling. In Terleckyj, N., ed. *Household production and consumption*, pp. 147–223. New York: Columbia University Press.

Haan, M., Kaplan, G. A. 1985. *The contribution of socioeconomic position to minority health.* Report to the NIH Task Force on Black and Minority Health. Berkeley: California Department of Health Services.

Haan, M., Kaplan, G. A., Camacho, T. 1986. Poverty and health: prospective evidence from the Alameda County study. Unpublished manuscript. Human Population Laboratory, California Department of Health Services, Berkeley.

Habbema, J. D. F., van Oortmarssen, G. J., van Putten, D. J., et al. 1986. Age-specific reduction in breast cancer mortality by screening: an analysis of the results of the Health Insurance Plan of Greater New York Study. *Journal of the National Cancer Institute* 77:317–320.

Hakama, M., Hakulinen, T., Pukkala, E., et al. 1982. Risk indicators of breast and cervical cancer on ecologic and individual levels. *American Journal of Epidemiology* 116:990–1000.

Harris, C. C. 1986. Tobacco smoke and lung disease: who is susceptible? *Annals of Internal Medicine* 105:607–609.

Haugen, A., Becher, G., Benestad, C., et al. 1986. Determination of polycyclic aromatic hydrocarbons in the urine, benzo(a)pyrene diol epoxide-DNA adducts in lymphocyte

DNA, and antibodies to the adducts in sera from coke oven workers exposed to measured amounts of polycyclic aromatic hydrocarbons in the work atmosphere. *Cancer Research* 46:4178–4183.

Heckman, J., Hotz, J., Walker, J. 1985. New evidence on the timing and spacing of births. *American Economic Review* 75:(2)179–184.

Henschke, U. K., Leffall, L. D., Mason, C., et al. 1973. Alarming increase of the cancer mortality in the U.S. black population, 1950–1967. *Cancer* 31:763–768.

Herberman, R. B., Ortaldo, J. R. 1981. Natural killer cells: their role in defenses against disease. *Science* 214:24–30.

Hinkle, L. E., Wolff, H. G. 1958. Ecologic investigations of the relationship between illness, life experiences, and the social environment. *Annals of Internal Medicine* 49:1373–1388.

Hirayama, T., Waterhouse, J. A. H., Fraumeni, J. F., Jr., eds., 1980. *Cancer risks by site*. UICC technical report series, Vol. 41. Geneva: Union Internationale Contre Cancer.

Holly, E. A. Petrakis, N. L., Friend, N. F., et al. 1986. Mutagenic mucus in the cervix of smokers. *Journal of the National Cancer Institute* 76:983–986.

Holman, C. D. J., Armstrong, B. K. 1984. Cutaneous malignant melanoma and indicators of total accumulated exposure to the sun. An analysis separating histogenic types. *Journal of the National Cancer Institute* 73:75–82.

Howson, C. P., Kinne, D., Wynder, E. L. 1986. Body weight, serum cholesterol, and stage of primary breast cancer. *Cancer* 58:2372–2381.

Jacobs, T. J., Charles, E. 1980. Life events and the occurrence of cancer in children. *Psychosomatic Medicine* 42:11–24.

Janz, N. K., Becker, M. H. 1984. The health belief model: a decade later. *Health Education Quarterly* 11:1–47.

Jenkins, C. D. 1983. Social environment and cancer mortality in men. *New England Journal of Medicine* 308:395–398.

Jones, D. R., Goldblatt, P. O., Leon, D. A. 1984. Bereavement and cancer: some data on deaths of spouses from the longitudinal study of Office of Population Censuses and Surveys. *British Medical Journal* 289:461–464.

Judd, E. S., New, G. B. 1923. Carcinoma of the tongue: general principles involved in operations and results obtained at the Mayo Clinic. *Surgery, Gynecology, and Obstetrics* 36:163–169.

Karvonen, M. J. 1982. Physical activity in work and leisure time in relation to cardiovascular diseases. *Annals of Clinical Research* 14 (Suppl. 34):118–123.

Kasl, S. V., Cobb, S. 1966. Health behavior, illness behavior, and sick role behavior. *Archives of Environmental Health* 12:246–266.

Kegeles, S. S., Kirscht, J. P., Haefner, D. P., Rosenstock, I. M. 1965. Survey of beliefs about cancer detection and taking Papanicolaou tests. *Public Health Reports* 80:815–823.

Kelsey, K. T., Christiani, D. C., Little, J. B. 1986. Enhancement of benzo(a)pyrene-induced sister chromatid exchanges in lymphocytes from cigarette smokers occupationally exposed to asbestos. *Journal of the National Cancer Institute* 77:321–327.

Kersey, J. H., Spector, B. D., Good, R. A., 1973. Immunodeficiency and cancer. *Advances in Cancer Research* 18:211–230.

Khosla, T., Lowe, C. R. 1972. Obesity and smoking habits by social class. *British Journal of Preventive and Social Medicine* 26:249–256.

Kiecolt-Glaser, J. K., Fisher, L. D., Ogrocki, P., et al. 1987. Marital quality, marital disruption, and immune function. *Psychosomatic Medicine* 49:13–34.

Kiecolt-Glaser, J. K., Garner, W., Speicher, C., et al. 1984. Psychosocial modifiers of immunocompetence in medical students. *Psychosomatic Medicine* 46:7–14.

Kiecolt-Glaser, J. K., Stephens, R., Lipitz, P., et al. 1985. Distress and DNA repair in human lymphocytes. *Journal of Behavioral Medicine* 8:311–320.

Kitagawa, E. M., Hauser, P. M. 1973. *Differential mortality in the United States: a study in socioeconomic epidemiology.* Cambridge: Harvard University Press.

Kitagawa, T., Hirakawa, T., Ishikawa, T., et al. 1980. Induction of hepatocellular carcinoma in rat liver by initial treatment with benzo(a)pyrene after partial hepatectomy and promotion by phenobarbital. *Toxicology Letters* 6:167–171.

Klein, G., Klein, E. 1985. Evolution of tumours and the impact of molecular oncology. *Nature* 315:190–195.

Kleinman, J. C., Gold, M., Makuc, D. 1981. Use of ambulatory medical care by the poor: another look at equity. *Medical Care* 19:1011–1029.

Knight, A. S., Dublin, L. I. 1917. *The relation of cancer to economic condition.* New York: Metropolitan Life Insurance Company.

Kogevinas, M. 1987. Socioeconomic status and cancer. Results from the OPCS Longitudinal Survey. Presented at the Conference on Socioeconomic Status and Health, Menlo Park, CA, March 25–27.

Kreyberg, L. 1938. The influence of extrinsic factors on the development of induced tumours in animals. *Acta Pathologica et Microbiologica Scandinavica* Suppl. 37:317–338.

Kutner, G., Makover, H. B., Oppenheim, A. 1958. Delay in the diagnosis and treatment of cancer: a critical analysis of the literature. *Journal of Chronic Diseases* 7:95–120.

Kwa, H. G., Cleton, F., Wang, D. Y., et al. 1981. A prospective study of plasma prolactin levels and subsequent risk of breast cancer. *International Journal of Cancer* 28:673–676.

Lancaster, H. O., Nelson, J. 1957. Sunlight as a cause of melanoma: a critical survey. *Medical Journal of Australia* 1:452–456.

Lancet. 1987. Editorial. Human papillomaviruses and cervical cancer: a fresh look at the evidence. 1:725–726.

Land, H., Parada, L. F., Weinberg, R. A. 1983. Tumorigenic conversion of primary embryo fibroblasts requires at least two cooperating oncogenes. *Nature* 304:596–602.

Laudenslager, M. L., Ryan, S. M., Drugan, R. C., et al. 1983. Coping and immunosuppression: inescapable but not escapable shock suppresses lymphocyte proliferation. *Science* 221:568–570.

Leach, J. E., Robbins, G. F. 1947. Delay in the diagnosis of cancer. *Journal of the American Medical Association* 135:5–8.

Lee, J. A. H., Strickland, D. 1980. Malignant melanoma: social status and outdoor work. *British Journal of Cancer* 41:757–763.

Lerner, M. 1986. Cancer mortality differentials by income: Baltimore, 1949–1951 and 1979–1981. Unpublished paper. Baltimore: The Johns Hopkins University, School of Hygiene and Public Health.

Leshan, L. L., Worthington, R. E. 1956. Personality as a factor in the pathogenesis of cancer: a review of the literature. *British Journal of Medical Psychology* 29:49–56.

Lewison, E. F., Montague, A. C. W., Kuller, L. 1966. Breast cancer treated at the Johns Hopkins Hospital, 1951–1956. *Cancer* 19:1359–1364.

Linden, G. 1969. The influence of social class in the survival of cancer patients. *American Journal of Public Health* 59:267–274.

Lipworth, L., Abelin, T., Connelly, R. R. 1970. Socioeconomic factors in the prognosis of cancer patients. *Journal of Chronic Diseases* 23:105–116.

Locke, S. E., Kraus, L., Leserman, J., et al. 1984. Life change stress, psychiatric symptoms, and natural killer cell activity. *Psychosomatic Medicine* 46:441–453.

Lombard, H. L., Doering, C. R. 1929. Cancer studies in Massachusetts. 3. Cancer mortality in nativity groups. *Journal of Preventive Medicine* 3:343–359.

Luft, H. S. 1975. The impact of poor health on earnings. *Review of Economics and Statistics* 57:43–57.

———. 1978. *Poverty and health.* Cambridge: Ballinger Publishing Co.

MacDonald, M. E., Hagberb, K. L., Grossman, B. J. 1963. Social factors in relation to participation in follow-up care of rheumatic fever. *Journal of Pediatrics* 62:503–513.

MacKie, R. M., Aitchison, T. 1982. Severe sunburn and subsequent risk of primary cutaneous malignant melanoma in Scotland. *British Journal of Cancer* 46:955–960.

MacMahon, B., Cole, P., Lin, T. M., et al. 1970. Age at first birth and breast cancer risk. *Bulletin of the World Health Organization* 43:209–221.

Maisin, J., François, D. A. 1928. Influence du régime alimentaire sur l'élosion et l'évolution du cancer du goudron. *Annales de Médecine* 24:455–467.

Manni, A., Trujillo, J. E., Pearson, O. H. 1977. Predominant role of prolactin in stimulating the growth of 7,12-dimethylbenz(a)anthracene–induced rat mammary tumor. *Cancer Research* 37:1216–1219.

Marchant, J. 1967. The effects of different social conditions on breast cancer induction in three genetic types of mice by dibenz[a,h]anthracene and a comparison with breast carcinogenesis by 3-methylcholanthrene. *British Journal of Cancer* 21:576–585.

Marmot, M. G., Kogevinas, M., Elston, M. A. 1987. Social/ economic status and disease. *Annual Review of Public Health* 8:111–135.

Marmot, M. G ., McDowall, M. E. 1986. Mortality decline and widening social inequalities. *Lancet* 2:274–276.

McGovern, V. J. 1952. Melanoblastoma. *Medical Journal of Australia* 1:139–142.

———. 1977. Epidemiological aspects of melanoma: a review. *Pathology* 9:233–241.

McKinlay, J. B. 1975. Who is really ignorant—physician or patient? *Journal of Health and Social Behavior* 16:3–11.

McTiernan, A., Thomas, D. B., Johnson, L. K., Roseman, D. 1986. Risk factors for estrogen receptor-rich and estrogen receptor-poor breast cancer. *Journal of the National Cancer Institute* 77:849–854.

Miller, E. C., Miller, J. A. 1952. *In vivo* combinations between carcinogens and tissue constituents and their possible role in carcinogenesis. *Cancer Research* 12:547–556.

Miller, J. A. 1980. Carcinogen activation and inactivation as keys to species and tissue differences. In Coulston, F., Shubik, P., eds. *Human epidemiology and animal laboratory correlations in chemical carcinogenesis*, pp. 133–151. Norwood, N.J.: Ablex Publishing Co.

Mohla, S., Sampson, C. C., Khan, T., et al. 1982. Estrogen and progesterone receptors in breast cancer in black Americans: correlation of receptor data with tumor differentiation. *Cancer* 50:552–559.

Montgomery, M., Trussell, J. 1986. Models of marital status and childbearing. Chapter 3 in Ashenfelter, O., Layard, R., eds, *Handbook of labor economics*. Vol. 1, pp. 205–271. Amsterdam: North-Holland.

Musey, V. C. Collins, D. C., Musey, P. I., et al. 1987. Long-term effect of a first pregnancy on the secretion of prolactin. *New England Journal of Medicine* 316:229–234.

Neser, W. B., Tyroler, H. A., Cassel, J. C. 1971. Social disorganization and stroke mortality in the black population of North Carolina. *American Journal of Epidemiology* 93:166–175.

Newacheck, P. W., Butler, L. H., Harper, A. K., et al. 1980. Income and illness. *Medical Care* 18:1165–1176.

Newman, J. F., Anderson, O. W. 1972. *Patterns of dental service utilization in the United States: a nationwide social survey.* Center for Health Administration Studies, Research Series 30. Chicago: University of Chicago.

Nomura, G., Kolonel, L., Rellahan, W., et al. 1981. Racial survival patterns for lung cancer in Hawaii. *Cancer* 48:1265–1271.

Nossal, G. J. V. 1987. Current concepts: immunology: the basic components of the immune system. *New England Journal of Medicine* 316:1320–1325.

Ownby, H. E., Frederick, J., Russo, J., et al. 1985. Racial differences in breast cancer patients. *Journal of the National Cancer Institute* 75:55–60.

Pack, G. T., Gallo, J. S. 1938. The culpability for delay in the treatment of cancer. *American Journal of Cancer* 33:443–462.

Papanicolaou, G. N., Koprowska, I. 1951. Carcinoma in situ of the right lower bronchus: a case report. *Cancer* 4:141–146.

Papanicolaou, G. N., Traut, H. 1943. *Diagnosis of uterine cancer by the vaginal smear.* New York: The Commonwealth Fund.

Parsons, D. O. 1977. Health, family structure, and labor supply. *American Economic Review* 67:703–712.

Pavlidis, N., Chirigos, M. 1980. Stress-induced impairment of macrophage tumoricidal function. *Psychosomatic Medicine* 42:47–54.

Pegoraro, R. J., Karnan, V., Dharamraj, N., Joubert, S. M. 1986. Estrogen and progesterone receptors in breast cancer among women of different racial groups. *Cancer Research* 46:2117–2120.

Pendergrass, T. W., Hoover, R., Godwin, J. D., II. 1975. Prognosis of black children with acute lymphocytic leukemia. *Medical and Pediatric Oncology* 1:143–148.

Pettingale, K. W., Greer, S., Tee, D. E. H. 1977. Serum IgA and emotional expression in breast cancer patients. *Journal of Psychosomatic Research* 21:395–399.

Pike, M. C., Krailo, M. D., Henderson, B. E., et al. 1983. 'Hormonal' risk factors, 'breast tissue age,' and the age-incidence of breast cancer. *Nature* 303:767–770.

Pill, R., Stott, N. C. H. 1982. Concepts of illness causation and responsibility: some preliminary data from a sample of working class mothers. *Social Science and Medicine* 16:43–52.

Pitot, H. C. 1982. The natural history of neoplastic development: the relation of experimental models to human cancer. *Cancer* 49:1206–1211.

Pottern, L. M., Morris, L. E., Blot, W. J., et al. 1981. Esophageal cancer among black men in Washington, D.C. I. Alcohol, tobacco, and other risk factors. *Journal of the National Cancer Institute* 67:777–783.

Rasmussen, A. F., Jr. 1969. Emotions and immunity. *Annals of the New York Academy of Sciences* 164:458–461.

———, Marsh, J. T., Brill, N. Q. 1957. Increased susceptibility to herpes simplex in mice subjected to avoidance learning stress or restraint. *Proceedings of the Society for Experimental Biology and Medicine* 96:183–189.

Reinherz, E. L., Schlossman, S. F. 1980. Current concepts in immunology. Regulation of the immune response—inducer and suppressor T-lymphocyte subsets in human beings. *New England Journal of Medicine* 303:370–373.

Reynolds, R. A. 1980. *A study of the relationship between health and income.* American Medical Association, Center for Health Services Research and Development. Chicago: American Medical Association.

Ries, L. G., Pollack, E. S., Young, J. L., Jr. 1983. Cancer patient survival: surveillance, epidemiology, and end results program, 1973–1979. *Journal of the National Cancer Institute* 70:693–707.

Riley, V. 1975. Mouse mammary tumors: alteration of incidence as apparent function of stress. *Science* 189:465–467.

Robbins, G. F., Conte, A. J., Leach, J. E., MacDonald, M. 1950. Delay in diagnosis and treatment of cancer. *Journal of the American Medical Association* 143:346–348.

Robbins, G. F., MacDonald, M. C., Pack, G. T. 1953. Delay in the diagnosis and treatment of physicians with cancer. *Cancer* 6:624–626.

Robbins, J. H., Kraemer, K. H., Lutzner, M. A., et al. 1974. Xeroderma pigmentosum: an inherited disease with sun sensitivity, multiple cutaneous neoplasms, and abnormal DNA repair. *Annals of Internal Medicine* 80:221–248.

Rodin, J. 1986. Aging and health: effects of the sense of control. *Science* 233:1271–1276.

Rosenstock, I. M. 1966. Why people use health services. *Milbank Memorial Fund Quarterly* 44:94–127.

———, Derryberry, M., Carriger, B. K. 1959. Why people fail to seek poliomyelitis vaccination. *Public Health Reports* 74:98–103.

Rous, P., Kidd, J. G. 1936. The carcinogenic effect of a virus upon tarred skin. *Science* 83:468–469.

———. 1938. The carcinogenic effect of a papilloma virus on the tarred skin of rabbits. *Journal of Experimental Medicine* 67:399–427.

———. 1941. Conditional neoplasms and subthreshold neoplastic states. A study of tar tumors of rabbits. *Journal of Experimental Medicine* 73:365–389.

Rowley, J. D. 1984. Biological implications of consistent chromosome rearrangements in leukemia and lymphoma. *Cancer Research* 44:3159–3168.

Ruberman, W., Weinblatt, E., Goldberg, J. D., Chaudhary, B. S. 1984. Psychosocial influences on mortality after myocardial infarction. *New England Journal of Medicine* 311:552–559.

Sackett, D. L. 1978. Patients and therapies: getting the two together. *New England Journal of Medicine* 248:278–279.

Sager, R. 1986. Genetic suppression of tumor formation: a new frontier in cancer research. *Cancer Research* 46:1573–1580.

Salonen, J. T. 1982. Socioeconomic status and risk of cancer, cerebral stroke, and death due to coronary heart disease and any disease: a longitudinal study in eastern Finland. *Journal of Epidemiology and Community Health* 36:294–297.

Schantz, S. P., Shillitoe, E. J., Brown, B., Campbell, B. 1986. Natural killer cell activity and head and neck cancer: a clinical assessment. *Journal of the National Cancer Institute* 77:869–875.

Schimke, R. N. 1978. *Genetics and cancer in man.* New York: Churchill Livingstone.

Schrier, P. I., Bernards, R., Vassen, R. T. M. J., et al. 1983. Expression of class I major histocompatibility antigens switched off by highly oncogenic adenovirus 12 in transformed rat cells. *Nature* 305:771–775.

Seidman, H. 1970. Cancer death rates by site and sex for religious and socioeconomic groups in New York City. *Environmental Research* 3:234–250.

Shapiro, M. F., Ware, J. E., Sherbourne, C. D. 1986. Effects of cost sharing on seeking care for serious and minor symptoms. *Annals of Internal Medicine* 104:246–251.

Shapiro, S. 1977. Evidence on screening for breast cancer from a randomized trial. *Cancer* 39:2772–2782.

Shekelle, R. B., Raynot, W. J., Jr., Ostfeld, A. M., et al. 1981. Psychological depression and 17-year risk of death from cancer. *Psychosomatic Medicine* 43:117–125.

Shillitoe, E. J., Greenspan, D., Greenspan, J. S., et al. 1982. Neutralizing antibody to herpes simplex virus type 1 in patients with oral cancer. *Cancer* 49:2315–2320.

Skillrud, D. M., Offord, K. P., Miller, R. D. 1986. Higher risk of lung cancer in chronic obstructive pulmonary disease: a prospective, matched, controlled study. *Annals of Internal Medicine* 105:503–507.

Sklar, L. S., Anisman, H. 1979. Stress and coping factors influence tumor growth. *Science* 205:513–515.

———. 1980. Social stress influences tumor growth. *Psychosomatic Medicine* 42:347–365.

Sklar, L. S., Bruto, V., Anisman, H. 1981. Adaptation to the tumor-enhancing effects of stress. *Psychosomatic Medicine* 43:331–342.

Smith, H. G., Horowitz, N., Silverman, N. A., et al. 1976. Humoral immunity to herpes simplex viral-induced antigens in smokers. *Cancer* 38:1155–1162.

Solomon, G. F., Amkraut, A. A., Kasper, P. 1974. Immunity, emotions, and stress. *Annals of Clinical Research* 6:313–322.

Sontag, S. 1978. *Illness as metaphor.* New York: Farrar, Straus and Giroux.

Stein, M., Schiavi, R. C., Camerino, M. 1976. Influence of brain and behavior on the immune system. *Science* 191:435–440.

Stoeckle, J. D., ed. 1987. *Encounters between patients and doctors.* Cambridge: M.I.T. Press.

Svarstad, B. L. 1986. Patient-practitioner relationships and compliance with prescribed medical regimens. In Aiken, L. H.,

Mechanic, D., eds. *Applications of social science to clinical medicine and health policy*, pp. 438–459. New Brunswick, N.J.: Rutgers University Press.

Swift, M., Reitnauer, P. J., Morell, D., Chase, C. L. 1987. Breast and other cancers in families with ataxia-telangiectasia. *New England Journal of Medicine* 316:1289–1294.

Sydenstricker, E. 1929. Economic status and the incidence of illness. *Public Health Reports* 44:1821–1833.

Syme, S. L., Berkman, L. F. 1976. Social class, susceptibility, and sickness. *American Journal of Epidemiology* 104:1–8.

Tanaka, K., Isselbacher, K. J., Khoury, G., Jay, G. 1985. Reversal of oncogenesis by the expression of a major histocompatibility complex class I gene. *Science* 228:26–30.

Tannenbaum, A. 1940. Relationship of body weight to cancer incidence. *Archives of Pathology* 30:509–517.

———. 1942. The genesis and growth of tumors. III. Effects of high fat diet. *Cancer Research* 2:468–475.

———, Silverstone, H. 1953. Nutrition in relation to cancer. *Advances in Cancer Research* 1:451–501.

Terris, M., Oalman, M. C. 1960. Carcinoma of the cervix: an epidemiologic study. *Journal of the American Medical Association* 174:1847–1851.

Townsend, P., Davidson, N. 1982. *Inequalities in health: the Black Report*. Harmondsworth, England: Penguin Books.

Trichopoulos, D., Day, N. E., Kaklamani, E., et al. 1987. Hepatitis B virus, tobacco smoking, and ethanol consumption in the etiology of hepatocellular carcinoma. *International Journal of Cancer* 39:45–49.

U.S. Department of Health and Human Services. 1982. *Health United States 1982*. D.H.H.S. Pub. No. (PHS) 83–1232. Washington, D.C.: G.P.O.

———. 1985. *Health United States 1984*. D.H.H.S. Pub. No. (PHS) 85-1232. Washington, D.C.: G.P.O.

Vågerö, D., Persson, G. 1984. Risks, survival, and trends of malignant melanoma among white- and blue-collar workers in Sweden. *Social Science and Medicine* 19:475–478.

Vågerö, D., Ringbäck, G., Kiviranta, H. 1986. Melanoma and other tumours of the skin among office, other indoor and outdoor workers in Sweden 1961–1979. *British Journal of Cancer* 53:507–512.

Watts, D. D. 1966. Factors related to the acceptance of modern medicine. *American Journal of Public Health* 56:1205–1212.

Wegner, E. L., Kolonel, L. N., Nomura, A. M. Y., Lee, J. 1982. Racial and socioeconomic status differences in survival of co-lorectal cancer patients in Hawaii. *Cancer* 49:2208–2216.

Weinberg, R. A. 1982. Oncogenes of spontaneous and chemi-cally induced tumors. *Advances in Cancer Research* 36:149–163.

Weinblatt, E., Shapiro, S., Frank, C. W., Sager, R. V. 1966. Re-turn to work and work status following first myocardial in-farction. *American Journal of Public Health* 56:169–185.

West, P. M., Blumberg, E. M., Ellis, F. W. 1952. An observed correlation between psychological factors and growth rate of cancer in man. *Cancer Research* 12:306–307.

Wilkinson, R. G., ed. 1986. *Class and health. Research and longi-tudinal data*. New York: Tavistock Publications.

Willett, W. C., MacMahon, B. 1984. Diet and cancer—an over-view. *New England Journal of Medicine* 310:633–638, 697–703.

Willett, W. C., Stampfer, M. J., Colditz, G. A., et al. 1987. Di-etary fat and the risk of breast cancer. *New England Journal of Medicine* 316:22–28.

Williams, R. R., Horm, J. W. 1977. Association of cancer sites with tobacco and alcohol consumption and socioeconomic status of patients: interview study from the Third National Cancer Survey. *Journal of the National Cancer Institute* 58:525–547.

Wilson, R., White, E. 1977. Changes in morbidity, disability, and utilization differentials between the poor and the non-poor: data from the Health Interview Survey 1964 and 1973. *Medical Care* 15:636–646.

Winkelstein, W., Jr., Shillitoe, E. J., Brand, R., Johnson, K. K. 1984. Further comments on cancer of the uterine cervix, smoking, and herpesvirus infection. *American Journal of Epi-demiology* 119:1–8.

Wynder, E. L., Cornfield, J., Schroff, P. D., et al. 1954. A study of environmental factors in carcinoma of the cervix. *American Journal of Obstetrics and Gynecology* 68:1016–1052.

Wynder, E. L., Rose, D. P., Cohen L. A. 1986. Diet and breast
    cancer in causation and therapy. *Cancer* 58:1804–1813.
Yeracaris, C. A., Kim, J. H. 1978. Socioeconomic differentials
    in selected causes of death. *American Journal of Public Health*
    68:342–351.
Young, J. L., Ries, L. G., Pollack, E. S. 1984. Cancer patient
    survival among ethnic groups in the United States. *Journal of
    the National Cancer Institute* 73:341–352.
zur Hausen, H. 1982. Human genital cancer: synergism between
    two virus infections or synergism between a virus infection
    and initiating events. *Lancet* 2:1370–1372.

Comments on Chapter 6

Mark R. Cullen

Dr. Harris makes a terrific case that factors related to SES could have tumor-promoter activity independent of well-observed chemical and physical factors like benzene or radiation. Unfortunately, the paper goes little beyond this plausibility argument. No data set "in need" of such variables (because of the clear failure of established factors to explain differences by SES) is presented, although some involving lung cancer, where attributability has been reasonably well worked out, could have been presented to illustrate the point. Furthermore, no clear model for research has been delineated, leaving unclear where this kind of reasoning would lead from an investigative point of view.

Mary N. Haan

This paper presents a stunning array of detail without tying it together in any overall picture. It is clear that in general lower SES people have higher incidence and mortality rates of many cancers (with the notable exception of breast cancer incidence). It is suggested that delay in seeking diagnosis may be contributory to increased mortality and that higher environmental stress might be a cofactor in the differential development of cancer. Why melanoma is selected for special discussion is not clear, especially since it is quite rare, albeit widely publicized.

The assumption is made that SES-cancer differences must mainly be due to SES differences in health behaviors, although evidence to support this is contradictory and sparse. A second thought is that the poor are more highly exposed to environmental carcinogens. The focus is toward the bottom of the hierarchy and little attention is given to explanation of the SES-cancer gradient. Is it reasonable to think that the middle SES strata and upper middle strata are at higher risk because they have poorer health behaviors and worse medical care than the top of the heap? If environmental carcinogens are important explanatory factors in the SES–cancer link, is it reasonable to think that middle and upper middle SES persons are more highly exposed to these factors than the top echelon?

George A. Kaplan

Harris's paper nicely reviews the biological underpinnings of some of the ways psychosocial characteristics related to socioeconomic status may influence tumor initiation, progression, and treatment. As he points out, there are a large number of unanswered questions.

This approach has a long history, extending back to Galen's belief that "melancholic" women were more cancer prone. Much later, this discussion of host characteristics was taken up by psychosomatic theorists, and still more recently, by those interested in psychoneuroimmunology (Robert Ader's book by the same name). Unfortunately there are numerous methodological and interpretive problems associated with the work on psychosocial factors/stress, perhaps the best presentation of these being Bernard Fox's 1978 paper in the *Journal of Behavioral Medicine*. Even some of the better studies—for example, Shekelle's on depression and cancer mortality—have not been replicated (Kaplan and Reynolds, "Depression and Cancer Mortality and Morbidity," *Journal of Behavioral Medicine*, 1988). Nonetheless, some of the current work in psychoneuroimmunology represents a methodologic and conceptual breakthrough by illustrating the ways in which the nervous, endocrine, and immune systems interact.

Although the work in this latter field is progressing rapidly, it suffers from both general problems and problems specific to our understanding of socioeconomic factors and cancer. First, the current state of the field is that there are a number of conflicting studies, studies that appear to be "mining" whatever immunologic measures are available, and an almost total focus on cross-sectional studies with all their problems of interpretation. Even more important is the general lack of any broad-based studies that focus, using epidemiologic techniques, on the relationship between immune function, psychosocial characteristics, and health outcomes in persons who are not already sick. This latter point is particularly important if these pathways are to explain, in general, socioeconomic gradients in health, and not be restricted only to the impact of socioeconomic factors on progression of detected disease.

Potentially even more important is the level at which the problem is conceptualized. Are the use of pap smears, multiple sexual partners, cigarettes, and exposure to stress to be seen only at the individual level? Why then do levels of risk factors cluster by socioeconomic group? It would seem that there needs to be more emphasis on the social causes of cancer as promised in the title of this chapter. Although there is some progress in defining the ways in which social and economic conditions *might* influence cellular transformation and growth, there is little discussion about how socioeconomic status comes to be associated with these possible pathways. This is an important issue: not to look for the socioenvironmental etiology of risk factors is to unnecessarily narrow our attempts at understanding socioeconomic effects. One of the consequences of this narrowing would be to direct interventions at individuals, rather than at the situations that cause those like them, now and in the future, to engage in such practices or be exposed to stress.

Two last points: Although I recognize the data limitations that lead Harris to consider black/white comparisons as proxies for socioeconomic comparisons, a good deal of caution is necessary here. There is a considerable correlation between socioeconomic position and black/white status, but it is far from a perfect correlation. Where possible, it is desirable to disentangle these two issues. Where we can't do this, there exists the possibility that we are misestimating, probably underestimating, the magnitude of socioeconomic effects. Finally, it is important to acknowledge the gradient between socioeconomic position and cancer outcomes, because it provides an additional test of our posited explanations. For example, are there gradients of exposure to stress, cigarettes, access to pap smears, etc., which are consistent with the observed mortality and morbidity gradients?

Part III
Reflections and Observations

7. General Comments of Conference Participants

Arnold M. Epstein

It seems clear that SES is related both to the incidence and course of disease, that for different conditions the relationship between SES and disease varies, and that, while our understanding of these phenomena is still very limited, in most instances we can posit a variety of overlapping hypotheses about plausible biological, psychological, and social mechanisms that may explain the relationship. Together, the four background papers in Part II review in depth available evidence and give substantial attention to gaps in our knowledge, to particular areas of investigation that may illuminate our understanding of causality, and to methodologic and conceptual approaches that may help us improve on previous research efforts.

Less attention is devoted to ways we might ameliorate the near and intermediate term health problems associated with these phenomena. Data presented in these papers strongly suggest that inequalities in the availability of medical care or utilization cannot explain a large portion of the link between SES and health and that many disease outcomes (e.g., the association between SES and injuries) may not be alterable through more intensive or effective medical treatment. Nevertheless traditional modes of medical treatment can make a difference. Indeed, for the near and intermediate term these may be the most effective vehicle for health promotion.

Starfield, in her book *The Effectiveness of Medical Care: Validat-*

ing Clinical Wisdom (1985) presented a variety of evidence that past public policies designed to improve access to medical care for the poor had been successful in reducing a number of social class differences in morbidity and mortality. Tyroler pointed out at this conference that, in carrying out its clinical trial, the Hypertension Detection and Follow-up Program provided follow-up and treatment of hypertension through a structure that reduced both financial *and* physical access barriers to anti-hypertensive drug therapy—a program that eliminated the trad-itional social gradient in mortality among hypertensives (Stam-ler et al. 1987). The policy implications for health promotion through education and design of health organizations discussed by Dutton and Levine and the areas of inquiry relating to the in-teraction of patient and providers underscored by Harris are both important contributions that might profitably be extended further.

Current trends in health policy have important implications for care of the poor and for health promotion. The federal sys-tem of prospective payment based on Diagnosis Related Groups (DRGs) is a particularly important example. This system pro-vides hospitals with a fixed payment per case that encourages re-duction in services and shorter lengths of stay. Early discharge may be especially harmful for patients with social environments that provide only minimal support. The system may also have deleterious implications for access. For a variety of reasons pa-tients of lower SES may require longer lengths of stay and more resources once hospitalized, irrespective of DRG. For example, initial difficulties in access may result in poor patients having greater severity of illness on admission. Greater general debility may retard healing of particular conditions. Difficulties in ob-taining follow-up and in structuring appropriate home supports may also necessitate longer and more costly hospitalizations.

Recently, a pilot study of patients with connective tissue dis-eases at the Brigham and Women's Hospital in Boston showed that after controlling for DRG, patients with lower household incomes, less education, and less prestigious occupations had lengths of stay that were 10 to 20 percent longer than other pa-tients. If these findings are generalizable across DRGs and insti-tutions, hospitals that care for the poor will receive inappropriately low payment. Unless supplementary payment is provided (it has been approved on an interim basis pending further research), hospitals will be encouraged to restrict access to hospital services for low income groups.

Another important example are the proposals in several states to encourage use of prepaid groups to care for the Medicaid population. While this plan has certain attractive features for coordination of services and cost containment, a recent RAND study (Ware et al. 1986) suggests that the outcome for the poor may be less than optimal. In that study, poor patients in initially poor health fared less well if they were randomized to an HMO (Health Maintenance Organization) rather than to fee-for-service practice. The reason for this result is unclear. The authors hypothesized it may be related to bureaucratic barriers in HMOs, as well as to less attention to ensuring continuity, follow-up, and compliance. Whatever the answer, there is an interesting parallel with studies of SES and health in other countries that have nationalized health systems and presumably provide more equality in access. In England, for example, the gradients of SES and mortality appear to have increased in recent years despite the advent of the National Health Service and the provision of free care (Whitehead 1987).

Such observations might lead one, as Harris suggested, to closer investigation of the context of care seeking and the content of care received by individuals with varying SES. Our own previous studies of medical communication showed that patient and doctor agreed less often about basic aspects of care, including symptoms, test results, therapy, and prognosis when the patient was of lower socioeconomic status (Epstein et al. 1985). Others have shown that effective communication is associated with greater patient satisfaction, increased compliance, and improved health outcomes. Perhaps insights gained from studying patterns of communication in the strict medical context may also benefit community-based programs directed at modifying behavior related to such health problems as coronary heart disease, cancer, and substance abuse.

All four papers clearly suggest that a problem exists. Individuals with lower SES do have poorer health outcomes. The suggestions to invest in a series of studies to define mechanism more accurately and determine causality seem meritorious. But the long-range problem is formidable. I suspect that the complex cultural, social, biological nexus underpinning the relation between SES and health may be difficult to reverse. Therefore at the same time I emphasize the need for parallel work focused on the types of medical care services and health policies that may make a more immediate difference.

Victor R. Fuchs

The background papers provide an excellent summary of widely held views regarding the effects of socioeconomic status on health. Although they are widely held, many of these views seem to me to be wrong, misleading, or incomplete. My comments indicate the reasons for my reservations and suggest some implications for policy and research.

SES has some value as a crude shorthand symbol, but it has outlived its usefulness for serious analytical work. Moreover, it does not provide a firm basis for policy making. In the United States, at least, the correlations between income, education, occupation, housing, ethnicity, lifestyle, and the like are not very high. For instance, the coefficient of correlation between education and income within age-sex-race groups never reaches as much as .50 and is typically around .40. Thus, 84 percent of the variance is unexplained. This is particularly relevant because the various components of SES do not have the same relationship to health. For instance, the correlation between mortality and education is usually much stronger than between mortality and income. In some cross-section studies mortality is actually positively correlated with income when education is held constant.

Furthermore, even a single component of SES can have very different effects on health, depending upon the particular problem, age, and other characteristics. For instance, income is much more significant for post-neonatal than neonatal mortality, and more significant for infant mortality in general than for mortality of teenagers or adults. Education is very significant for lung cancer in men, but less so for breast cancer in women. Black/white differentials for many health problems disappear or are sharply reduced after controlling for education and income, but the higher incidence of low birthweight (and mortality) among black infants remains in even the most detailed multivariate analyses.

Some relationships that are significant within individual countries disappear in cross-country comparisons for reasons that have never been adequately explained. Life expectancy, for instance, which usually has some relationship to income within countries, bears no relationship to real GNP (Gross National Product) per capita across developed countries. Does this mean that an individual's *relative* position matters more than his or her *absolute* position? And if so, is the relevant reference group a country? A state? A city?

There are other anomalies. In U.S. cross-section studies, the incidence of low birthweight infants is negatively correlated with income and education; many observers have inferred a strong causal relationship running from the SES variables to low birthweight. Why, then, have the huge increases in income and education of the past 30 years had so little effect on birthweight distributions? And why do Mexican Americans have few low birthweight babies despite poor education and meager income?

Even the most robust part of the SES connection, the effect of additional education on health, is increasingly suspect. The correlation is strong, but is the causal connection just as strong? Any survey of high school students *at the same grade level* will show that they have already begun to sort themselves into groups characterized by different behavior with respect to smoking, alcohol, drugs, reckless driving, unprotected sex, and the like. On average, those with the more harmful behaviors are least likely to finish high school or attend college and graduate school.

The foregoing comments are not merely academic quibbles. Without a firm understanding of the causal significance of the individual SES variables, it is difficult to decide which ones should be targeted for policy. We need better data and more sophisticated statistical models to sort out causal links as distinct from correlations. Consider the finding that occupation and place of residence are frequently related to health status even after controlling for income, education, race, and other socioeconomic variables. Does this indicate causality, or does it mean that individuals with poorer health (not adequately explained by the SES variables) tend to sort themselves by occupation and place of residence?

It is doubtful that the existing SES variables tell the whole story. The time has come to pursue research on the so-called "missing" variables that may help to explain some of the correlations and anomalies. The following show some promise:

- *Time preference.* It is well known that people differ greatly in the extent to which they take the future into account in making present decisions. In common parlance this is spoken of as "living for the moment." Sociologists talk about delay of gratification, and economists describe this phenomenon as time preference or time discount, a quantitative measure that indicates the present value of future costs and benefits. Individuals with high rates of time preference will tend to invest less in the future and on average will have less education, lower income, and worse health behaviors.

- *Self-efficacy.* Individuals differ in their ability to control their lives and in their confidence in their ability to control their lives. Two individuals may feel equally strongly about the desirability of giving up cigarette smoking, but one may be much more effective than the other in doing so. Differences in self-confidence or self-control are probably correlated across many domains such as health, work, and education. It may be possible to increase self-efficacy directly, and thus to improve health.

- *Physical, mental, and emotional stamina.* It is a commonplace of everyday experience that people differ greatly in their drive, ability to work long hours, ability to function effectively with little sleep, and so on. Some people get frequent colds or headaches and some are easily depressed by unfavorable events. Individual differences in these respects have not been well studied, but they may contribute significantly to individual variation in income, education, and health, and to the correlations among these variables.

- *Multiplier effects.* It is also possible that chance events, either favorable or unfavorable, can start a reinforcing cycle that puts people on an upward or downward course with respect to income, health, and other variables. The process is well illustrated by the story of a general who was asked to explain his chest full of medals: "I found the first," he said, "and the rest came naturally." With respect to health, a chance illness can set a person on a downward spiral through adverse drug reactions, hospitalization, and the like. The deterioration in health can affect income and other variables. Similarly, one lucky or unlucky break in a career can set a favorable or unfavorable spiral in motion that can spread across domains to produce the observed correlations. (See Mechanic's introductory comments in chapter 1.)

In summary, the papers and conference call attention to a significant range of problems, but much work remains to be done. We need to move forward with a major effort to understand the interplay between socioeconomic factors and health outcomes and to develop interventions that will improve those outcomes.

Steven Gortmaker

I found all the papers stimulating and informative; my comments focus upon what I consider to be some major issues that were either overlooked or where I disagree with what was said.

I agree with Haan et al. that the relationship between socioeconomic status (SES) and health status (HS) "is one of the most profound and pervasive observations ever made in public health." However, I also believe we are not going to further our understanding of these relationships in all their complexity by merely noting that this relationship is unvarying and pervasive. Rather, we need to study how the relationship between SES and HS varies, test hypotheses concerning why this is so, and do so in a manner that is relevant to variables that policies and programs can influence.

This approach is illustrated in the paper by Harris where a complex set of relationships between SES and HS are detailed for the case of cancer. Harris notes that for some cancers positive relationships to SES are found, and for others negative relationships are observed.

I myself am most familiar with the variety of SES/HS relationships found in the study of infant and childhood mortality and morbidity. Whereas in the aggregate a simple relationship may appear (e.g., as SES increases, rates of mortality and morbidity decrease) as more specific causes of death and disorder are examined, much more complex patterns emerge.

For example, infant mortality rates are higher among black infants than white infants, yet rates of neonatal mortality among low birthweight black infants born in tertiary centers are lower than rates of similar weight white infants born in these same centers (Gortmaker et al. 1985). Rates of infant deaths due to congenital anomalies are similar for both blacks and whites (Berry et al. 1987). Rates of many chronic childhood disorders are similar for blacks and whites, with some being higher for whites (e.g., cystic fibrosis) and others being higher for blacks (e.g., sickle cell anemia). Rates of a variety of chronic physical disorders show little relationship to SES. Poor adolescents are more likely to die of homocides, whereas wealthier adolescents tend to die in automobile accidents (Wise et al. 1985).

In addition to examining specific causes of death and disease, we need to make further differentiation with respect to the construct of SES. When used as a crude control variable, SES can be usefully conceptualized as a unitary construct. But when we are thinking causally, it is imperative to conceptualize at the very minimum the distinct constructs of income, education, and occupation. Each of these can be expected to have distinct effects independent of the others. For example, occupational exposures can lead to certain diseases like asbestosis; income (or the lack of it) can affect many aspects of life. For example, higher income could lead to increased consumption of food, perhaps explaining the higher rates of obesity observed among white and wealthier children in the United States (Gortmaker et al. 1987), and the lack of it could explain the higher rates of malnutrition found among the poor. Education can have a myriad of effects, including making persons "more efficient producers of health" as noted by Grossman and Joyce in their paper.

What this sort of disaggregated approach leads to is a more complex view of the SES/HS connection. I don't believe the search for a few global, unifying constructs to explain these complex relationships is going to be fruitful. Such global explanations run the risk of creating the false impression that poverty dooms an individual to a miserable and unhealthy life. In fact, many behaviors of the poor and the working class are quite "healthy," and there are plenty of highly intelligent people living on low incomes in the United States who live long, healthy, happy lives.

The task before us is thus not simple. *Many* causal relationships need to be identified and explained. The fact that individuals at the bottom of the income, educational, or occupational ladders are disadvantaged in terms of their risk of death and disease can be explained by the effects of inequality, by the selection processes whereby individuals come into these statuses, or by explicating the mechanisms linking these inequalities to health outcomes (with allowance for some feedback). Haan et al. present a nice framework for thinking about these issues, as well as some good evidence that the selection argument does not in general hold (with some caveats). It is also a fact that inequalities of income, occupation, and education are not easily eliminated, although experiments such as the income maintenance experiments and educational interventions such as Head Start hold obvious importance.

Missing from these analyses is a recognition of the limits placed upon our present knowledge by current inadequacies in measurement. Haan et al. cite some of the results from the important Alameda County Study, indicating that relationships between income and mortality could not be accounted for by a wide range of behavioral risk factors, such as smoking, alcohol consumption, physical activity level, etc. No mention was made of the fact that substantial measurement error is associated with many of these variables: Dietary and activity measures, for example, can have notoriously low reliability, and lack of reliability will lead to underestimates of these mediating mechanisms. Given that controlling for the variables as measured in the Alameda County Study resulted in a substantial reduction in the relationship between income and mortality, I believe it is quite premature to reject the notion that these behavioral risk factors (and others as yet unmeasured or poorly measured) can account for much of the observed relationship.

Another, more basic issue was not addressed in these papers. An implicit assumption that appeared throughout the discussions is that we would like to produce a society where the relationship between SES and HS is nonexistent. However, I believe we need a much more clearly specified goal: We need to clarify how we should decide if a relationship between SES and HS is acceptable or not. Perhaps we should be less concerned if a highly paid, stressed executive experiences disabling depression because of the failure of a million-dollar deal in contrast to our feelings for the infant who died because the mother happened to be an illegal immigrant who received no medical care during a high risk pregnancy. What do you think?

Therefore, given our current state of knowledge, I believe attention needs to be focused upon explication of the most important mechanisms connecting SES to HS. *Creative demonstration and experimental programs need to be implemented and evaluated.* These often produce the most important data from a policy-oriented point of view. Obviously this approach is complex, and it is true that many causal processes will be unsuitably studied because of the limitations of data and research/evaluation designs. However, as our quantitative knowledge concerning these mechanisms grows, we will be able to specify areas where SES differentials could be eliminated if we applied known interventions. In some areas today SES differentials in mortality can be reduced through the equitable provision of effective medical care, through health promotion interventions, and through alterations of the work, home, and school environment by means of policies, programs, and publicity.

Discussions at the conference reinforced for me some areas of particular importance that the Foundation might consider for foci of future intervention efforts. One of these areas concerns early intervention programs that work to develop skills early in a child's life and that build upon the successes reported for programs such as Head Start. Another area of limited discussion at the conference, but one that cannot be ignored, is the potential impact of the spread of HIV (human immunodeficiency virus)—particularly among poor and minority populations in the United States. Substantial disparities in the incidence of AIDS (acquired immunodeficiency syndrome) have already appeared, and there has been remarkably little development of health education and health promotion interventions aimed at behaviors related to spread of the virus. It also seems clear that health promotion efforts aimed at reducing the spread of HIV need to be integrated into a wide variety of other health promotion efforts if substantial progress is to be made in avoiding a major public health catastrophe.

Michael Grossman

In attempting to explain the relationship between health and socioeconomic status, one might want to take account of the endogeneity of such intervening factors as medical care, cigarette smoking, and diet. Failure to do so may lead to an underestimation of their impacts. To be specific, persons with poor health endowments may select a different mix of health inputs than other persons. Since one can never fully control for the endowment, the intervening factors are likely to be correlated with the disturbance term in the health outcome equation.

A related point is that if one has data on all relevant intervening variables and takes the endogeneity of these variables into account, one would want to estimate the health outcome equation by simultaneous equations methods and omit socioeconomic status from the equation. Thus, it may be somewhat misleading to adjust health for risk factors and then examine the SES effect if the adjustments are based on ordinary least squares or related techniques.

There is a flip side to my first two comments. As I point out in my paper, the use of two-stage least squares rather than ordinary least squares may involve a trade off between a reduction in simultaneous equations bias and increases in specification or omitted variables bias and multicollinearity. Specification bias becomes a problem because certain variables must be omitted from the structural outcome equation to achieve identification. The degree of multicollinearity in the data rises because the predicted values of the intervening variables tend to be more highly correlated than the actual values.

Howard H. Hiatt

The background papers present comprehensive summaries of studies on the relationships of nonbiological factors—

economic, educational, occupational, and political—to health. The relationships are strong—across age, sex, and national boundaries. The pernicious effects on health outcomes of adverse social conditions are multiple and multifactorial. This is no surprise, since all disease, even that seemingly caused by a single biological factor, is invariably influenced by other conditions. For example, the pneumococcus may cause pneumonia, but susceptibility to, and severity of, the illness are determined by a range of other factors as well—nutritional and occupational, to name two. And, just as depressed social conditions breed ill health, so illness increases the likelihood of poverty, joblessness, inadequate education, etc.

The papers convincingly present the need for more research so as to understand better the relationships of specific factors to ill health. They indicate the impossibility of unravelling completely the web of causation. But since medical care cannot fully, or even in large measure, compensate for the effects of the many nonmedical factors that promote ill health, it is crucial that those factors be defined as carefully as possible, and that efforts be directed at their control.

Harris develops the multifactorial theme elegantly for cancer. Multiple biological factors, most still unknown, affect the development of the clinical picture of cancer in any single individual. Similarly, a range of social factors, even less well understood, may also play important roles. Harris poses convincingly the need for a research agenda that includes both biological and social scientists. Implicit is the indispensable role of scientists like himself who bridge both areas.

Two conclusions from these papers and from the discussion at the conference seem to me worth special note, in addition to the need for more research:

- Medical care, including primary preventive care, is of universal importance, particularly among disadvantaged populations. Drugs directed at the bacteria that cause tuberculosis and rheumatic fever, for example, are effective against these diseases even among the most deprived people. But better living conditions, improved nutrition, more education, and other social measures are also crucial for control of these and most other diseases.

• Health policy is social policy, and major progress in improving the nation's health will require not only the provision of medical care to the millions of Americans now without it, but also attention to education, employment, housing, and other social problems.

In our world of limited resources, we must increasingly think in terms of tradeoffs. Decision makers need to be made aware of the relationships between SES and health to which this conference was committed, so that the priorities they set can be informed. Since there will never be enough money to meet all needs in both the health and the education fields—to take two of today's neglected areas—the effects on health of more medical measures and more education should be compared before allocation decisions are made. The Kaiser Family Foundation's community-based health promotion programs present unique opportunities to focus the attention of the public and their elected representatives on such tradeoff issues.

Neil A. Holtzman

I will limit my comments to the role of genetic factors in disease. That genetically determined differences could explain why some people are more likely to become ill than others is not mentioned at all by Dutton and Levine or Haan, et al., and only fleetingly by Grossman and Joyce or Harris. There are, I think, three reasons for this lack that I will examine in detail:

First, it has not been possible to determine the extent or nature of allelic diversity that contributes to differences in susceptibility to disease.[1]

Second, in contrast to the risk factors for which class differences often are found (e.g, housing, nutrition, occupation, smoking), allele frequencies are unlikely to differ between classes within a given culture or race.

Third, the use of genetics as an instrument of social policy has had disastrous consequences.

Grossman and Joyce explicitly recognize the first point. It is, however, becoming much easier to assess the role of inherited factors in a wide range of diseases. As this knowledge accumulates, to maintain, as Harris does, that "what matters [in consid-

ering socioeconomic gradients] is the acquired, not the inherited" will be to disregard valuable information on variance in
disease incidence and severity.

*It has not been possible to determine the extent or nature of allelic
diversity that contributes to differences in susceptibility to disease.*

The barriers to elucidating the genetic role in many diseases
were largely methodological. They were removed with the discovery of recombinant DNA techniques, which for the first
time permitted direct examination of the human genome. In just
a few years, the new technology has succeeded in locating the
genes for Huntington's disease, retinoblastoma, cystic fibrosis,
Duchenne's muscular dystrophy, some forms of hyperlipidemic
heart disease, and—in some families—Alzheimer's disease and
bipolar affective disorder. (This is not a complete list.)

Heterozygote carriers of the alleles for some rare, severe, recessive disorders have been found recently to be at increased risk
for fairly common disorders that are generally milder and of
later age of onset than the associated recessive disorders. The
frequency of such heterozygotes for each predisposition is in the
range of 0.1 to 1 percent of the population. Heterozygotes for
familial hypercholesterolemia alleles occur in about 0.2 percent
of the population and account for about 5 percent of myocardial
infarctions before age 60 in the U.S. Heterozygotes for ataxia telangiectasia, estimated to make up about 1 percent of the U.S.
white population are at increased risk for cancer, particularly
breast cancer in women. The 2 percent of the population that are
heterozygotes for an alpha$_1$-antitrypsin deficiency allele may be
at increased risk of emphysema from cigarette smoke or other
lung irritants.

Some common genetic variants (polymorphisms) occurring
in more than 1 percent of the population increase susceptibility
to harm from environmental exposures. The possession of certain alleles at the histocompatibility (HLA) loci increases the risk
of insulin-dependent diabetes mellitus, ankylosing spondylitis,
and narcolepsy, to name but a few. The contributing environmental factors have not been elucidated. It would be surprising
if there were not genetically determined differences at the HLA

or other loci that influenced the immune responses to stress as Harris notes in chapter 6.

Polymorphic differences in a cytoplasmic receptor for certain chemicals (benzpyrene and other aromatic hydrocarbons) determine the rate of P450I enzyme synthesis (*induction*) following exposure of the organism to these chemicals. Among the 10 percent of the U.S. population that are high inducers of P450I enzymes, the risk of bronchogenic cancer in smokers is 10 to 40 times higher than in smokers who are low inducers. Polymorphic differences at the locus for another P450 enzyme, which metabolizes the antihypertensive drug debrisoquine, also account for differences in the risk of lung cancer in smokers. Extensive metabolizers are at greater risk for lung cancer if they smoke. Approximately half the population have a polymorphism that limits their rate of acetylation of a number of drugs and other chemicals. They are at greater risk for peripheral neuropathy following prolonged isoniazid therapy, a lupus erythematosus-like reaction following treatment with certain antihypertensive and antiarrhythmia drugs, and bladder cancer following exposure to arylamines.

The high frequency of alleles that predispose to disease can be accounted for by the relatively late onset of such diseases and the delay in exposure to, or effect of (latency), the contributing environmental factors. As a result, the predisposing allele may already have been transmitted to offspring before the diseases become manifest. Moreover, humans have evolved under drastically different conditions from those that confront the species today. Alleles that were beneficial to hunter-gatherers may not be beneficial to modern humans; an insufficient number of generations has passed since the dawn of the industrial revolution, and perhaps even since the start of agriculture, to eliminate alleles whose benefit has turned to risk.

Allele frequencies are unlikely to differ between classes within a given culture or race.[2]

Although poverty, and class status in general, tend to perpetuate from one generation to the next as noted by Haan et al. in chapter 4, it is difficult to account for this on genetic grounds.

The number of generations for which U.S. families, especially those of nonnative Americans, have been in the same socioeconomic stratum is insufficient to result in genetic differences between strata, even if there were no interstrata matings. Among any wave of immigrants (or slaves), alleles at most loci were randomly distributed among individuals in the pool and remained so as members of the pool moved into different classes.[3]

Two attributes of genes make it highly unlikely that they play much of a role in determining socioeconomic status. First, any single gene has a small effect. Even discrete traits such as hair or eye color are determined by more than one gene. Second, except for those on the same segment of one chromosome (and humans have 24 chromosomes), genes are inherited independently of each other. This is often the case for genes that influence related functions, such as sequential steps in a metabolic pathway. It is inconceivable, therefore, that anything as complex as coping ability or intelligence could be determined by one or a small number of genes (although a defect in a single gene could have a negative effect, for instance, phenylketonuria). Nor is it probable that the combination of alleles at different loci that *might* contribute to a complex response (e.g., "resilience," "coping") to complex environmental stimuli would all be inherited together. Instead, they will be reshuffled with every passage to one's offspring.

If, then, there is no evidence that allele frequencies differ between classes, what contribution do genetic factors make to the differences in morbidity and mortality between classes? The answer lies in the interactions between gene-products (enzymes and other proteins) and environmental agents. For while the genetic factors do not differ between classes the environmental factors do. This interaction has some predictable effects on disease patterns.

In the absence of adverse environmental factors we should expect that genetic factors will predominate in disease causation. Since there are fewer adverse environmental factors among the upper socioeconomic strata, genetic factors should be more apparent. In one report (Marmot, Shipley, and Rose 1984), a history of a first degree relative with coronary heart disease (CHD) was three times more likely among the highest grade of British civil servants (21 percent) than among the lowest (7 percent). The authors used this to argue, correctly I believe, "against genetic determination of the higher CHD risk in lower grades" (Marmot et al., p. 1003). Moreover, the proportion of deaths from all causes between ages 40–64 that occurred between ages 40–49 was 24 percent in the two upper grades compared to 8 percent in the two lower grades. Both of these observations are consistent with a greater role of genetic factors in the upper grades. Those forms of a disease in which genetic factors predominate have earlier ages of onset than the forms in which there is less evidence for genetic factors and more for environmental. The data in this study are ecological; they do not indicate whether those few administrators and professionals who died young had the positive family history.

In the study of Marmot et al. (1984), the death rates from CHD and all causes in *every* age category were always highest in the lowest two civil service grades. I hypothesize that adverse environmental exposures, which admittedly occur in a higher proportion of lower than upper class individuals, are insufficient to account for the excess of deaths in the lower classes at young ages; what is needed in addition is the presence of susceptibility-conferring alleles. The frequency of these alleles (which is the same in each class) must be greater than the frequency of adverse environmental exposures in the upper classes. As more and more disease-causing and susceptibility-conferring alleles are identified and simple tests for them developed, it will be easier to test the hypothesis.

The use of genetics as an instrument of social policy has had disastrous consequences.

The early eugenicists, including many in the United States, maintained that "feeble-mindedness" and "criminality" could be reduced by preventing those with such disorders from reproducing. This view was supported by the Supreme Court in 1927 in the Buck v. Bell decision. Speaking for the majority, Justice Oliver Wendell Holmes declared that sterilization on eugenic grounds was within the police power of the state. "Three generations of imbeciles are enough," he said. By 1931 thirty states had passed compulsory sterilization measures; they remain on the books, although seldom enforced, in twenty-two states. In the absence of cures for many of the disorders held to be inherited, the early eugenicists in this country were among the first to use cost-benefit analysis to justify their policies. Class bias among the eugenicists was neatly summed up by the British biologist Lancelot Hogben when he commented that "no eugenicist had publicly proposed sterilization as a remedy for defective kingship" despite hemophilia in the royal houses of Europe.

The evidence on which the early eugenicists based their claims of inheritance of deleterious traits lacked scientific credibility. Recombinant DNA technology makes it possible to determine with considerable accuracy the genetic factors in a wide range of diseases. Although this will improve understanding of etiology and pathogenesis, the use of the technology to predict those at risk for disease—or whose offspring are at risk—could once again lead to the use of genetics as an instrument of public policy without regard for individual autonomy.

For many diseases the capability of predicting those at risk will precede by many years any capability to treat effectively. Carrier screening, prenatal diagnosis, and abortion of affected fetuses will, however, be possible, and will often turn out—particularly for common diseases—to be less expensive than treatment after the disease becomes manifest. Although mandatory abortion is unforeseeable in this country, people could be pressured to accept abortion even when it was offensive to them. Their affected offpsring could be denied health insurance. Or, public support for their long-term care could be reduced. As prenatal diagnosis became the norm, those who rejected it could be socially ostracized. If the magnitude of the disease were to be diminished by widespread use of prenatal diagnosis, research directed toward finding effective means of preventing the manifestations or curing them might not be supported.

Genetic tests can be used to discriminate in other ways. Those with predispositions could be denied insurance or employment in order to save the private sector money. Although genetic traits are of equal frequency in all classes, their discriminatory effects will be felt hardest by the lower classes. Genetic testing may be used most frequently to screen applicants for jobs for which there is a surplus labor pool. Moreover, the poor will have the fewest resources to cope with the manifestations of the diseases predicted by genetic tests. In addition, by relying on excluding the genetically predisposed, efforts to reduce harmful environmental exposures may be neglected.

In summary, genetic factors play a significant role in the etiology of many common as well as rare diseases. As a result of new technology, it is now possible to elucidate these factors. Although their frequency would not be expected to differ between classes, genetic predispositions promise to explain why some people exposed to a given environment or stress situation become sick while others do not. Genetic tests could be used to exclude the genetically predisposed from adequate health care coverage or employment. An increase in the disparity in health between rich and poor could result. Pressure could be exerted on those at risk for having offspring with genetic diseases to avoid their conception or birth without adequate assurance of individual or parental autonomy. Whether to learn more about variance in illness or to influence public policy, genetics can no longer be ignored.

Brian Jarman

The case for a strong link between socioeconomic factors and health has been established by the papers circulated beyond any serious element of doubt, as has the link with specific causative factors, such as tobacco, alcohol, and, to a certain extent, diet. The difficulty remains of how a group of health professionals should proceed to implement changes that will lead to improved health, particularly of the lower socioeconomic groups. The main problem is that action would need to be taken at a political level in many instances and there are strong vested interests for the powerful tobacco and alcohol companies to maintain their market share. I think there is a danger, which may not be openly expressed in the medical forum, that discussion of the minutiae of these socioeconomic health differences could be used to avoid the more difficult task of implementing changes.

It is appropriate that health professionals should recommend any action that is necessary to improve the health of the populations they are studying and should continue to draw attention to the action needed with all government and other bodies concerned. I believe more research would be desirable on how to do this most effectively.

Michael Marmot

RESPONSES TO THE FOUR BACKGROUND PAPERS

These papers provide a very good background to the general topic of socioeconomic position and health. What follows are reactions to the papers rather than detailed critiques of them.

- Why have socioeconomic differences in mortality apparently increased in England and Wales, despite general improvements over time in mortality in the population as a whole? If the decline in mortality is due to general improvement in socioeconomic conditions, does this mean that things are improving for everyone but at differential rates?

- These observations raise the whole question of "deprivation versus inequality." People in the 1980s are, presumably, less deprived than early generations of the 1930s. Yet the interclass differences appear to have become exaggerated. As pointed out in the papers, this is a likely effect of hierarchies or inequalities per se. This is an important issue. In Britain at least, we currently have a government that believes that inequalities are the fuel that drives the engine of the economy. The government believes that only by following policies that exaggerate inequalities will general prosperity for all be increased. If worsening mortality, and other health parameters, follow from this, it has important political implications.

- The whole question of a general pattern versus the search for specific causes is raised in different ways by Harris, Haan et al., and Dutton and Levine. Harris appears to be further down the line in looking for specific causes, although allowing for some general effect on cancer promotion. Haan et al. appear to be further along the line in the other direction. Dutton and Levine suggest some sort of combination, as in their statement: "multiple adversities and processes undermine endurance." This suggests the existence of some general phenomenon such as endurance that would account for a general effect across a wide range of specific causes. But it leaves open the possibility that endurance may be affected by a wide range of specific factors. Until we get our models right, it is going to be difficult to know both what should be the appropriate study design and what should be the form of analysis. My associates and I are similarly confused in our own work. We have tended towards a model of general susceptibility and yet have noted that diseases such as coronary heart disease appear to have changed their social class distribution, depending on the level of economic development. This should not be too challenging to a model of general susceptibility, as the relation between social class and variety of specific "exposures" such as smoking and diet, will be contingent.

- Dutton and Levine and Haan et al. make clear that socioeconomic factors can affect health very early in life. Yet they both cite the relationship of education with ill health as refuting the hypothesis of downward mobility being caused by ill health. While in general I think they are correct, their argument could be attacked. If the ill health caused by poor social position begins in utero and in the first years, ill health could certainly lead to poorer educational performance and to ill health subsequently in life. While this is not downward mobility, it is ill health affecting education rather than the reverse. In practice, I think it is more likely to be the play of a common antecedent—i.e., poor social position leads to ill health and poorer educational achievement, which in turn leads to lower status occupation and lower income level.

- The question of the contribution of medical care to inequalities in health is apparently not solved. My associates and I have followed the statisticians who have used Rutstein's approach (1976) in dealing with "amenable" causes of death—i.e., those diseases "amenable" to medical care. This approach suggests that only a minority of the social class differences in mortality could be attributed to differences in medical care. It should be noted, however, that where the authors assume that the medical care argument is refuted by the existence of social class gradients in countries with equal access, they potentially fall into the trap of equating potential equality of access with actual equality of access. This is now very difficult to sort out as consulting rates clearly reflect both perceived need, actual need, and access. Another approach is to take, as Harris does, specific diseases such as cancer and ask what could the contribution of medical care be. We have been analyzing the British data and our preliminary conclusions are that social class differences in survival from cancer could not account for social class differences in mortality from cancer.

- The potential importance of "area characteristics" as laid out by Haan et al. is intriguing. It is challenging to know how to take this further. Their area characteristics include variables such as high proportions of men over sixty-five, widowers, persons without cars, deteriorated housing, and housing without heat. While the latter two may possibly have a direct effect on mortality, lack of access to cars could be some indicator of wealth or have a more prosaic connection with ill health. Presumably the first two are indicators of something else. The research question is how to narrow down on what the relevant characteristics of an area are that are susceptible either to further study or to intervention.
- The suggestions both for further study and intervention could lead to a whole program of work that would need to be carried out in different cultural settings.

COMMENTS ON FUTURE RESEARCH ON SOCIAL INEQUALITIES

The papers in this volume and in the conference that gave rise to it touch on a number of important questions: why look at socioeconomic differences in health; do we need research, action, or a combination—action-research; if research, what types of data and models are needed; should the focus of intervention to improve health be on high risk individuals or should it be at a societal/population level?

Why examine socioeconomic differences in health?

To interpret the world or to change it? The answer is surely both. In studying socioeconomic differences, we are seeking clues to the determinants of health and disease in general, to the determinants of social class differences in particular, and to ways of reducing those differences.

Action? Research? Or action-research?

There is a view that research, particularly that on social inequalities, is neverending. Why wait while the research community struggles with the mass of interconnected variables related to social class? Why not try action-research? On the surface, this sounds attractive: do it and see if it works; program and evaluation.

My reservations come from involvement with translating research findings into policy for the prevention of cardiovascular disease. The view had taken hold that the controversy over whether coronary heart disease (CHD) was preventable would not be settled by further observational studies on risk-related behaviors or risk factors. It was argued that questions both of etiology and efficacy of prevention could be settled only by trials of intervention: behavioral change and/or drug treatment of high levels of plasma lipids and blood pressure. In any event, these trials settled little. The most celebrated, the Multiple Risk Factor Intervention Trial (MRFIT) was inconclusive; others were negative, e.g., the British Medical Research Council trial of treatment of mild hypertension had no effect on CHD. Even where the trial was positive (e.g., the Lipid Research Center's primary prevention trial where lowering plasma cholesterol by cholestyramine reduced CHD incidence), critics argued that the trial participants were so atypical with diet-resistant hyperlipidemia, that results could not be extrapolated to those with more moderate elevations of risk.

We were therefore thrown back onto observational data to make judgments as to whether there was a causal connection between risk factors and CHD, and as to whether changing population levels of risk factors would change population rates of

CHD. It could be argued that at least the trials told us if it was possible to modify risk behaviors and how to do it. Even here, the conclusions are of doubtful generalizability. In the Multiple Risk Factor Intervention Trial, the effort and resources put into modifying individual behaviors far outstripped those available in the real world. The practical lesson learned is, therefore, questionable. Similarly, even if a community level intervention, such as that in North Karelia in Finland, successfuly modifies behaviors, we are left wondering: What worked? Which of the many actions taken produced the desired change? These questions are important because the level of resources available outside the research setting are likely to be a faint shadow of those available for a special trial.

If the reservations about the interpretation of action-research apply to so relatively "simple" a problem as whether high intakes of dietary fat lead to CHD, how much more do they apply to a truly complex area such as the link between socioeconomic status and disease? It may well be appropriate to plan interventions on the basis of observational studies, and this should influence the research agenda.

What types of data and models?

To the uninformed bystander (e.g., this epidemiologist) there appears to be a tendency in some social science/economic research to proceed as if statistical models equated with reality: if you cannot model it, it does not exist; and if you can model it, it does. An extension: a statistical model can sort out the relative strength of association of different factors with an "outcome" such as disease rates or health status, and can help make judgments on which of several factors is primary. This tendency looms large in epidemiology as well. This leads to the following type of statements: A number of socioeconomic factors were put into a multivariate statistical model; years of education showed the strongest independent association with health status; therefore, differences in education are the main cause (out of the factors considered) of differences in health status; education, therefore, provides the best prospect for reducing socioeconomic differences in health status. This sequence is plausible, but it may be quite wrong. Years of education might, for example, show the strongest association with health status simply because it is measured more precisely than social characteristics of residence or occupational status. Education may be a precise marker of social position, but may not be in itself a determinant of health status.

Multivariate statistical models are invaluable, but they should serve social/biological models, not pre-empt them. What may be needed is more attention to study design and the "natural" experiment that may help to disentangle intercorrelated variables. The Alameda County data provide such an example (see chapter 4 by Haan et al.).

Individual or society?

One of the achievements of the *Black Report* on inequalities in health (Townsend and Davidson 1982) was to crystalize the arguments as to the causes of inequalities. In particular, having dismissed artifacts and health selection, the report concentrated on differences in material conditions of life as against simply individual differences in behavior. Many of us would feel that one influences the other (Marmot et al. 1987), but the distinction is important. Should the approach to reducing social inequalities in health be to attempt to alter individual behaviors or should it be to modify the social environment? In Britain, the *Black Report* reacted against the view (still expressed) that individuals are responsible for their health and ill health by virtue of the decisions they make about their personal behavior. To caricature only slightly: if they smoke or eat badly, it must be through bloody-mindedness or ignorance. They should, therefore, be blamed and/or educated. The point of intervention should be the individual.

Versions of the "individual responsibility—therefore individual intervention" argument surface often through the papers in this volume. The objection to this is twofold: First, "individual choices" cannot account for the broad and consistent social trends in disease patterns observed; and second, there is little evidence to encourage us that an approach to intervention based on individuals will be effective in reducing social inequalities. In

TABLE I. MAJOR RISK FACTORS IN DIFFERENT GRADES: AGE-ADJUSTED MEANS AND PERCENTAGE SHOWING INCREASED VALUES

	GRADE			
VARIABLE	*ADMINISTRATIVE*	*PROFESSIONAL/ EXECUTIVE*	*CLERICAL*	*OTHER*
Systolic BP (mmHg):				
Mean (SEM)	133.7(0.67)	136.0(0.19)	136.8(0.42)	137.9(0.64)
Percentage ⩾160	10.7	12.2	13.8	16.5
Plasma cholesterol (mmol/1):				
Mean (SEM)	5.20(0.04)	5.13(0.01)	5.08(0.03)	4.96(0.04)
Percentage ⩾6.72	12.6	10.2	10.5	7.8
Smoking: Percentage				
smokers	28.8	37.3	53.0	60.9
Never smoked	33.0	23.2	17.0	14.8
Ex-smokers	38.1	39.6	29.9	24.3
BMI (weight/height^2) (kg m-2):				
Mean (SEM)	24.5(0.09)	24.8(0.03)	24.6(0.07)	25.0(0.10)
Percentage ⩾28	9.9	11.8	13.8	17.4
Leisure physical activity: Percentage				
inactive	26.3	29.5	43.0	56.0
Height (cm):				
Mean (SEM)	178.5(0.20)	176.3(0.05)	174.0(0.13)	173.2(0.23)
Percentage >183 (6 ft)	21.1	12.8	7.6	8.7
Family history: 1st-degree relatives with heart disease (%)	21	16	10	7

Marmot et al. 1984.

Britain, for example, to the extent that attempts at prevention of cardiovascular disease have been successful, they have selectively benefited the middle classes. Over the decade from the early 1970s to the 1980s, the gap in mortality between nonmanual and manual classes increased (Marmot and McDowall 1986).

In our "Whitehall" study of civil servants (Marmot et al. 1984), several major risk factors cluster by social class, the lower grades of employment (clerks and messengers) having higher levels than more senior grades (see Table 1). The study showed a step-wise association of level of employment with mortality: the lower the grade, the higher the mortality. Such a study allows some sorting out of a number of intercorrelated variables usually associated with social class: (1) the study is confined to office employees, it therefore excludes physicochemical industrial hazards; (2) these are men in stable jobs, so there can be no effect of unemployment, or frequent job changes; (3) they all work in and around London, so there is no effect of variations, geography, or climate; (4) they are overwhelmingly one ethnic group; (5) although income closely matches grade of employment, even the lowest grades are not subject to poverty in any absolute sense, so the deprivation is relative. Despite this, the social gradient in mortality is steeper than in the country as a whole, using the Registrar-General's social classes I–V. Perhaps this is because in the civil service, there is more homogeneity within and more heterogeneity between grades than in social classes nationally.

The Whitehall study is a useful illustration because it demonstrates that there are powerful social causes of individual behaviors. As in other surveys, men of lower status are more likely to smoke and less likely to take exercise in their leisure time. If individual choice were the best way to view risk-related behaviors, one might have expected a random distribution of these behaviors. The focus of our question should not be why do some individuals smoke, but why are some groups more likely to smoke? The aim of intervention should not be to reduce smoking levels of individuals, but to reduce smoking levels of the least advantaged social group to those of the most advantaged.

Mortality provides another similar example. In our Whitehall study, the socioeconomic gradient in mortality could not be explained completely by known biological risk factors. The question is not why are some disadvantaged individuals at higher risk, but why are whole disadvantaged groups at higher risk? In seeking reasons for the higher risk of men in lower grades, we are looking at the social environment: the nature of work and social relationships. Work is of particular interest because, in the civil service at least, the nature of working relationships and the structure of jobs (work stress) is on the agenda for discussion between management and unions. Data on the health effects of work characteristics, and their contribution to social inequalities, will have great real world significance and will become part of the discourse. The potential is there for tangible benefits of research efforts. That is, in the end, the reason for them.

David Mechanic

The papers are excellent and all make clear the robustness of the relationship between socioeconomic status (SES) and health, however these be measured and whatever the outcomes examined. A critical challenge is to define the question more clearly and more specifically, particularly in light of the Foundation's interest in identifying points of leverage for interventions in promoting health. Knowing about aggregate relationships between SES and health is not particularly helpful in identifying strategies. SES includes a broad set of factors that affect almost every aspect of living from exposure to environmental risks to cognitive sets, interaction styles, and child rearing. These factors affect varying disease processes and health risks in *different* ways, and specificity of condition and possible causative processes are essential. Harris's discussion of intervening factors as they affect cancer is a useful way to proceed. In some instances the SES relationship will be explained by occupational exposure, in other cases by differential access to care, and in still other cases by varying processes of socialization that affect health risks. It is pointless to try to account for the relationship in the aggregate since so many different and complex processes are involved.

The paper by Haan, Kaplan, and Syme is instructive, but I find the demands-resources model too general to be useful except as a way of organizing discussion. Similarly, Dutton and Levine make a persuasive case that inequality is a major contextual influence; but while I agree with their concerns, I would suggest that no society has ever managed to eliminate inequalities and thus a more specific focus seems warranted in addition to any efforts we make at the macro level. If the effects of SES on health are *relative* as well as *absolute*, and I believe they are, then a multifaceted strategy seems most appropriate.

SES is basically a proxy variable for hundreds of different influences. No multivariate model ever controls more than just a few of these intervening factors, and thus it is no surprise that all SES effects cannot usually be explained. In any given area, if we can isolate the more proximate influences, we have a more promising chance to intervene since they are likely to have effects on health beyond those explained through SES. Such lifestyle areas as smoking, diet, and contraceptive behavior are just a small selection of the intervening factors that affect health outcomes. Moreover, intervention strategies require better understanding of the causal influences on the risk factors themselves.

Because SES factors are influential in almost every aspect of living well, over and beyond health, it is sometimes argued that the optimal strategy with the broadest effects would be to increase educational attainment and reduce income inequalities. While I endorse efforts to reduce educational and other inequalities, we should at the same time seek a better understanding of the intervening processes that affect health, which might turn out to be more practical points of intervention for Foundation programs.

These considerations lead me to the following conclusions:

- First, an examination of the area of concern and the discussions at the conference suggest that research in the area of SES and health is still greatly underdeveloped. Many important issues remain unresolved and further development of our understanding of causal processes is needed. Some part of the Foundation's efforts should be directed to enhancing our grasp of basic processes as they affect outcomes of interest. The area of the Foundation's concern is extraordinarily large. A well-targeted research program could be helpful in identifying promising points of leverage.

- Second, as I argued in chapter 2, many of the important influences on children and adolescents occur in family settings and involve the quality of relationships that children develop with parents that affect motivation and coping strategies. Family interventions are difficult and raise serious ethical considerations. But we should seek new ways of involving families in the health interventions we attempt, using the resources of peer groups, schools, churches, and other agencies for reinforcement.

- Third, the effort to change health behavior should be seen as a sequence of steps, reinforced over time, and not simply as a single intervention. Each step may involve different strategies and techniques. For example, many health campaigns fail not because they are conceptually wrong but because they fail to elicit people's attention. The efforts of various foundations to affect health behavior using television as in the "Feeling Good" series failed because few people watched the programs. Here I believe we have much to learn from promotional efforts, such as the various mobilization techniques used by Hands Across America.

Attracting people's interest is only the initial step, because interest must be sustained over a long period of time. The techniques for reinforcing and sustaining interest may be very different from those necessary to attract it in the first place. Then, of course, the basic materials used to influence behavior must be effective. Good intentions may not only have no effect, but may have consequences different from or contrary to those intended. In short, we have to know what we are doing, and formative evaluation helps in the process.

Ultimately, the success of efforts to change behavior depends on the extent to which the goals and behaviors have been internalized by the target populations and are self-sustaining. Again, the interventions that facilitate internalization may be very different from those that elicit interest or sustain it. I am impressed by how often good health behavior arises not from specific health motivations, but from other values that structure everyday activities and behavior. We are truly in the business of changing culture and we should recognize it as a formidable task.

Herbert Nickens

Following the tradition that where you stand is determined by where you sit, my particular interest is in the interaction between socioeconomic status (SES), ethnicity/race, and health. There is little doubt from the literature that SES is inversely related to the overwhelming majority of health status indices. All of the conference papers in somewhat different ways make this point abundantly clear.

An additional contribution of the Harris paper is to remind us that all of these correlates between SES and health must ultimately be mediated by physical mechanisms. Put another way, in this discussion we must move between at least two epistemologically different frames: the physical and the metaphysical. If we talk of "sense of control," for example, as being a significant variable in these discussions, we must be prepared to *ask* at least, how problems in sense of control are mediated to physical outcomes.

It appears to be true that within ethnic/racial groups there are clear gradients in health status by SES. However, the data also suggest that the overall or average health statuses of different ethnic/racial groups are often quite different from one another, and that these differences cannot be accounted for by income differences. Examples:

- Black and Hispanic income status in the aggregate appears to be similar, yet our best evidence is that their respective health status is quite different, with black mortality rates being markedly worse. Both groups have worse health status as measured by mortality rates than the white population.
- My reading of Figure 21-A in Haan, Kaplan, and Syme is that adjusting for income narrows, but does not remove, the differential effect of race on the survival curves.
- The most important contributor to infant mortality is low birthweight. Black infant mortality has historically been about twice that of the white population. The low birthweight rate for blacks is slightly more than twice that for whites. Two points are important in this context:

  1. Many other minority groups with no better economic status have low birthweight rates very similar to those for whites.

  2. Even if you control for important variables such as education, early prenatal care, smoking and drinking during pregnancy, marital status, and age of mother, black mothers still have about twice the incidence of low birthweight as white mothers.

My assertions are first, that ethnicity/race can have an effect on health status that interacts with SES but is independent of it; and second, that the degree to which ethnicity/race exerts this effect is dependent on the psychosocial *meaning* that that particular race or ethnic group has in a given society. Blacks provide an easy example. The experience and legacy of the slave trade, the slave system, and "Jim Crow" regulations, all of which served to institutionalize the degradation of black people, still have clear health and mental health impact today. The mechanisms are likely legion.

My final point concerns ameliorative strategies. It is probably true, for example, that risk factors for given diseases do not operate the same way in different ethnic/racial or different SES groups; and that excesses of a given risk factor (e.g., high fat diet) may not fully (or at all) explain differences in health outcome between groups. Yet in a simple-minded way, aren't those of us in the public health business in the position of trying to make positive changes where and how we can, even if we know we are not making the most "fundamental" change we theoretically could? Put more simply, even given our current state of knowledge, can't we do more?

Barbara Starfield

These remarks are organized into three parts: existing research, future research, and applications of research to the design of interventions.

EXISTING RESEARCH

Despite a general consensus about appropriate measures of social class (generally wealth or income, education, and/or occupation) the literature often uses race as a proxy for class. In fact, one of the papers prepared for the conference focused largely on race. While a greater proportion of blacks (as compared to whites) are poor, the majority of the poor population (adults as well as children) is white. It is important to be especially careful in extrapolating from relationships of race and health to class and health. It is much easier to pose a possible biological explanation for some aspects of health in the case of race—much more so than for class. The use of race as a proxy for class is, therefore, particularly unfortunate.

The various components of social class do not necessarily influence health in the same way. Occupation and place of work have a direct effect on environmental exposures. Income also influences the likelihood of exposure but in different ways, through its impact on place and type of residence, crowding, and amenities, but it also reduces exposure to beneficial agents, such as a well-balanced diet. Income is also directly related to the seeking of health services early in illnesses and hence to a better outcome of medical care. (See Starfield 1985 for documentation in the case of child health.) Education, on the other hand, seems to have its effect on preventive health behavior, such as the seeking of medical care for indicated checkups, immunizations, and dental care. Theory (as well as empirical evidence) suggests that conclusions about social class may differ depending on which measure of social class is used.

Why is it that epidemiologic studies often fail to employ social class (or its separate components)? This deficit is especially noticeable in United States studies, as contrasted with those from western Europe and Scandinavia. There have been several major reports on the relationship between social class and health from the United Kingdom and Scandinavia, but little on the subject in U.S. annals. If it is because the data are often lacking, what can be done about it?

Stereotypes regarding the relationship between adverse individual behaviors and social class should be avoided. Despite evidence that lower income women are less likely to smoke and drink, the notion that the lower class uniformly practices more adverse behaviors (and is less healthy as a result) persists.

Implications for Future Research

The assumption of linearity in relationships between the independent variable (social class) and the dependent variable (the measure of health) is often violated in the application of statistical tests. The science of statistics needs to be challenged to develop more appropriate methods of analysis. In addition, the assumption of linearity thwarts the search for possible threshold effects. Demonstrations of threshold effects where they exist could shed light on mechanisms of effect as well as potential solutions.

There is an opportunity to explore susceptibility by examining clustering of illnesses in individuals and subpopulations. In our own research, we have found a way to express this clustering (Starfield et al. 1984) and have found it to be related to the extent of use of services in a middle class population enrolled in an HMO (Starfield et al. 1985). The hypothesis of heightened susceptibility to illness among the lower classes would receive support if there were increased clustering of conditions among lower class individuals. In fact, recent research using the Child Health Supplement indicates the greater clustering of illness and especially disability from illnesses among children in lower income families (Newacheck and Starfield 1988).

The argument (made by Dutton and Levine) that longitudinal data could provide better information about dynamics of the relationship between class and health is well taken. In this light, the efforts of the National Center for Health Statistics to incorporate a longitudinal follow-back to the National Health Interview Survey should be strongly supported. Proactive support is required because the budget to support these new efforts, as well as to maintain existing ones, is continually threatened. Another opportunity for longitudinal analyses arises in the course of "natural experiments." As a nation, the United States is notoriously flexible in its health policy initiatives, which sometimes change virtually overnight. A wealth of data is potentially available to examine the impact of these changes on specific population subgroups, depending on the type of change. It ought to be national policy that any major alteration in organization or financing should be accompanied by serious efforts to evaluate its impact and to capture information that helps in understanding the dynamics between intervention and effect.

International comparisons of health status remain a largely untapped source of information on the relationship between class and health. Do countries that have compressed social class differentials and/or educational differentials continue to show differentials in health of specific population subgroups? If so, in what aspects of health? Does the elimination of social class differences in access to health services reduce the extent of class differences in health? If so, in which aspects of health? Two types of research have considerable potential: research to examine the consistency of the relationship between class and health, and research to explore the contribution of health services to reducing the gaps in health status across classes.

Haan et al. suggest the utility of combining the techniques of community analysis and individual analysis. Such an approach would greatly facilitate the examination of resilience under apparently adverse circumstances. How do some people living under adverse conditions manage to remain healthy?

Applications of Research to the Design of Interventions

Evidence indicates the beneficial impact of interventions on the health of children. This evidence shows that the frequency of occurrence of preventable conditions declines in response to the provision of medical care, that early detection prevents asymptomatic conditions from becoming symptomatic, and that indicated interventions reduce the severity of conditions or the occurrence of sequelae. Furthermore, population groups in poorest health (those in low income families) appear to benefit the most from improved access to services (Starfield 1985). Therefore, appropriate interventions can reduce disparities across the social classes.

After theory and evidence have suggested alternative interventions, decisions about the most appropriate interventions should be guided by the following considerations:

- address needs as elicited from the targets of the intervention
- be practical
- operate as early as possible in the lifecycle
- operate in a family context when feasible
- have a low probability of failing

Interventions related to the subject of day care seem to fulfill these criteria. An increasing proportion of mothers are entering the work force; many of these are the sole wage earner and/or are of low social class. Low cost child-care arrangements are of high priority to these families and there are few available options. Child-care facilities that are situated in proximity to the work site would appear to have the greatest potential, because they also provide opportunities to engage the mothers in health-enhancing activities as well as activities that improve their child-rearing skills. Employee-sponsored day-care facilities are attractive to employers because they reduce absence and improve productivity. Interventions targeted at preschoolers operate very early in the lifecycle and therefore are of greatest potential. The existing evidence suggests that, if care is taken in the design of early educational interventions, the impact is considerable.

Herman A. Tyroler

The papers by Dutton and Levine, Haan et al., and Harris provide comprehensive, critical syntheses of a vast literature. The documentation of the empirical observations of the SES-health association is accompanied by new insights, conceptualizations, and testable hypotheses in each paper.

Specific comments that follow are organized within the categories of descriptive findings, explanatory concepts, potential for intervention and control, observational research methods, and experimental research methods.

DESCRIPTIVE FINDINGS

Dutton and Levine emphasize the consistency, pervasiveness, and invariance over person, place, and time of the inverse association of SES and health. They note that there are some exceptions to these general patterns but devote only one paragraph to a description of these exceptions. Haan, Kaplan, and Syme similarly catalogue the pervasiveness of the health-SES relationship across ages, time, countries, and diseases. Harris, in contrast, addressing the focused question of socioeconomic factors and cancer, illustrates the different relationship of SES to two of the major malignancies of women, breast and cervical cancer. Thus, while not challenging the impression of the Dutton and Haan papers regarding the near universality of the inverse association, the Harris paper highlights the existence of exceptions to the general finding. Explorations of these exceptions may shed light on the factors responsible for the general finding.

EXPLANATORY CONCEPTS

There is agreement in the Dutton and Haan papers that socioeconomic status is multidimensional and that each of the components that enters into its assessment has a generally similar association with health. There is some disagreement, as Haan believes that position rather than status reflects the conceptually meaningful dimension. Dutton considers the potential contributions of social and environmental stressors, individual resistance and coping resources, and physiological responses. Haan argues that a composite of individual and environmental explanations are incomplete and that what is required is the simultaneous evaluation of demands and resources. Harris focuses on the biological gradient of tumors and the influence upon it of social factors. In this latter approach, considerations of processes operative from the molecular to the health care levels are reviewed and their potential modification by social factors identified. Thus, these papers collectively cover processes that range across levels of organization extending from the molecular to the community. Each level provides observations explainable by processes ranging from the biochemical-physical to the physiologic, psychological, medical care, and social organizational. Investigations at each level can be presumed to offer increased understanding. However, the utility of each for intervention is not discussed.

INTERVENTION AND CONTROL

Dutton and Levine interpret the observations of multiassociations as indicating combined interactive effects and predict that ". . . narrow piecemeal strategies for improving health among lower class groups may be less effective than expected." Counter examples are not discussed. Harris, by his in-depth study of the biologic gradient, natural history, and clinical course of different malignancies with different associations with social factors at different points in the life history of these illnesses, implies the need for a reductionistic approach, at least for understanding if not also for the control of inequalities. Haan et al. do not explicitly discuss the potential for control that would emerge from their new conceptualization, which argues for "integration for the individual, interactive, and environmental levels at which the SES-health link is seen," thereby implying (to this reviewer) that understanding of the relationship is a worthwhile endeavor in its own right.

OBSERVATIONAL RESEARCH METHODS

Without making the methodologic issue explicit, the papers reviewed rely primarily upon observational studies. Dutton and Levine discuss limitations involved in conventional analyses of survey data using multiple regression analyses to investigate causal relationships. They propose the use of path analytic techniques as a more effective method. This approach, while making putative causal mechanisms and their pathways explicit, cannot overcome the limitations of the observational approach. Particular emphasis is placed upon the existence of interaction among the components of SES and their effects upon health. The Haan model of strain research, extrapolated from the work site to the community level, interprets the SES-health association as one reflecting the imbalance between demands and resources and argues that resources must be conceptualized in terms of physical and social environmental attributes as well as individual attributes. There is no explicit treatment of the potential use of experimental approaches among these papers.

EXPERIMENTAL RESEARCH METHODS

The use of experimental approaches for either the understanding or elimination of SES inequalities in disease has had limited application. However, there are examples of randomized clinical trials whose primary objectives of assessment of treatment efficacy provided relevant SES-disease association information. For example, the Hypertension Detection and Follow-up Program demonstrated through a community-based, randomized clinical trial that the sizeable SES gradient in mortality among hypertensives using usual community care was eliminated, with overall reductions in morbidity and mortality, by follow-up and treatment of hypertension within a program that reduced financial and physical access barriers to antihypertensive drug therapy. This clinical trial demonstrated the feasibility of evaluating efficacy of medical intervention across social status groups with elimination of an SES-mortality gradient. In addition to efforts to reduce socioeconomic inequalities per se, public health extensions of experimental approaches beyond the clinical trial, which is directed at patients, to the social units of factories, towns, and regions have been undertaken focused on cardiovascular disease in this country and other areas of the world. These experiments offer promise of eliminating some of the SES-health inequalities by the introduction and evaluation of strategies for treatment of disease, prevention of disease, and health promotion in natural social settings.

Fernando E. Viteri

My contribution to the conference focuses on the possible role that food and the nutritional habits of individuals and populations play in explaining the well-documented relationship between socioeconomic status and health, and suggests possible directions in research where considerations in nutrition, health, and development could provide new insights into the causal relationship between SES and health.

From the start, I would like to indicate that in the minds of human-nutrition professionals nutrition cannot be considered independent of functional capacity and health, and that nutritional status is perceived in the classic Leavell and Clark (1965) scheme as a result of the interaction of biological factors, including biological metabolic variability in health and disease (host characteristics), environmental factors including sanitation, socioeconomic and cultural determinants of human food practices (environmental characteristics), and foods as carriers of nutrients as well as of desirable and nondesirable nutritional compounds (agent characteristics).

Nutrition, as it contributes to the health (or lack of it) of different socioeconomic groups, must be conceptualized as only a part of the complex setting where the individual lives, interacting with many factors such as stress, genetic makeup, age, sex, and drug intakes, and contributing to the wide spectrum of health problems affecting from the lowest to the highest socioeconomic strata. Indeed, food and nutritional factors have been well established as important contributors to low birthweight; to child development, morbidity and mortality; to certain cognitive abilities and behavioral manifestations; to physical work capacity; to reproductive function and performance; to immune functional capacity; to the aging processes; and to adult chronic diseases, including type II diabetes, obesity, hypertension and stroke, coronary heart disease, liver disease, and cancer.

The problem is to try to clarify conceptual approaches and causal mechanisms by which SES and health are related, with the aim of defining research needs and suggesting policies, plans, and programs to address health needs more effectively.

The papers provided as background for the conference are most informative and provide provocative insights into the well-documented relationship between socioeconomic status and health in general and cancer in particular. The following are some general comments on the four background papers, not confined to the nutritional aspects of health and SES, but reflecting what I consider an effort at the integration of various disciplines that contribute to a better understanding of health and nutrition within socioeconomic groups.

First, the papers refer almost exclusively to stable populations of industrialized societies in the developed world, predominantly white and Anglo-Saxon. Some information is provided on black population groups in Alameda County and very slight reference is made to other "minority groups," who however constitute a progressively important segment of the population of the United States and other industrialized societies and are more highly represented in the lower SES categories. Little attention is given by the authors to cultural factors and characteristics. This lack of information may actually be hiding the contribution of minority and less stable groups to the data presented.

Dutton and Levine express the important concept that a host of factors is embedded in poverty, indicating that many of these factors constitute or contribute to hardships that may interact nonlinearly in creating a situation characterized by multiple adversities, loss of control, and ill health. The logical and crucial consequence of this picture is that narrow, piecemeal strategies to improve health among the poor leads to failure. I fully agree with this evaluation of poverty and its consequences as well as with Dr. Mechanic's statement that interventions based on deeper understanding of the situation offer greater potential. However, I find in this and the other papers a vacuum in the areas of culturally based nutritional and health behavior.

Socioeconomic status is a broad conceptual composite of predominantly physically definable characteristics among which I include earnings and/or expenditures, schooling (by grades of formal education), and even certain key aspects of lifestyle such as the division of time by broad activity categories, access to information, etc. The problem of measuring SES is quite evident and most studies rely on proxies that often are highly intercorrelated, thus posing problems of analyses and interpretation of results. Defining culture and expressing it in "measurable" components is hardly a simple task. However, scales of culturally determined concepts and behaviors exist, which are just beginning to be applied to conditions like nutritional status, stress, and health.

We all agree that SES, by modulating certain conceptual frameworks and values, can modify behavior. In fact I contend that just as there is a host of factors embedded in poverty, similarly a host of factors exists embedded in wealthy groups and in any SES category that we define. We, as a group of university graduates, generally belong to an SES category that is more distant to poverty so that we see it as a strange situation that we do not fully understand. Moreover, we are rightly concerned with it because there is an SES-related gradient in health that favors the better-off categories.

However, I challenge us, studious people, to evaluate the effectiveness and efficiency of the health behavior of upper SES categories in relation to the theoretical level of health achievement possible, given the facilities and resources available to them, and then compare it to the effectiveness and efficiency of the health behavior of the lowest SES categories, given their facilities and resources. I suspect that the poor as a group exhibit in general a very efficient behavior leading to their survival given their circumstances. Its effectiveness, on the other hand, may be hampered by the overwhelmingly negative environment that surrounds poverty, including the pressure to accept as desirable unhealthy "modern practices" as was, until recently, the case when formula feeding was encouraged instead of breast feeding, or to accept "recreational habits" such as smoking, alcohol, or drugs, which are most often developed, cleverly advertised, and pushed by economically powerful groups. All this is to say that we lack vital information about the cultural basis for behavior (including health-related and nutrition-related behavior) without which the analyses of the SES associations with health may fall short of providing fundamental answers leading to pertinent, culturally acceptable actions favoring health.

Some of the models proposed, such as the demands-control model and others that scale stress-producing and stress-dampening factors can be useful in addressing certain mechanisms by which SES and health interact (Dressler 1980). The study of positive and negative deviants provides useful information in determining basic characteristics and how they interact with deviant characteristics. I favor strongly the potential of research based on positive and negative deviants along the SES-culture, nutrition-health relationships. Unless we understand the basis for behavior (oftentimes implicating survival), we run the risk, with best intentions, of promoting actions that can break the fragile equilibrium by which the poor survive efficiently.

There is ample evidence that poverty and ignorance tend to perpetuate themselves and that this unfortunate combination breeds concepts, values, and behaviors that are difficult to change or abandon precisely because throughout generations they are perceived as having allowed survival within a hostile environment. An example is the highly prevalent behavior among the "lesser developed" societies that favors the male sex and assigns little social and/or economic value to women, and this discrimination is still manifested (painful to say) among most industrialized societies.

Why stress this discrimination? Because nutrition and health at the family level pivot around women in most societies, including those presently under Western influence and their improvement depends on improving women's social status. Examples of the perceived lower social value of the female sex in less developed societies are many, more prominent among the poorer and less modern or more traditional cultures and societies:

- The birth of a boy is more an occasion of joy.
- Breast-feeding and weaning practices favor boys: girls are not supposed to grow as robust as boys, and the proportion of undernourished girls is higher, partly because boys are fed preferentially since they are perceived as a "better investment" for the economic and social future of the family or clan.
- Girls often are educated in the home environment without exposure to formal schooling and external modern influences; thus many remain illiterate and the training provided by mothers and others in the household perpetuates the biases of lower self-esteem and self-sacrifice that favor men (this includes eating what is left after men are satisfied).
- Girls are encouraged and enticed to marry early in order to diminish the length of "economic burden" they constitute, either by moving to another household or bringing an able-bodied and productive man to the girl's household.
- Girls under these circumstances, with teenage pregnancies superimposed on chronically poorly nourished bodies, give birth to small, undernourished babies, who begin their lives with the handicap of poor nutrition and frail health. Thus the perpetuation of poor nutrition and poor health is well on its way through these mechanisms, all dependent on the low social value of the female sex in many societies.

Female sex discrimination is a "theme" that can easily be expanded, and many others can be cited that document the cultural roots of nutrition and health behavior. Societies undergoing transculturation in a rapidly developing technical age, most of them belonging to lower SES, provide unique opportunities for determining behaviors and other characteristics that lead to different degrees of success in the process. Here the positive and negative deviance approach can be particularly fruitful. The knowledge derived from such studies is also essential in developing policies, plans, and programs in which individuals, in low SES populations in particular, participate actively in their own health maintenance.

It must be recognized that when the ever more abundant destitute groups (underdeveloped in the midst of development) are faced with rising health and "true food costs" and with greater difficulties in joining welfare programs while they are at the same time poorly informed of desirable and available modern medical facilities, they tend naturally to make greater use of local wisdom, as well as of their own traditional and less expensive healers in the case of multicultured societies. The use of community-based healers, who exercise traditional, culturally accepted medicine and have the local respect universally accorded to health providers, should be recognized in an active and positive way rather than in a punitive way. The repudiation of local healers as a matter of principle often translates into the rejection of a whole cultural value system. I want to indicate that the presence of these healers and their value as members of a working health team, often parallel to our "scientific medical care," must become better known and understood. Traditional healers can bridge wide cultural gaps. A future aim could be to incorporate them into medical care systems, with full knowledge of their capacities and limitations and after providing them further training and guidance in the limits of their practice, including when to refer their patients to modern, western facilities and health care.

At the same time, we should be taught by these culturally accepted traditional healers the intricacies of health care concepts and practice among groups whose cultures and resources are different from ours. These traditional medical men and women, together with other community health promoters, have been effectively incorporated into health teams by national health systems in several parts of the world. They can be extremely useful and efficient in many aspects of primary health care including preventive medicine, chronic rehabilitation programs, and first-level-of-complexity care. Once a clearly established relationship based on mutual trust and including mutual reference of patients is achieved, the role of traditional healers in expanding medical coverage and providing a permanent and dynamic cultural bridge can be extremely valuable.

Dutton and Levine, using arthritis as an example, state that class gradients in health cannot be attributed simply to the differential perception of symptoms by people of different SES levels because comparable gradients occur in both subjective measures of disease and objectively defined measures. In other conditions, the limits of what is perceived as a healthy status are very culturally dependent so that, for example, obesity among Caribbean women is a desirable trait and thus not perceived as a health problem. Similarly, but in another extreme, severe marasmus in infants in certain regions of Pakistan is considered a normal event in the process of growth.

Medical attention is sought when there is a perception of ill health; unfortunately, in nutrition-related health problems the perception of the limits between normality and abnormality can be particularly difficult, which may help to explain why health risks and actual diseases are more prevalent among lower SES groups. There is evidence that chronic diseases are associated with nutritional behaviors within defined lifestyles and social classes; infectious diseases in childhood are also associated with nutritional behavior and undernourishment among lower SES groups. This association can be so strong that Dubos et al. (1966) attributed to better nutrition the most important role in the impressive decline in infant and child mortality documented in New York City early in this century.

Furthermore, nutrition definitely contributes to the change in specific pathology as time progresses. Research over time is recommended in areas where these changes can cause changes in specific morbidity and mortality. Again, populations in active transculturation and SES mobility can provide particularly dynamic relationships that can clarify tendencies in an abbreviated time: Culturally ingrained nutritional and general behavior show their importance in health achievement among all socioeconomic groups but particularly among the growing members of lower SES populations who have different cultures from those of the middle-upper socioeconomic group of Anglo-

Saxon origin. In this regard, I strongly believe that now more than ever the need to explore in depth these SES-health relationships in key areas of the United States is essential for the improvement of nutrition and health for lower SES groups, as well as for the important insights to be gained.

Finally, it is important to realize that most countries (and regions) when under economic hardships do two things: First, they limit or even decrease their social investment programs, including health; and second, they tend to keep the politically more attractive medical care programs at the expense of preventive programs (including those in food and nutrition). To some extent this has been happening in the United States. These changes convey the wrong perception that on the one hand health is a luxury and not a human right, and that on the other hand curative medicine is more cost-effective than preventive medicine. Among lower SES groups this shift in emphasis promotes physicians' manipulations, often out of context with cultural understanding and needs.

Until better living conditions, lifestyles, health education, and schooling are achieved among the underprivileged, preventive medicine is even more important. Socioeconomic inequality will persist, including its stressful components. The need is to protect those at greater risk by long-standing, dynamic preventive programs, including appropriate and pertinent programs in communication and education in health and nutrition. In this regard, I believe all the authors agree there is urgent need for carefully designed and longitudinally evaluated action-oriented research programs that approach the nutrition and health issues in a comprehensive manner, with a holistic cultural and SES-based approach.

NOTES

1. Variant forms of the same gene are called *alleles*. When I use the term *gene* I usually mean the position (locus) occupied by a segment of DNA that is responsible for some specific function, usually by determining synthesis of a specific enzyme, hormone, or other protein. The alternate segments (alleles) that can reside at the locus can differ in their ability to perform the specific function.

2. My use of the term *class*, for purposes of genetic analysis, denotes a socioeconomic stratum within a single ethnic/racial group. The frequencies of alleles at some gene loci will differ between such groups, but not necessarily between classes within any single ethnic/racial group.

3. A case could be made that the early deaths of those most likely to succumb to the scourges of the past (which accounted for extraordinary rates of infant and child mortality) removed a fraction of susceptibility-conferring alleles from the gene pool. This might leave classes that were most likely to suffer the scourges with a lower frequency of such alleles than others. Since the diseases that afflict humans today are different from the earlier killers, it is doubtful that such "culling" accounts for class-related differences in susceptibility to modern diseases.

REFERENCES

Berry, R. J., Buehler, J. W., Strauss, L. T., et al. 1987. Birth-weight-specific infant mortality due to congenital anomalies, 1960 and 1980. *Public Health Reports*, 102:171–181.

Dressler, W. W. 1980. Coping dispositions, social supports, and health status. *Ethos* 8(2): 146–171.

Dubos, R., Savage, D., Schaedler, R., et al. 1966. Biological Freudianism: lasting effects of early environmental influences. *Pediatrics* 38:789–800.

Epstein, A. M., Taylor, W. C., Seage, G. R. 1985. Effects of patients' socioeconomic status and physicians' training and practice on patient–doctor communication. *American Journal of Medicine* 78:101–106.

Gortmaker, S. L., Dietz, W. H., Jr., Sobol, A. M., and Wehler, C. A. 1987. Increasing pediatric obesity in the United States. *American Journal of Diseases of Children* 141: 535–540.

Gortmaker, S. L., Sobol, A. M., Clark, C., Walker, D. K., Geronimus, A. 1985. The survival of very low birthweight infants by level of hospital of birth: a population study of perinatal systems in four states. *American Journal of Obstetrics and Gynecology* 152: 517–524.

Leavell, H. R., Clark, E. G. 1965. *Preventive medicine for the doctor in his community: an epidemiologic approach.* 3rd ed. New York: McGraw-Hill.

Marmot, M. G., Kogevinas, M., Elston, M. A. 1987. Social/ economic status and disease. *Annual Review of Public Health* 8:111–137.

Marmot, M. G., McDowall, M. E. 1986. Mortality decline and widening social inequalities. *Lancet* 2:274–276.

Marmot, M. G., Shipley, M. J., Rose, G. 1984. Inequalities in death—specific explanations of a general pattern? *Lancet* 1:1003–1006.

Newacheck, P., Starfield, B. 1988. Children's health and use in health services. In Schlesinger, M., Eisenberg, L., eds. *Children: a changing health system.* Baltimore: The Johns Hopkins University Press.

Rutstein, D. D., Berenberg, W., Chalmers, T. C., et al. 1976. Measuring the quality of medical care: a clinical method. *New England Journal of Medicine* 294:582–588.

Stamler, R., Hardy, R. J., Payne, G. H., et al. 1987. Educational level and five-year all-cause mortality in the hypertension detection and follow-up program. *Hypertension* 9:641–646.

Starfield, B. 1985. *The effectiveness of medical care: validating clinical wisdom.* Baltimore: The Johns Hopkins University Press.

———, Hankin, J., Steinwachs, D., et al. 1985. Utilization and morbidity: random or tandem? *Pediatrics* 75:241–247.

Starfield, B., Katz, H., Gabriel, A., et al. 1984. Morbidity in childhood: a longitudinal view. *New England Journal of Medicine* 310:824–829.

Townsend, B., Davidson, N., eds. 1982. *Inequalities in health: the Black Report.* Harmondsworth, England: Penguin Books.

Ware, J. E., Brook, R. H., Rogers, W. M., et al. 1986. Comparison of health outcomes at health maintenance organizations with those of fee-for-service care. *Lancet* 1:1017–1021.

Whitehead, M. 1987. *The health divide: inequalities in health in the 1980's.* London: The Health Education Council.

Wise, P. H., Kotelchuck, M., Wilson, M. L., Mills, M. 1985. Racial and socioeconomic disparities in childhood mortality in Boston. *New England Journal of Medicine* 313:360–366.

8. Pursuing the Links Between Socioeconomic Factors and Health: Critique, Policy Implications, and Directions for Future Research

Alan M. Garber

THE RESEARCH DISCUSSED in this conference attests to the regularity with which socioeconomic factors are associated with health status. Those at the bottom of the social and economic order suffer more disability, more illness, and earlier death. As we deepen our understanding of disease at the molecular level, the papers prepared for the conference remind us that those who study the determinants of disease must also take note of its social, psychological, and economic linkages. To know who suffers ill health and why often means discovering how the individual interacts with his or her social and physical environment.

Those whose primary interest is health promotion will find that studies of the linkages between socioeconomic factors and health can guide efforts to improve health by producing insights into the determinants of disease and disease outcomes. Since 1775 when Sir Percival Pott noted an increased incidence of scrotal cancer among chimney sweeps, occupational associations have led to the discovery of several environmental causes of disease. Even when the reason for their association with health is obscure, socioeconomic factors can identify individuals at high risk of disease. The yield of a screening program for hypertension, for instance, will be greater in the ghetto than in the suburbs, and a campaign to stop smoking will find more smokers among high school dropouts than among college graduates.

Socioeconomic factors have been measured by broad indices, such as social class and socioeconomic status (SES), and by specific components of such indices. In accordance with the consensus reached by the participants in the conference, the following discussion emphasizes three components of SES: occupation, educational attainment, and financial status. Financial status refers to wealth and income, which I use interchangeably. As a predictor of health status, wealth may be superior to income, but the two aspects of financial status are highly correlated with one another, and few surveys have accurate wealth data. I examine these components of SES, rather than social class or SES itself, since the components are unequally associated with health, even though they are correlated with one another. Furthermore, social interventions, which include policies to increase educational attainment, redistribute income, and promote occupational safety, are usually targeted toward specific socioeconomic factors.

This paper addresses the ways that future research into socioeconomic factors and health can identify areas for intervention. An extensive literature has documented that the socioeconomic gradient in health extends across diseases, places, and time. This literature has been less successful at identifying the mechanisms that lead to the linkages; in many cases, it has not been possible to measure the direct effects of socioeconomic factors. As I argue, the inability to measure causal links has made it hazardous to draw policy inferences from this literature. In the first section, I examine some of the factors that link socioeconomic factors and health, exploring behavioral mechanisms that underlie the association. Understanding these mechanisms is a crucial task, since the interpretation of the association between socioeconomic factors and health depends on the underlying cause of the association. The second section explores some of the methodological challenges that frustrate attempts to elucidate these mechanisms. Statistical pitfalls have led studies of the relationship between socioeconomic factors and health to underestimate the effects of conventional risk factors on health outcomes, while some of the problems have led such studies to overestimate the effects of the socioeconomic factors. Despite the uncertainties, the best of these studies have important implications for policy.

The third section examines the lessons that these studies have for social policy, exploring in detail a particular occupational hazard, asbestos. One might reason that because socioeconomic factors are associated with health outcomes, they are causes of the health outcomes, so that interventions targeted toward the socioeconomic factors would be the best means of improving health. However, as I argue, even if the socioeconomic factors are causes of variation in health, socioeconomic interventions might not be the most efficacious or the most desirable means of improving health. Research that addresses the policy issues directly is needed to compare the alternative approaches to improving health. The kinds of data that can best guide such research efforts are discussed in the final section. With better data, appropriate methodology, and a focus on policy, future research efforts can progress from an indictment of inequality to an agenda for improving the health of populations.

Interpreting Socioeconomic Gradients in Health

Controversy inevitably attends studies of socioeconomic gradients in health. The political implications of the *Black Report* on inequalities in health in Great Britain (Townsend and Davidson 1982) doubtless contributed to its icy reception by the Conservative government. Controversy, however, does not arise solely from the political sensitivity of the results. It also grows from disagreements over the inferences that can be drawn from the association between socioeconomic factors and health. The assumptions of studies of SES and health often remain unstated. They range from the purely technical—that the variables are measured properly, that error terms have a normal distribution, that the functional form for a regression equation is correct—to fundamental beliefs about which relationships are important, which outcomes matter, and which aspects of health are subject to individual control. These assumptions determine whether the studies can answer the central questions in research on socioeconomic gradients: is there a causal relation, and if so, how large is the effect? Since causal inferences can only be drawn with strong assumptions, many of them implicit, the scope for disagreement and ambiguity is immense.

In this section I discuss some of the processes that underlie the association between behavioral or socioeconomic factors and health. Using an economic framework, I explore the ways that individual behavior can interact with external circumstances to generate associations between socioeconomic factors and health. The next section examines the methodologic implications of this analysis.

Endogeneity and the Response to Interventions

Because they seldom can perform population-wide experiments, social scientists usually analyze observational data to infer the effects of interventions. To draw inferences, they must judge which factors the intervention can determine, which factors the individual can control, and which factors neither the policy nor the individual can influence.

As the second section explains, the validity of statistical analysis of observational data depends on these distinctions. In the language of statistics, the factors that the individual cannot modify are *exogenous* or purely causal variables. Intervention or policy variables are exogenous; other exogenous variables that affect health and socioeconomic success, such as age, sex, and natural catastrophes, are beyond the reach of policy and individual choice. The factors that the individual can influence are called *endogenous* variables. Because behavioral responses modify their values, the targets of interventions—such as educational attainment, income, and health—are endogenous. They are not subject to direct policy control. For example, a government can use taxes and support payments to redistribute income, but it cannot directly *fix* each person's income, since the intervention will trigger changes in individual behavior. Even in a communist economy, government control over income is eroded by black market trading and barter.

Sometimes the distinction between the two categories of variables is subtle. The current values of some variables, such as measures of health, are exogenous, while their future values are endogenous. Endogenous variables can have causal impacts on other endogenous variables, and two variables can influence one another. For example, as I claim below, health status affects income, and income influences health status.

Because the endogenous variables are outcomes of individual choices, economic analysis of individual decision making can help identify the factors that influence decisions. The economic framework can illuminate any decision characterized by choice under constraints. The decisions might concern how much money to save, what health insurance policy to buy, and where to live, and the constraints might arise from resource limitations. For example, expenditures cannot exceed wealth indefinitely. Earned income, in turn, is limited by the number of hours an individual can work and the wage he or she can obtain.

The decisions need not involve money, but the constraints imply that there are tradeoffs: a decision to walk in the park means forgoing another activity such as jogging, reading, or watching television. Much of modern economics is concerned with constrained decisions in which money is not the central issue. Notable examples include studies of fertility, child rearing, marriage, and divorce (Becker and Lewis 1973, Willis 1973, Becker et al. 1977); studies of the decision to engage in criminal behavior (Ehrlich 1974), and, as I discuss below, studies of decisions regarding health. While these applications of economics are often controversial, they have focused attention on key determinants of social behavior and on potential interventions.

The economic perspective offers little insight when there are no constraints on choice, or when the constraints are so restrictive that there is no real choice. Neither view characterizes decisions regarding health or the determination of socioeconomic factors in twentieth century America. If choices involved no constraints, all material desires could be satisfied, people could take whatever jobs they desired, and there would be no poverty or inequalities in health.

Somewhat more evidence supports the opposite view: that constraints are limiting enough to preclude real choice. Choice has little influence on health when random events and other factors over which the individual has no control, such as heredity, are crucial. People who diet, exercise, and pursue a "healthy" lifestyle are making a choice to try to prolong their lives. Yet 30 to 50 percent of all heart attacks occur in people who do not have any of the three major modifiable risk factors—cigarette smoking, hypertension, and elevated cholesterol (Werko 1987). Similarly, by wearing seat belts, installing air bags, and obeying traffic signals, automobile passengers can reduce, but not eliminate, the likelihood of accidental death.

Random and other uncontrollable events can also influence socioeconomic outcomes. The economic fortunes of an industry or occupation, which individual workers can do little to change, affect their wages and the likelihood that they will keep their jobs.

These exogenous factors are important. But choice, even when subject to severe limitations, plays a critical role in outcomes. People with similar opportunities make different choices, and these choices have repercussions throughout life. Smokers can reduce their risk of cardiac disease and lung cancer by giving up tobacco. Hypertensives can reduce their mortality by taking medications. The choices may be difficult, poorly informed, and painfully limited. As long as people are free to make decisions that affect health or socioeconomic factors, however, the economic perspective can illuminate the decisions.

Within this framework, choices differ because either constraints or preferences differ. But since preferences cannot be influenced by policy, only the constraints are amenable to intervention. Further, as long as preferences vary, equal constraints will not lead to equal outcomes.

The decision to undergo treatment for hypertension illustrates how variations in preferences can frustrate attempts to eliminate socioeconomic gradients in health. Hypertensive patients considering treatment must weigh several factors, including the costs of treatment, the gain in life expectancy, side effects of medications, and freedom from morbidity. Medication costs are a component of the constraints that might explain a wealth gradient in treatment. But compliance with treatment also varies because people do not equally value the benefits or side effects of treatment. Those who particularly value good health are more likely to comply, whereas those who care less about longevity and more about side effects, such as depression or impotence, are less likely to comply. Thus differences in preferences and wealth can lead to diverse decisions regarding treatment.

To overcome the socioeconomic differences in treatment, or to promote compliance with treatment, interventions might redistribute income. Generally, this will increase consumption of all desired material goods and services, including the hypertension medication. Unless income is the only difference between those who undergo treatment and those who do not, however, this will be a blunt instrument for lowering mortality. A more promising alternative is to lower the price of medications to the patient. The subsidy will have two effects. The first is a *substitution* effect. Because the price of the medication will fall relative to all other goods and services, hypertensive patients will be more likely to purchase it. The second is an *income* effect. When the price of a consumer good falls, its purchasers can spend more on other goods and services while continuing to buy the lower-priced good, and thus effective income rises. Usually the substitution effect will be far more important than the income effect, unless the good accounts for a substantial portion of the purchaser's expenditures.

The combination of income and substitution effects makes the subsidy a powerful tool for inducing people to undergo treatment. Will it eliminate the income gradient in treatment? In general, it will not. While the change in constraints alters the incentives for treatment, if the relatively wealthy value longevity more, they will continue to have a greater propensity to comply with treatment.

Constraints and preferences are also responsible for the determination of socioeconomic factors themselves. A government, for instance, cannot directly control the number of years that people go to school (even antitruancy laws have loopholes), although it can make education more attractive. In schooling as in programs to improve health, behavioral responses modify the impact of government interventions.

Interventions to promote education have similar limitations. Income redistribution is likely to boost educational attainment, but as long as income is not the only difference between the poor and the well-off, the formerly poor presumably will still not stay in school for as many years as the formerly well-off. Tastes for education—some find school enjoyable, while others find it onerous—can lead one person to finish college while another drops out of high school. The "costs" of education depend on tuition and foregone earnings, as well as less readily quantified factors as aptitude and academic preparation. The returns to schooling may differ because some individuals are better able to convert education into earnings than others. The variability of costs and financial benefits, most of which are exogenous to the individual, lead to differing incentives to stay in school (Ben-Porath 1967, Mincer 1974). As I shall discuss, the value that students place on delayed rewards is another factor that influences their desires for more schooling.

Interventions may not be able to change tastes for schooling, but they can promote schooling by changing constraints—lowering its costs and increasing its benefits. Scholarships and tuition subsidies can lower monetary costs of education; affirmative action programs for well-schooled minorities can boost the financial returns to educational investments. As long as preferences differ, however, these programs may not eliminate inequality in education.

In summary, by altering constraints, interventions can sway the decisions that determine health, education, income, and other important outcomes. But preferences, which may not be manipulated easily, also influence the decisions. As long as preferences vary, individuals with the same endowments of wealth, ability, and health will not follow the same paths of future socioeconomic attainment or health. Furthermore, differences in preferences will cloud predictions of the effects of interventions.

I now turn to the links between the individual socioeconomic factors and health. What is the evidence for each direction of causality, and what mechanisms underpin the links?

How Health Affects Socioeconomic Factors

There is little mystery about this direction of causality: health can constrain socioeconomic attainment. A frail individual may be unable to perform demanding work or to invest in education, and poor health will frequently keep him or her from work. Several studies have examined the effects of health on economic well-being. Luft claimed (1978) that disability often leads to poverty by reducing individual and family earnings. Bartel and Taubman (1979) analyzed earnings and employment of about 4,300 middle-aged men for whom medical diagnoses at five different times were available. The diagnoses were obtained from Veterans Administration and military records and by self-report. The authors found that several diseases markedly lowered earnings; the reduction associated with some diagnoses, such as arthritis or bronchitis, emphysema and asthma, was between 20 percent and 30 percent. Similarly, some longitudinal studies have found a "downward drift" in the economic well-being of the mentally ill (Myers and Bean 1968).

Other authors have argued that this direction of causation is unimportant (Townsend and Davidson 1982; Fox et al. 1985; Wilkinson 1986). For the most part their arguments rest on a narrow definition of health, which incorporates observed acute events and chronic diseases that occur late in life, or specific illnesses in childhood. Because some of these health events occur late in life, it is argued, they cannot be responsible for the differences in wealth, income, occupation, or education with which they are associated. But the ways in which good health may be persistent throughout life are difficult to measure or even to recognize. Acute health events later in life may manifest adverse health conditions that were present much earlier, just as a stroke results from years of elevated blood pressure. Early health means more than freedom from childhood ailments: it may include endurance, drive, and other aspects of hardiness that can eventually lead to greater educational attainment and higher income.

How Financial Status Influences Health

There can be little doubt that wealth acts as a constraint in decisions regarding health. Because they command more resources, the wealthy can obtain more of all commodities that are bought and sold, including those that improve health. Health maintenance is costly—it comes from safe work and the commitment of time and money to health-related activities. Further, increasing longevity can mean giving up some goods and services that produce utility but do not produce health improvements. All else being equal, the wealthy can live in safer housing, drive safer automobiles, and devote more time and money to health-promoting activities. If the demand for health rises with income or wealth, health and financial status will be positively associated.

Differences in utilization of medical services do not appear to be the principal reason for the socioeconomic gradient in health in the United States or Great Britain. Although the wealthy can afford comprehensive health insurance and go to the best doctors when they become ill, they do not receive substantially more medical care. The poor in America are seen in physicians' offices and hospitals as frequently as the middle class and wealthy. In 1985, persons whose family income was less than $10,000 averaged 5.8 annual physician visits, while whose whose family income exceeded $35,000 averaged 5.4 physician visits (in their offices and elsewhere) each year (National Center for Health Statistics 1986, p. 137). The poor may need more services, and these figures say little about ease of access or quality of the care they receive. However, the numbers indicate that financial gradients in health outcomes cannot be explained solely by large barriers to obtaining care. In Great Britain, the pronounced socioeconomic gradient in health is widening despite universal health care coverage under the National Health Service (Whitehead 1987).

The sinking of the *Titanic* proved to be a telling, if unusual, example of how wealth can reduce mortality. As at least two earlier reviews of socioeconomic gradients in health have noted (Hollingshead and Redlich 1958; Antonovsky 1967), the mortality rate among women travelling first class on the *Titanic* was lower than in second class, which in turn was lower than third class (Lord 1955).

How Occupation Influences Health

Because they define social class by occupation, most British studies of class gradients (see, for example, the *Black Report* [Townsend and Davidson 1982]; studies based on the Office of

Population Censuses and Surveys [OPCS] Longitudinal Study, such as Fox and Adelstein 1978, and Fox et al. 1985; and the Whitehall study, as reported in Rose and Marmot 1981) are studies of occupational gradients. Almost uniformly these studies have found that mortality rates are highest in the low status, low income occupations. Links between occupation and health have also been found among American workers.

Several occupational causes of poor health have been discovered. Some of the best-established environmental hazards are found in the workplace. Occupational exposures are thought to contribute to a high percentage of lung cancers among males (Pastorino et al. 1984), and about twenty occupational carcinogens have been identified (Ernst and Theriault 1984). These figures may underestimate the role of occupational carcinogens, since the connection between a case of cancer and an occupational exposure that occurred years before is often obscure. Blue-collar workers—such as miners, furniture makers, and leather workers—are most likely to have contact with occupational carcinogens. Blue-collar workers are also most likely to suffer an injury on the job (Ashford 1976; Gordon, Akman, and Brooks 1971). In contrast to cancer, workplace injuries bear an immediate and obvious relationship to occupation.

An increased incidence of rare cancers due to exposures to chemicals on the job and a high rate of industrial accidents provide striking evidence of occupational effects on health. Work may also tax health by more subtle mechanisms. Unpleasant working conditions, stresses, and loss of a sense of control characterize the jobs held by many blue-collar workers. These factors might lead, in turn, to adverse health outcomes. Because they are subtle and because there is no reliable metric for these factors, their roles are easily overlooked. Because such factors are pervasive, they may be important causes of ill health.

It is self-evident that painting bridges and building skyscrapers are more hazardous than accounting. But why is risk concentrated among the blue-collar occupations? In *The Wealth of Nations*, Adam Smith claimed that workers would need to be paid a premium over the usual wage, or a compensating differential, before they would accept particularly hazardous or onerous work. Modern studies of variation in occupational mortality rates have confirmed Smith's claim, showing that higher wages accompany riskier work (Thaler and Rosen 1976; Viscusi 1979). If the wealthy are inclined to pay more for improved longevity or health, then they would need to be paid more than less prosperous workers to accept risky work. Workers who accept hazardous jobs will in fact earn more than they otherwise would; nevertheless it is those workers who command less wealth and are less educated and thus have lower earnings potential who take risky jobs (Leigh 1986). If job tenure, education, and other characteristics that affect earnings are not held constant, it will appear that hazardous work pays less, when the opposite is true.

Hazardous work is not the only cause of the excess mortality associated with some occupations. Some jobs that are not particularly hazardous are associated with high mortality rates, perhaps because they attract unhealthy or risk-loving workers. For example, the mortality rate for male bartenders is much higher than for police officers or firefighters (Thaler and Rosen 1976). When selection is responsible for excess occupational mortality, an occupational intervention may have little effect on health outcomes.

How Schooling Influences Health

Health is linked more tightly with education than with any other socioeconomic factor (Kitagawa and Hauser 1973). In an analysis of cross-state data, Auster, Leveson, and Sarachek (1969) found that a 1 percent increase in average years of school attendance was associated with a 0.2 percent decrease in mortality, while a 1 percent increase in health expenditures was only associated with a 0.1 percent decrease in mortality. They found that when health expenditures, education, and several other factors were held constant, income was *positively* associated with mortality. The authors argued that other studies attributed positive health effects to income because they failed to control for medical care and education. Furthermore, the authors claimed that higher income might be associated with deleterious lifestyles. Using different techniques and data sets, other investigators have reported that there is a strong association between health and education, and that the association with earnings or income becomes insignificant when education is held constant (Newhouse and Friedlander 1980; Leigh 1983).

Grossman's extensive work on this subject attributes greater efficiency in the production of health to better education (1972; see also Grossman and Joyce in this volume). The better educated may know more about prevention and may use medical services more effectively, or their education may furnish better strategies for dealing with stress.

There can be little doubt that schooling has a strong association with health, but it has been difficult to establish how education improves health. More schooling is associated with better health at all levels of education, even though college and graduate studies usually do not address health explicitly. Could another factor lead some people to have both better health and more education? Concern that "third factors" might drive the correlation between health and socioeconomic factors often stymies efforts to establish causality.

How Third Factors Can Influence Health and Socioeconomic Factors

Sometimes the absence of a compelling biological explanation arouses suspicion that the association between a particular socioeconomic factor and a health status is spurious. One or more "third factors" that influence both the socioeconomic factor and the health outcome might generate the association. If the association is spurious, modification of the socioeconomic factor will have no effect on health unless it alters the underlying third factor(s) as well.

Attitudes toward risky activities can act as third factors. People who are less deterred by risk or who enjoy risky activities tend to die younger. Riding motorcycles, climbing mountains, parachuting, and hang-gliding are dangerous and, at least to their enthusiasts, pleasurable. The health risks need not be dramatic. Some people sacrifice months or years of life-expectancy in order to "live well"—eating an unhealthy diet, drinking too much alcohol, and smoking cigarettes despite the health risks. Since many health risks are discretionary, differences in preferences can lead to varied health outcomes.

If such attitudes or preferences are responsible for differences in health, why are the poor and less educated more likely to possess them? The time preference hypothesis offers one explanation. According to Fuchs (1982), people who have a high rate of time preference—i.e., who discount future costs and benefits heavily—tend not to exhibit positive health behaviors. They also devote relatively few resources to other activities, such as education, that produce delayed benefits. A high rate of time preference is likely to be associated with cigarette smoking, since the benefits of cigarette smoking are immediate while for the most part its toll on health is delayed for years.

Fuchs's hypothesis implies that the health effects of policies to promote education will be smaller than predicted by studies that fail to account for differences in time preference. The students who stay in school for many years without the help of the education-promoting intervention have a lower rate of time preference, on average, than those who stay in school only because of the intervention. Since students with lower rates of time preference tend to pursue positive health behaviors more avidly, then, given the same level of education, the health improvement resulting from the extra schooling would be smaller than anticipated.

Establishing the role of time preference is elusive, since it is difficult to measure directly. Fuchs tried to assess rates of time preference by distributing a questionnaire regarding the timing of monetary rewards, but the respondents gave inconsistent answers (1982). Their responses mirror inconsistencies that have been found in surveys designed to measure attitudes toward risk (Kahneman and Tversky 1979). These and other uncertainties have led Grossman and Joyce to conclude (in this volume) that differences in the rate of time preference do not explain most of the association between schooling and health. However, it seems likely that either the rate of time preference or other third factors play a large role. The persistence of the association between schooling and health at high levels of education is not easily explained if education has a purely causal effect on health, but is compatible with the effects of third factors. Furthermore, where they have been measured, personal characteristics, such as academic ability, have been found to be important determinants of educational attainment; it is very likely that some of these factors also influence health.

In addition to time preference, these factors might include motivation, a sense of purpose, and a host of other characteristics that reflect psychological and social adjustment. Such third factors are important because statistical analyses that fail to account for them are misleading. These third factors can also be the targets of an intervention. Even though they are not easily changed in adults, they may be malleable early in life. Parental behavior and environment, which are conditioned by economic status and education, help shape the beliefs and values of the children. If these attitudes are formed during childhood, social interventions would have relatively small immediate effects on adult health. But they could have a large impact years later, when the children who were exposed to the intervention reach adulthood.

Each direction of causality can underlie the association between socioeconomic factors and health. Meticulous statistical analyses are needed to weigh the relative importance of each component of this web of causality. Faced with complex phenomena that violate the assumptions required for the application of such basic satistical techniques as linear regression analysis, few studies have been able to isolate the direct causal effects of socioeconomic factors on health. The following section explains why.

METHODOLOGIC LIMITATIONS OF STUDIES ON SOCIOECONOMIC FACTORS AND HEALTH

How will an intervention directed toward socioeconomic factors affect health? Most studies have had to infer the answer by examining observational data, with all the uncertainties and pitfalls that implies.

Analysis of observational data presents different methodological challenges from those encountered in the analysis of randomized clinical trials or other experimental data. Observational studies depend on statistical techniques to control for confounding factors, while experimental studies can either control such variables directly or nullify their effects by randomization. Even the most appropriate statistical techniques, when applied to observational data, are less likely than experimental studies to produce definitive estimates of the impact of a variable. But an observational study that applies suitable methodology can be a satisfactory alternative, and sometimes experimental is impossible.

Unfortunately, many studies of the relationship between socioeconomic factors and health have applied standard statistical methods to data and phenomena that violate the assumptions under which the methods are valid. This problem is ubiquitous in the social sciences; rarely, if ever, are all of the conditions assumed by standard linear regression methods completely satisfied. Even flawed methods can yield important and useful insights, but it is crucial to identify the sources and direction of bias before drawing inferences from the studies that use such methods.

This section examines some of the most important statistical pitfalls of studies of socioeconomic gradients in health, exploring the reasons for these problems, the biases they generate, and methods that can be used to surmount them.

Measurement Error

Despite assiduous efforts by researchers, key variables frequently are measured imprecisely. The substitution of a flawed proxy for the (unavailable) variable of interest may give rise to such imprecision. For example, even though health is more tightly linked with schooling than with any other socioeconomic factor, schooling may only serve as a proxy for specific knowledge or other aspects of education. Not all schools or curricula are equal. Not all pupils learn the same material, nor do they learn equally well. If years of schooling is an imperfect measure of "true" education, we will underestimate its effects on health and overestimate the effects of other factors that are positively correlated with education, such as wealth or father's and mother's schooling attainments (Chow 1983, pp. 105–107).

In the presence of measurement error, attempts to appraise the contributions of particular risk factors to health outcomes are hazardous. Cigarette smoking is perhaps the best-established risk factor for cardiovascular and cancer mortality, yet self-reported cigarette smoking is an inexact measure of actual cigarette use, as reflected in concentrations of tobacco metabolites (Schwartz and Rider 1978; Vesey et al. 1982) and cigarette sales figures (Jackson and Beaglehole 1985). Some studies have concluded that the SES differential in lung cancer rates cannot be attributed to differential smoking rates (see, for example, Haan et al. in this volume), since the gradient persists after controlling for cigarette smoking. But the poor and less educated are more likely to smoke cigarettes (Schoenborn and Cohen 1986; Millar and Wigle 1986), and if cigarette smoking is measured inaccurately, multiple regression analysis and related techniques will overestimate the effects of the socioeconomic factors and underestimate the effects of smoking.

Expanding the size of the study population will not eliminate the biases that result from measurement error. At least two solutions hold promise. First, the measurement can be improved. Better questionnaire design and interviewing procedures or improved measurement of metabolites might sharpen assessments of tobacco and alcohol consumption. While better measurement is always desirable, it is essential when a conclusion turns on the assumption that measurement error is negligible.

Second, statistical techniques that remain valid in the presence of measurement error can be applied. Two such techniques, instrumental variables and two-stage least squares (Theil 1971), use alternative measures of the "noisy" variable that are correlated with its systematic component (its "true" value) and uncorrelated with the error in its measurement. Sometimes repeated measurements of a variable can be the basis for such a technique. This statistical procedure mirrors clinical practice; for example, an individual's blood pressure varies substantially from one measurement to the next, so it is standard practice to measure the blood pressure on at least two separate occasions before starting drug treatment for mildly or moderately elevated blood pressure. These approaches are not always satisfactory. They cannot always be applied, since data on the additional variables may not be readily available. Furthermore, while they produce *consistent* estimates of the effects of each factor (that is, in large samples the estimated values of the regression coefficients are unbiased), these statistical methods also increase the variance of the estimates (Leamer 1978; see also Grossman and Joyce in chapter 5 of this volume). Consequently, the power to detect a significant effect is reduced and larger samples are needed to obtain the same precision.

Without knowing the true value of the variable that is measured with error and its correlation with the other variables, one cannot determine the magnitude of the biases that result from measurement error. Bias affects the estimated impacts of the variables that are measured with error as well as the variables that are correlated with them. The size of such effects may be large. Hence statements that only a small percentage of variance in health outcomes can be explained by observed risk factors must be qualified if the risk factors are measured with error.

Time Specification of Explanatory Variables

Risk factors may not produce overt disease for many years. For example, cancer may first become apparent years after exposure to a carcinogen (see Harris in chapter 6 of this volume). In other instances, clinical disease may appear long after first exposure because the *cumulative* exposure produces disease. A chronically elevated blood cholesterol appears to promote cardiovascular disease this way; a transient elevation does not increase mortality, but a sustained rise in cholesterol increases the rate of accumulation of deposits on blood vessel walls. These deposits cause angina pectoris, heart attacks, and death from heart disease. Thus the entire past history of cholesterol values, not the current value, determines current mortality. Other risk factors, such as diabetes mellitus, hypertension, smoking, and alcohol consumption, also appear to cause morbidity through cumulative effects. There is every reason to believe that delayed and cumulative effects of risk factors are common.

These lagged effects pose a difficult challenge for epidemiological studies. First, few studies have comprehensive data on the past history of disease and exposure to risk factors. Frequently epidemiologic studies can only measure the current values of such variables, which may be associated with health outcomes only because they are correlated with past values of the risk factors. Sometimes the past values of a risk factor are obtained by survey, but recall for exposures that occurred in the distant past is imperfect. Thus either measure correlates weakly with the actual levels of past exposure.

Second, when the past history of risk factors is available, epidemiologic studies must specify the precise functional relationship between past values of the risk factor and current health. Is lung cancer mortality a function of the number of pack-years of smoking (average number of packs of cigarettes smoked per day multiplied by the number of years of smoking)? Is a pack-year twenty years ago equivalent to a pack-year five years ago? We know that the number of pack-years correlates well with the risks of lung cancer and heart disease, and that the risks diminish with years since quitting, because cigarette smoking has been studied extensively for more than three decades. We know much less about most other risk factors.

The precise form by which past values influence current risks needs to be determined, but only a small subset of the vast number of possibilities can be tested. The literature on distributed lags addresses methods for testing the functional form of lagged variables, primarily in the context of time-series data (Griliches 1967; Hendry et al. 1984), but often prior assumptions about the structure of the lag are needed. At least in theory, biology can provide useful qualitative information by narrowing the range of plausible alternatives. To determine specific functional forms, independent samples of epidemiologic data are usually needed, so that the lag form measured in one data set can be tested on another. These problems are exacerbated when we do not know which lagged variables matter, since then the number of possible relations to be tested becomes daunting.

The impact of a risk factor will be underestimated if its effect is either cumulative or lagged, and if the measured value is imperfectly correlated with the lagged values. Since few studies of socioeconomic factors and health have adequate measures of lagged values of risk factors, they will tend to underestimate the effects of conventional risk factors. Proper measurement of the history of risk factors is essential. When delays and cumulative effects are significant, even a controlled clinical trial can underestimate the effects of a risk factor intervention, since its health benefits may not become apparent for many years. For example, a randomized clinical trial of one cholesterol-lowering drug, niacin, did not demonstrate a reduction in overall mortality after six years, when the trial was terminated. However, after nine more years, the group treated with niacin had significantly lower all-cause mortality than the control groups (Canner et al. 1986). Few investigations could detect benefits delayed for so many years.

Simultaneity

The statistical consequence of reverse causality is simultaneity bias. The repeated observation that causality may run from health to socioeconomic status or in the opposite direction, or that both may be affected by a third factor, suggests that failure to account for each direction of causality may vitiate statistical analyses. Simultaneity occurs when one of the explanatory variables in a regression equation is a consequence as well as a cause of the dependent variable.

The effects of exogenous variables on the outcome variables can be assessed by linear regression techniques. A series of linear regressions whose dependent variables are the endogenous variables and whose explanatory variables (also called regressors or covariates) are fully exogenous is called the *reduced form*. When applied to the reduced form, linear regression is a statistically consistent method for forecasting the effects on the endogenous variables of changes in the exogenous variables (Koopmans and Hood 1953). However, unlike path analysis or other methods designed to explore the interrelations among endogenous and exogenous variables, the reduced form does not separate the direct effects of the exogenous variables from their indirect effects. If schooling is treated as exogenous, the reduced form approach does not make it possible to distinguish the direct health effects of schooling from such indirect effects as the improvements in health that result from increases in earnings made possible by more schooling. Thus the reduced form approach is more appropriate for forecasting than for elucidating mechanisms, since it yields valid estimates of the changes in outcome (endogenous) variables that can be expected to result from a change in policy (exogenous) variables.

Alternative methods seek to estimate the *structural* form of a model. The structural form of a set of relationships estimates the effects of changes in both exogenous and endogenous variables on other endogenous variables. Thus the structural form is able to distinguish direct effects of exogenous variables from their indirect effects. Several techniques are available for the estimation of structural forms, including instrumental variables, two-stage least squares, path analysis, three-stage least squares, and full information maximum likelihood (Malinvaud 1970). Because these techniques sometimes cannot be applied, it is not always possible to obtain consistent estimates of the structural form of the model. Generally, the techniques can be used when a sufficient number of variables correlated with socioeconomic factors, but not influenced by health, are available.

The selection of such variables is far from mechanical. It requires a careful definition of health, a clear understanding of the chronology of events, and support for the assumption that the variables are truly exogenous. For example, a heart attack at age 60 could not have contributed to lower socioeconomic status at age 20. But facets of health present during adolescence, such as coping behaviors and the ability to manage stress, could affect occupational and educational attainments as well as the likelihood of later suffering cardiac disease. Only when we have specific information that makes it unlikely that a health event affected the socioeconomic factors can we perform analyses free of simultaneity bias.

Heterogeneity, Omitted Variables, and Interactions

In any statistical analysis, omitting an important causal variable will lead to biased estimates of the effects of the included variables. Several investigators have scrutinized the importance of omitted variables bias in estimating the effects of education on earnings. Critics claimed that early estimates of the financial returns to schooling were overly optimistic. They argued that individuals who obtained more years of formal education were fundamentally different from those who did not; the better educated may have had more aptitude for academic pursuits and would have enjoyed higher earnings even if they had not attended school longer (Griliches and Mason 1972). Thus schooling might serve as an indicator of earnings potential, not a cause of it. The subsequent literature concluded that deletion of measures of aptitude or ability led to overestimates of the financial rewards of schooling, but the rewards were still substantial (Griliches 1977).

The severity of omitted variables bias depends on the size of the effect of the omitted variable(s) and the correlation between the included and the omitted variables. If the omitted variable is positively correlated with an included variable, and both variables affect the dependent variable in the same direction, then the omission will lead to an overestimate of the effect of the included variable. Many studies of socioeconomic gradients in health include social class or income but not conventional medical risk factors, such as smoking or hypertension (Nagi and Stockwell 1973; Jenkins 1983; Devesa and Diamond 1983; Marmot and McDowall 1986), thereby overestimating the direct effects of the socioeconomic factors. Failure to control for significant "third factors," such as the rate of time preference, will also lead to omitted variables bias.

Interactions, if neglected, can also lead to omitted variables bias. Whether the direction of the bias that results from failure to measure an interaction term will be upward or downward depends on the distribution of risk factors in the study sample. Cardiovascular mortality, for example, increases in a greater than additive fashion when several risk factors are present (Kannel et al. 1979). Failure to account for these interactions would bias the estimated effects of each risk factor. More importantly, it would obscure the importance of targeting interventions toward patients with multiple risk factors. The mortality reduction from treating hypertension is greater for patients who smoke and have an elevated cholesterol than for patients who have no other cardiovascular risk factors.

Several methods can correct for biases arising from omitted variables (Aigner and Goldberger 1977; Chamberlain 1984; Gorsuch 1974; Goldberger 1972; Joreskog and Goldberger 1975). Corrections for omitted variables depend on assumptions about the nature of the variables, such as their statistical distribution, and on their correlations with other variables.

Omitted variables are an example of heterogeneity, or differences among individuals that are not fully measured by the explanatory variables. Several statistical methods can detect heterogeneity in longitudinal data. This is an area of active research in biostatistics, econometrics, and demography (Heckman and Singer 1984; Trussel and Richards 1985; Yashin et al. 1985). The methods that are being developed may be particularly useful for studying the relationship between socioeconomic factors and health, since heterogeneity appears to be one of the most important obstacles to developing valid estimates of causal effects.

These statistical problems are not unique to research on socioeconomic factors and health. As in other areas of empirical investigation, after recognizing that the problems exist, it is important to judge their significance. When the effects of simultaneity, heterogeneity, measurement error, and other problems are especially severe, standard statistical methods are inappropriate, and more suitable methods should be applied. We will be misled if we fail to anticipate the biases that result from using flawed statistical methods to assess the likely effects of an intervention.

Policy Implications of Studies on Socioeconomic Factors and Health

Policy implications drawn from studies that simply measure the association between socioeconomic factors and health should be greeted with skepticism. However, skepticism should not blind us to the potential usefulness of research into the socioeconomic determinants of health. I now turn to the central question of this volume: How can research on socioeconomic factors and health contribute to better health? Instead of confirming that there is a socioeconomic gradient in health, future efforts should explore the causes of the gradient and assess the consequences of interventions aimed at improving health. After finding, for example, that the poor are more likely to die in automobile accidents, our efforts are more likely to bear fruit if we investigate the reasons for the phenomenon rather than further demonstrating that the association with poverty is consistent or pervasive.

Health interventions fall into one of four categories: social interventions, occupational interventions, public health interventions, or medical interventions.

Social interventions. Even if a so-called third factor accounts for part of the association between health and education, education may nonetheless have a direct effect on health. If so, efforts to raise educational attainment, a social intervention, will improve health. This approach is particularly promising if poverty or poor education is the fundamental cause of the socioeconomic gradient in health, and risk factors and other specific mechanisms are merely the channels through which poverty exerts its harm.

On the other hand, even if socioeconomic factors (rather than an unknown third factor) directly cause disease, social interventions may not be the best way to promote health. Attempts to remove the cause of a disease can be costly and less effective than treating or preventing it by other means (Russell 1986). For example, the high prevalence of hypertension among American blacks has been attributed to psychological, social, and other environmental stresses. Even if the social environment is wholly responsible for the excess rate of hypertension in blacks, pharmacological treatment may be more effective than attempts to remove such causes of hypertension.

In addition, health effects are often a small part of the consequences of a social intervention. Educational interventions affect employment, earnings, and the distribution of workers among different occupations. Schemes to redistribute wealth also have diverse effects. The most ambitious income redistribution experiment ever attempted in the United States, the Seattle/Denver Income Maintenance Experiment (SIME/DIME), compared groups of individuals who received varying levels of income support under a negative income tax. Income support improved the financial well-being of the recipients, but it diminished labor force participation (Robins and West 1983) and had mixed or insignificant effects on health. It did not significantly alter psychological distress, duration of disability, hospitalization rates, or perceived health status. Thus, while it increased expenditures for health care, "SIME/DIME probably did not affect the health of participants" (Davis and Kehrer 1983, p. 390). Because redistributive efforts reduce labor supply and change consumption patterns, they are also likely to diminish economic efficiency and overall wealth (Okun 1975). The public cares a great deal about these consequences. To recognize that a social intervention imposes costs is not to conclude that it should be rejected; rather, it calls for a broad view of the costs and benefits. The impact on overall welfare, not the health effects alone, determines the merit of an intervention.

Occupational interventions. The consequences of occupational interventions also extend beyond their health effects. Supported by compelling evidence that some occupational hazards cause severe disability and early death, occupational interventions promise to improve health and diminish its socioeconomic gradient. Such interventions might include, for example, rules that are highly specific to particular occupations or work sites as well as general interventions designed to reduce job stress or discomfort. Well-designed interventions that reduced toxin exposures and the number of industrial accidents would surely improve health.

Any such intervention, however, would have important economic ramifications. Voluntary acceptance of hazardous work implies that the hazardous job is preferable to alternative opportunities available to the employee—as long as the employee is fully aware of the health risks and other conditions of employment. The employee might choose the hazardous work because the pay is better, because it involves fewer hours of work, or because the job is desirable in other respects. Under these conditions, an intervention that raised employer costs by imposing workplace safety rules might result in lower wages or loss of employment. In some cases, safety regulation can be costly enough to close down companies or industries. If employees choose the hazardous work, with its higher pay and other advantages, costly interventions that improve their health may worsen their overall welfare.

There may, however, be compelling reasons to pursue an occupational intervention despite these considerations. If workers are not informed of the health risks, there should be no presumption that they would consent to the level of risk to which they are exposed. If workers receive subsidized health insurance or health care, they might not have sufficient incentives to avoid risk, so that we might choose to promote health at the expense of other aspects of employee welfare. Finally, hazardous employment might be an appropriate target for intervention because, as a society, we care more about the health of workers than about their economic welfare. Rather than drawing broad conclusions about all occupational interventions, we should recognize that they are appropriate instruments for health intervention only if we would choose them after a complete accounting of their costs and benefits.

Public health interventions. The historical accomplishments of public health interventions, such as immunization programs and advances in sanitation, have been remarkable. Some contemporary public health actions, such as the detection and removal of toxic chemicals and other environmental hazards, are likely to benefit blue-collar workers and the poor. Adverse health behaviors and other risk factors associated with lower SES can be attacked at the population level. The Stanford Five City Multifactor Risk Reduction Program is an example of a population-based intervention that combines education, advertising, and other modes of reinforcement to modify risks; such efforts may prove to be more effective than individual education, preventive efforts, and treatment.

Medical interventions. Like public health interventions, preventive and therapeutic medical interventions can also be targeted toward the poor and less educated. Individual medical care may be the best way to prevent the complications of hypertension and other risks that are common in this group. The rationale for this approach is clear: these factors are established causes of mortality and they can be modified. By applying interventions whose effectiveness has already been proven, medical interventions may be able to reduce socioeconomic gradients in health.

When we spend government funds on medical care of the disadvantaged, however, we should be satisfied that health care is superior to alternative uses of the money. The disadvantaged might be willing to forgo a small health benefit if public funds were spent instead to improve housing, nutrition, or schooling.

We might well decide that health improvements merit public funds more than do housing and education, but we should make the rationale for our decision explicit.

Interventions need not be limited to any one of these four categories. At times, a combination of approaches will be most effective. Choosing among the alternatives is conceptually simple: selecting the intervention (or combination of interventions) that, at a given cost, improves health the most. Discovering which interventions satisfy this criterion is rarely straightforward.

Although the path from discovering an association between socioeconomic factors and health to selecting a health intervention is often tortuous, it can lead to an effective intervention. That is what happened when investigators pursued an association between occupational asbestos exposure and excess mortality; although decades-old asbestos exposure continues to produce morbidity and death, regulations in the United States and Great Britain have diminished occupational exposure since the 1960s. The example of asbestos illustrates two important aspects of this discussion. First, exposure is strongly associated with low occupational class. Second, the significant interaction between cigarette smoking and asbestos exposure demonstrates the importance of attention to methodology. Asbestos, of course, is not completely representative of occupational hazards; its health effects could be detected more easily than those of many other hazardous substances since it produces distinctive patterns of disease. As a result, more is known about the health consequences of asbestos than virtually any other occupational carcinogen.

The relation of exposure to occupational class is striking. In a British study of 31,150 asbestos workers, most either manufactured asbestos products or were insulation, maintenance, shipyard, or construction workers (Hodgson and Jones 1986). In another large British study, all asbestos factory workers fell into the two lowest social classes in the Registrar General's classification (Berry et al. 1972). Most Americans exposed to asbestos were also blue-collar workers.

The diseases caused by asbestos include asbestosis, a form of scarring of the lung that can lead to severe, irreversible respiratory impairment; mesothelioma, a cancer of the lining of the lung or the abdominal cavity; and lung cancer. The link between asbestos and lung cancer was established decades ago (Doll 1955; Selikoff et al. 1964) and the association with cancer and other lung disorders has been confirmed by numerous subsequent studies. Several clues suggested that asbestos exposure led to the lung diseases. Asbestos workers frequently had lung complaints. Because asbestos produced distinctive radiographic abnormalities, X-ray examinations of the chest often confirmed that the respiratory symptoms were associated with asbestos exposure. Finally, the incidence of mesothelioma, an otherwise rare cancer, was found to be increased 100-fold among asbestos workers (Hammond et al. 1979).

Although lung cancer is the most frequent cause of death linked to asbestos exposure, most asbestos workers were also exposed to another cause of lung cancer—cigarette smoke. About 70 percent of Selikoff and Lee's sample of 12,000 American and Canadian insulation workers smoked cigarettes, and in several studies of asbestos workers (Selikoff and Lee 1978; Selikoff et al. 1968; Berry et al. 1972) nearly all of the lung cancer deaths occurred in smokers. The added risk of lung cancer from asbestos exposure among nonsmokers was small (Selikoff et al. 1980; Steenland and Thun 1986), whereas asbestos workers who smoked had more than six times the expected lung cancer mortality rate and nearly four times the expected all-cancer mortality rate. None of these studies compared the all-cause mortality of nonsmoking asbestos workers to nonsmoking controls, but Selikoff and Lee found that overall mortality was *lower* for nonsmoking asbestos workers than for all white American males, not adjusted for smoking.

These studies provide important insights into policies to improve occupational health. First, they demonstrate that asbestos exposure, which occurred in blue-collar occupations, is associated with cancer. Second, although the estimates of the risk in nonsmokers vary, all of the studies found that the risk of lung cancer from asbestos exposure and cigarette smoking is greater than additive. Third, a high percentage of exposed workers smoked cigarettes, so they had an elevated risk of lung cancer on that basis alone. Because lung cancer was (and usually is) incurable, only prevention can significantly diminish the mortality of this disease. With such data in hand, we now ask, what policies would most effectively prevent the disease?

The following example illustrates how the epidemiological data can be used to obtain an answer. The following table, adapted from Steenland and Thun (1986), is based on data from Hammond et al. (1979). The control population was a panel of 74,000 white males in blue-collar occupations followed by the American Cancer Society. The exposed group consisted of 891 nonsmokers and 6,841 smokers.

LUNG CANCER DEATH RATES
AMONG SMOKERS AND NONSMOKERS

| | *NONSMOKERS* | | *SMOKERS* | |
	Exposed	Not exposed	Exposed	Not exposed
Death rate/100,000 man-years	58.4	11.3	590.3	120.2

From these figures we can calculate that there will be about 471 lung cancer deaths per 100,000 man-years among a group of asbestos workers, if 70 percent of them smoke cigarettes. An employer might reduce this mortality rate by building a facility for asbestos manufacturing that eliminated asbestos exposure among employees. If 70 percent of the workers smoke, and their risk falls to the level of nonexposed workers, the mortality rate will drop to 88 per 100,000 man-years. Instead of reducing asbestos exposure, the employer might either hire only nonsmokers or persuade workers to quit smoking. If their risk of lung cancer becomes the same as the risk for exposed nonsmokers, the lung cancer mortality rate will fall to 58 per 100,000 man-years. After smoking is removed as a risk factor, eliminating asbestos exposure reduces the death rate by an additional 47 deaths per 100,000 man-years, leaving 11 per 100,000 man-years. Smokers who are not exposed to asbestos have twice the lung cancer mortality of nonsmokers who are exposed, so smoking cessation prevents more deaths than removal of the asbestos.

By themselves, these figures cannot tell us which intervention would be best. That depends on the costs and other benefits of the intervention. Although cigarette smoking is a more deadly risk factor than asbestos exposure, smokers do not give up tobacco easily. Uncontrolled clinical trials have found that intensive programs to help smokers quit achieve six-month abstinence rates of about 25 to 75 percent (American College of Physicians 1986). Since these studies enrolled highly motivated individuals, the quit rate in a randomized trial would likely be smaller. Completely preventing exposure to asbestos will avert more deaths than an ineffective smoking cessation program. But eliminating asbestos exposure by banning its use in manufacturing and construction might be costly to the general population, since substitutes for asbestos are usually more expensive and lack some of its desirable physical features (Craighead and Mossman 1982). It might also prove costly to the workers, some of whom might lose their jobs or undertake other equally risky work.

It will nearly always cost more to save a life by attempting to eliminate both smoking *and* asbestos exposure than by attempting to eliminate either one. Either smoking cessation or a reduction in asbestos exposure will reduce mortality substantially, but after one risk factor is eliminated, the additional gains from eliminating the second are smaller. Consequently, eliminating both risk factors will be less cost-effective than eliminating either one alone. However, declining cost-effectiveness is not sufficient reason to reject the second intervention; even though the cost of preventing an additional death rises, the additional lives saved may justify the expense.

These inferences about the effects of interventions are, of course, subject to qualification. Similar qualifications apply to any nonexperimental study. If other factors associated with either cigarette smoking or asbestos exposure generated the association with lung cancer, removing either risk factor might have a smaller effect than anticipated. Furthermore, the estimate of the relative risk due to asbestos exposure is sensitive to the duration and intensity of exposure, the particular form of asbestos fiber, and the number of years that the study population is observed. Because of the lag between exposure and the development of clinically detectable cancer, studies of cohorts followed for brief times after asbestos exposure underestimate the relative risk observed in later years. These quantitative relationships become important when we weigh the cost of risk factor reduction against the mortality gain, as any policy evaluation must.

When observational data cannot fully resolve the importance of lagged effects and the full impact of a causal variable, confirmatory biological or medical data can be helpful. Laboratory studies (Selikoff and Lee 1978) have demonstrated that exposure to cigarette smoke and to asbestos, alone or together, can cause cancer in laboratory animals. Furthermore, the risk of mesothelioma is so elevated among asbestos workers that any third factor responsible for the association would have to be very tightly linked to asbestos. Identifying such a third factor would be extremely difficult and have little practical importance. Thus, even though these studies do not reveal the exact gains in life expectancy to expect from alternative policies to reduce asbestos exposure or smoking among asbestos workers, they have told us a great deal that is useful, including which risk factor modifications will reduce mortality the most. Thus the observation of a link between occupation and health effect led to lifesaving policies.

In summary, when a disease is tightly linked with a socioeconomic factor, an intervention can be directed toward the socioeconomic factor itself (occupation), the proximate cause of the disease (asbestos), or an aspect of behavior (smoking). In this example, researchers avoided a methodological pitfall by discovering the interaction with smoking. The presence of an interaction may be the only clue that removal of an associated risk will prove fruitful. The aggressive pursuit of the linkages with a research approach that combined epidemiology, clinical investigation, and basic laboratory studies verified that asbestos caused death and disability. Smoking cessation efforts have continued, with mixed success, and the discovery of these linkages led to successful efforts to reduce asbestos exposure in homes, schools, and the workplace.

DIRECTIONS FOR FUTURE RESEARCH

While previous research on socioeconomic gradients in health has fallen short of sending a clear policy message, its implication for future research is clear: the next task is to distinguish cause from correlation. Much of the research on socioeconomic factors and health points to the existence of a problem, but not to a solution. Often the research does not examine the mechanisms behind an association in sufficient detail to suggest a way to proceed. Is a diet high in cholesterol and saturated fats the cause of increased cardiac mortality among the poor? Do the poor have higher lung cancer mortality rates because they are more likely to smoke, and smoke more? Do the less educated smoke cigarettes because they are unaware of the health consequences of smoking? The success of alternative policies to improve health depends on the answers to questions such as these.

Nonmedical interventions can be powerful tools for improving health. To avoid overestimating the effects of such interventions, however, future research must account for behavioral variation that modifies responses to the interventions. Consider alternative approaches to heart disease prevention in the framework of the four categories of intervention described. Broad social interventions might include income redistribution through progressive taxation, and such an intervention might reduce heart disease mortality by reducing social and psychological stresses or by improving diet and other risk factors. But underlying differences in tastes and education make it likely that wealth redistribution will not reduce the prevalence of cardiac disease to the level of those who were wealthy before the intervention.

Occupational interventions might relieve job stress and provide exercise for sedentary workers. But the work itself may not be the cause of poor health. Since selection of high risk individuals may account for much of the added risk of heart disease among workers in the lowest occupational classes, the occupational gradient will not disappear with an occupational intervention. Public health interventions, such as educational programs to improve diet and other health behaviors, and medical interventions, such as screening for high cholesterol, might be targeted to less educated or less wealthy populations. To choose from the large menu of possible interventions, we must determine the portion of the observed association with socioeconomic factors that represents causality.

The best measures of causality will come from the application of suitable statistical methods to valid, reliable data. Not all data collection efforts are equally likely to produce the desired information. The data requirements for some of the techniques that control for heterogeneity are much more demanding than for multiple regression and similar methods. Data collection strategies will be most successful if they are based on a clear understanding of the questions to be answered and the techniques to be applied.

Aggregate time-series data, such as mortality rates and income levels by population groups or geographic units, tend to be an inadequate basis on which to judge causality. Since government agencies routinely collect and report aggregate data, they can be obtained inexpensively. However, such data provide little insight into the specific mechanisms and subtle questions of causality that are crucial in this area. The inability to employ appropriate statistical methods often means that time-series data cannot be used to detect the presence of third factor mechanisms underlying the association between SES and health.

Collecting cross-sectional data on individuals is more expensive, since the requisite surveys are usually detailed and time-consuming. Furthermore, analyses of data obtained at a single point of time permit only limited conclusions about causality. Without repeated measurements, even individual data can seldom deal effectively with endogeneity or heterogeneity.

A randomized trial is more likely to establish causality and measure the efficacy of alternative interventions than any other data collection effort. Unlike purely observational approaches, randomization eliminates the influence of unmeasured variables. However, randomized trials of medical interventions are expensive, and studies of social or behavioral interventions introduce additional complexities. A social intervention may have a measurable effect only after a long delay, and important endpoints frequently are "soft." Furthermore, it is often difficult to ensure that all treated subjects get the same intervention, since, unlike medications, social interventions are not neatly defined and packaged.

Randomized trials can compare multiple treatments, but most often they compare a single treatment to a control. Rarely

can a randomized trial investigate multiple treatments simultaneously, because unless it has large numbers of study subjects, it
will lack the statistical power to detect clinically significant differences among the treatment groups. Instead of testing several
different interventions, a randomized trial might examine an intervention that has multiple components. Studies that use this
approach may be unable to dissect the contribution of each component of the intervention. For example, the treatment group
of MRFIT (Multiple Risk Factor Intervention Trial Research
Group 1982) participated in a program designed to reduce smoking, improve diet, increase exercise, and aggressively treat high
blood pressure. Mortality was roughly the same in the treatment
and control groups. This finding has been attributed to an un-
expected drop in mortality in the control group, but the intervention may have been unsuccessful because some of its
components were deleterious, while others lowered mortality.
Unfortunately, it has been difficult to separate the impacts of individual components of the intervention.

Although randomized trials can assess the effects of an intervention in an unambiguous way, they have other limitations.
Strictly speaking, the results of the randomized trial apply only
to populations identical to the sample studied. Major trials of
cholesterol reduction in this country included only men (Coronary Drug Project Research Group 1973, Lipid Research Clinics
Program 1984, and MRFIT); do the results apply to women,
whose age-adjusted cardiac mortality rates are lower? If a trial
seeks to broaden generalizability by studying a heterogeneous
population instead, it may not be able to detect differences in
benefits among particular subgroups.

Since the randomization applies only to the intervention, randomized trials are no more useful than observational data for investigating other issues, such as the impacts of variables that are
not randomized. A randomized trial of an intervention to decrease smoking, for instance, will not tell us more about the effects of race on lung cancer mortality than a purely observational
study would.

These limitations do not vitiate the usefulness of randomized
trials. If the trial is planned with sufficient foresight, it will produce information about many phenomena besides the efficacy of

treatment. Randomized trials can serve as the focus of a more general longitudinal data collection effort. For example, the major study of coronary artery bypass surgery in this country, the Coronary Artery Surgery Study (CASS), included both a randomized trial of surgical management of coronary artery disease and a much larger registry of patients who underwent cardiac catheterization but were not eligible to participate in the randomized trial. Both the randomized trial and analyses of the longitudinal data collected as part of the registry have been influential.

Longitudinal observational data, whether collected as part of a therapeutic trial or as an independent investigation, have several advantages over cross-sectional data and over aggregate time-series data. Methods that avert the biases caused by measurement error, simultaneity, heterogeneity, and other violations of the basic assumptions of linear regressions, can be applied to longitudinal data. These methods can approximate the experimental control achieved in randomized trials.

The collection of longitudinal observational data has some of the drawbacks of randomized trials: It is costly, and repeated surveying of individuals over long periods of time raises concerns about confidentiality violations and sample attrition. But these drawbacks are far outweighed by the versatility of the data. The Framingham study, a prospective longitudinal study of residents of one town in Massachusetts, did not include a randomized trial. Yet it has proven to be an extremely important source of information about numerous aspects of health and has been an inspiration for subsequent clinical trials.

If the follow-up information is limited, it need not cost substantially more to collect longitudinal data than cross-sectional data. Extensive baseline information about an individual (such as variables representing the home environment, measures of health, welfare, assets, and education), along with less detailed follow-up information, will be adequate for many purposes. Since important supplementary data can be obtained from government sources (such as mortality information from the National Death Index or health expenditure information from Medicare claims files), the longitudinal aspect of the data might be an inexpensive addendum to a cross-sectional survey.

The most promising approaches combine several data types and paths of investigation. By demonstrating that a causal relationship is plausible, laboratory investigation has proven to be an important adjunct to epidemiologic studies of cigarette smoking and of asbestos exposure. Longitudinal studies can confirm that causality is likely in a human population and can suggest which interventions might succeed. An interventional trial—randomized or not—can directly assess the consequences of an action taken to improve health. The process is an iterative one, since new epidemiologic findings can suggest new avenues of laboratory investigation, and results of a clinical trial can suggest new epidemiologic or laboratory hypotheses. We will not always need to wait for the results of numerous studies to choose a strategy. However, when the potential benefits appear to exceed the risks by little, or the uncertainty is great, investigation is an essential prelude to action.

CONCLUSIONS

This paper began with the claim that studies of the linkages between socioeconomic factors and health could lead to interventions to improve health. Many studies have taken a first step toward this goal by documenting the association between health and socioeconomic factors. But they have faltered on the second step: demonstrating that the association is a causal relation. When only observational data are available, it is never easy to prove that an association represents cause and effect, and many investigations of the socioeconomic gradient in health have used statistical methods that are ill-suited for this purpose. Few have attempted to take the final and most important step: assessing the effectiveness of specific interventions. Thus the literature on the relationship between socioeconomic factors and health has uncovered a problem, but it has not been able to explain its causes, nor has it identified the best course of action to alleviate it.

Despite the shortcomings of much of this research, some important conclusions can be drawn from it. First, the effects of an intervention to improve health, for instance, will tend to be smaller than might be predicted on the basis of simple associations. For example, neonatal mortality rates are higher among the poor than among the middle class. Income redistribution might not improve health outcomes substantially, because income is only one of the differences between the poor and the wealthy. Other characteristics—such as time preference, other psychological factors, exposure to cigarettes and other conventional risk factors, and underlying "frailty"—may also contribute to the health gradient. Unless the intervention modifies these other factors as well, its impact will be smaller than expected.

Second, policies that raise educational attainments are the most promising social interventions. Although some of the association between health and education probably reflects the impact of third factors rather than a direct causal impact of education on health, education may have a significant, positive influence on health status. Furthermore, inasmuch as income improves health, education will benefit health indirectly by raising earnings.

This literature also suggests that interventions applied early in life may be particularly effective (see Mechanic in this volume). There are at least three reasons for directing our efforts toward children. First, observational studies tend to underestimate the roles of risk factors whenever their health effects are cumulative or delayed. Thus the benefits of an intervention applied to children are likely to be larger than most studies imply. Second, motivation, time preference, and other third factors that contribute to the association between health and socioeconomic factors may themselves be the targets of intervention in childhood, when they are likely to be malleable. Third, clinical observations support intervening early to prevent some diseases. Unlike most preventive activities in adults, the costs of prevention are less than the costs of treatment for some interventions applied to children. For example, savings in medical expenditures from cases of disease averted exceed the costs of vaccinating children for measles (Russell 1986).

The long delay before health benefits accrue from some childhood interventions partially offsets the advantages of targeting children. Social interventions, for example, may produce their greatest impact long after they are initiated. Future benefits from any action or expenditure are worth less, all else being equal, than immediate benefits, since any future cost or benefit must be discounted (Keeler and Cretin 1983). However, even when delayed benefits are discounted, vaccination programs still result in a net saving of health expenditures, and this may hold true for other early interventions as well.

Investigators can begin to resolve the uncertainties in the relationship between socioeconomic factors and health by shifting to an explicit policy focus. The greatest opportunity to assess the effects of an intervention, short of a randomized trial, will come from the application of sophisticated methodology to longitudinal data. For example, excess cancer mortality among the poor might reflect increased incidence, delayed detection, inadequate treatment, or a combination of these factors. Intervention-oriented research will analyze longitudinal data in order to assess the reasons for the elevated mortality and will search for factors that policy might modify. If increased breast cancer mortality is due to delayed detection, screening programs may save more lives than improved access to treatment. If inadequate treatment accounts for the excess mortality, an alternative approach is warranted.

Any thoughtful discussion of a contemplated intervention should account fully for its potential consequences, including its financial impact, indirect health effects, and other benefits and costs. A less comprehensive view will be of limited value to policy makers. For example, social and economic interventions seem promising because of the consistent and pervasive socioeconomic gradient in health. But the health effects are likely to be only a small part of the total impact of such interventions. Even if interventions designed to raise educational attainments provide negligible health benefits, they may be desirable, since they raise lifetime earnings and seem to enhance the quality of life in other respects. A comprehensive, disinterested view is important even when the choice is limited to alternative forms of medical care. Sometimes it is more efficacious to treat a health problem than to attempt its prevention (e.g., pneumonia in healthy young people), while at other times the opposite is true (e.g., lung cancer); we should choose our policies accordingly.

Studies in this area may never produce the unambiguous answers that we would like. The social and behavioral mechanisms are complex; often the biological mechanisms are obscure. Yet this literature has mapped a fruitful area for inquiry and intervention. It has exposed some of the weaknesses of a purely biomedical approach to human health, while uncovering clues to the etiology of disease that laboratory investigation alone might never have discovered. With better data and more suitable methods, the perspectives of social science and public health can further illuminate the causes of the socioeconomic gradient, suggest strategies to improve health, and catalyze the adoption of effective solutions.

REFERENCES

Aigner, D. J., Goldberger, A. S., eds. 1977. *Latent variables in socioeconomic models.* Amsterdam: North-Holland.

American College of Physicians, Health, and Public Policy Committee. 1986. Methods for stopping cigarette smoking. *Annals of Internal Medicine* 105:281–291.

Antonovsky, A. 1967. Social class, life expectancy, and overall mortality. *Milbank Memorial Fund Quarterly* 45:31–73.

Ashford, N. 1976. *Crisis in the workplace: occupational disease and injury.* Cambridge, MA: M.I.T. Press.

Auster, R., Leveson, I., Sarachek, D. 1969. The production of health, an exploratory study. *Journal of Human Resources* 4:411–436.

Bartel, A., Taubman, P. 1979. Health and labor market success: the role of various diseases. *Review of Economics and Statistics* 61:1–8.

Becker, G. S., Lewis, H. G. 1973. On the interaction between the quantity and quality of children. *Journal of Political Economy* 81:S279–S288.

Becker, G. S., Landes, E. M., Michael, R. T. 1977. An economic analysis of marital instability. *Journal of Political Economy* 85:1141–1187.

Ben-Porath, Y. 1967. The production of human capital and the life-cycle of earnings. *Journal of Political Economy* 75:352–365.

Berry, G., Newhouse, M. L., Turok, M. 1972. Combined effect of asbestos exposure and smoking on mortality from lung cancer in factory workers. *Lancet* 2:476–479.

Canner, P. L., Berge, K. G., Wenger, N. K., Stamler, J., et al.

1986. Fifteen-year mortality in Coronary Drug Project patients: long-term benefit with niacin. *Journal of the American College of Cardiology* 8:1245–1255.

Chamberlain, G. 1984. Panel data. In Griliches, Z., and Intriligator, M. D., eds. *Handbook of econometrics, vol. 2.* Amsterdam: North-Holland.

Chow, G. C. 1983. *Econometrics.* New York: McGraw-Hill.

Coronary Drug Project Research Group. 1973. The Coronary Drug Project: design, methods, and baseline results. *Circulation* 47 (suppl. I):1–179.

Craighead, J. E., Mossman, B. T. 1982. The pathogenesis of asbestos-associated diseases. *New England Journal of Medicine* 306:1446–1455.

Davis, M. R., Kehrer, K. 1983. Overview of research on health, consumption, and social behavior. In *Final report of the Seattle-Denver Income Maintenance Experiment, vol. 1: design and results.* Menlo Park, CA: SRI International.

Devesa, S. S., Diamond, E. L. 1983. Socioeconomic and racial differences in lung cancer incidence. *American Journal of Epidemiology* 118:818–831.

Doll, R. 1955. Mortality from lung cancer in asbestos workers. *British Journal of Industrial Medicine* 12:81–86.

Ehrlich, I. 1974. Participation in illegitimate activities: an economic analysis. In Becker, G. S., Landes, W. M., eds. *Essays in the economics of crime and punishment.* New York: Columbia University Press for the National Bureau of Economic Research.

Ernst, P., Theriault, G. 1984. Known occupational carcinogens and their significance. *Canadian Medical Association Journal* 130:863–867.

Fox, A. J., Adelstein, A. M. 1978. Occupational mortality: work or way of life? *Journal of Epidemiology and Community Health* 32:73–78.

Fox, A. J., Goldblatt, P. O., Jones, D. R. 1985. Social class mortality differentials: artefact, selection, or life circumstances? *Journal of Epidemiology and Community Health* 39:1–8.

Fuchs, V. R. 1982. Time preference and health: an exploratory study. In Fuchs, V. R., ed. *Economic aspects of health.* Chicago: University of Chicago Press.

Goldberger, A. S. 1972. Maximum-likelihood estimation of regressions containing unobservable independent variables. *International Economic Review* 13:1–15.

Gordon, J., Akman, A., Brooks, M. 1971. *Industrial safety statistics: a re-examination.* New York: Praeger.

Gorsuch, R. L. 1974. *Factor analysis.* Philadelphia: W. B. Saunders Co.

Griliches, Z. 1967. Distributed lags: a survey. *Econometrica* 35:16–49.

———. 1977. Estimating the returns to schooling: some econometric problems. *Econometrica* 45:1–22.

———, Mason, W. M. 1972. Education, income, and ability. *Journal of Political Economy* 80:S74–S103.

Grossman, M. 1972. *The demand for health: a theoretical and empirical investigation.* NBER Occasional Paper 119. New York: Columbia University Press for the National Bureau of Economic Research.

Hammond, E. C., Selikoff, I., Seidman, H. 1979. Asbestos exposure, cigarette smoking, and death rates. *Annals of the New York Academy of Sciences* 330:473–490.

Heckman, J., Singer, B. 1984. A method for minimizing the impact of distributional assumptions in econometric models for duration data. *Econometrica* 52:271–320.

Hendry, D. F., Pagan, A. R., Sargan, J. D. 1984. Dynamic specification. In Griliches, Z., and Intriligator, M. D., eds. *Handbook of econometrics, vol. 2.* Amsterdam: North-Holland.

Hodgson, J. T., Jones, R. D. 1986. Mortality of asbestos workers in England and Wales 1971–1981. *British Journal of Industrial Medicine* 43:158–164.

Hollingshead, A. B., Redlich, F. C. 1958. *Social class and mental illness.* New York: Wiley.

Jackson, R., Beaglehole, R. 1985. Secular trends in underreporting of cigarette consumption. *American Journal of Epidemiology* 122:341–344.

Jenkins, C. D. 1983. Social environment and cancer mortality in men. *New England Journal of Medicine* 308:395–398.

Joreskog, K. G., Goldberger, A. S. 1975. Estimation of a model with multiple indicators and multiple causes of a single latent variable. *Journal of the American Statistical Association* 70:631–639.

Kahneman, D., Tversky, A. 1979. Prospect theory: an analysis of decision under risk. *Econometrica* 47:263–291.

Kannel, W. B., Castelli, W. P., Gordon, T. 1979. Cholesterol in the prediction of atherosclerotic disease: new perspectives based on the Framingham study. *Annals of Internal Medicine* 90:85–91.

Keeler, E. B., Cretin, S. 1983. Discounting of life-saving and other non-monetary effects. *Management Science* 29:300–306.

Kitagawa, E. M., Hauser, P. M. 1973. *Differential mortality in the United States: a study in socioeconomic epidemiology.* Cambridge, MA: Harvard University Press.

Koopmans, T. C., Hood, W. C. 1953. The estimation of simultaneous linear economic relationships. In Hood, W. C., and Koopmans, T. C., eds. *Studies in econometric method.* Cowles Commission for Research in Economics, Monograph 14. New York: Wiley.

Leamer, E. 1978. Least-squares versus instrumental variables estimation in a simple errors in variables model. *Econometrica* 46:961–968.

Leigh, J. P. 1983. Direct and indirect effects of education on health. *Social Science and Medicine* 17:227–234.

———. 1986. Who chooses risky jobs? *Social Science and Medicine* 23:57–64.

Lipid Research Clinics Program. 1984. The Lipid Research Clinics coronary primary prevention trial results: I. Reduction in incidence of coronary heart disease. *Journal of the American Medical Association* 251:351–364.

Lord, W. 1955. *A night to remember.* New York: Henry Holt.

Luft, H. 1978. *Poverty and health: economic causes and consequences of health problems.* Cambridge, MA: Ballinger.

Malinvaud, E. 1970. *Statistical methods of econometrics.* 2nd ed. Amsterdam: North-Holland.

Marmot, M. G., McDowall, M. E. 1986. Mortality decline and widening social inequalities. *Lancet* 2:274–276.

Millar, W. J., Wigle, D. T. 1986. Socioeconomic disparities in risk factors for cardiovascular disease. *Canadian Medical Association Journal* 134:127–132.

Mincer, J. 1974. *Schooling, experience, and earnings.* New York:

Columbia University Press for the National Bureau of Economic Research.

Multiple Risk Factor Intervention Trial Research Group. 1982. Multiple risk factor intervention trial: risk factor changes and mortality results. *Journal of the American Medical Association* 248:1465–1477.

Myers, J., Bean, L. L. 1968. *A decade later: a follow-up of social class and mental illness.* New York: Wiley.

Nagi, M. H., Stockwell, E. G. 1973. Socioeconomic differentials in mortality by cause of death. *Health Services Reports* 88:449–456.

National Center for Health Statistics. 1986. *Health United States 1986.* D.H.H.S. Pub. No. (PHS) 87-1232. Public Health Service. Washington, D.C.: G.P.O.

Newhouse, J. P., Friedlander, L. J. 1980. The relationship between medical resources and measures of health: some additional evidence. *Journal of Human Resources* 15:200–218.

Okun, A. 1975. *Equality and efficiency: the big tradeoff.* Washington, D.C.: The Brookings Institution.

Pastorino, U., Berrino, F., Gervasio, A., Pesenti, V., et al. 1984. Proportion of lung cancers due to occupational exposure. *International Journal of Cancer* 33:231–237.

Robins, P. K., West, R. W. 1983. Labor supply response. In *Final report of the Seattle-Denver Income Maintenance Experiment, vol. 1: design and results.* Menlo Park, CA: SRI International.

Rose, G., Marmot, M. G. 1981. Social class and coronary heart disease. *British Heart Journal* 45:13–19.

Russell, L. B. 1986. *Is prevention better than cure?* Washington, D.C.: The Brookings Institution.

Schoenborn, C. A., Cohen, B. H. 1986. Trends in smoking, alcohol consumption, and other health practices among U.S. adults, 1977 and 1983. *Advance Data from Vital and Health Statistics,* No. 118. D.H.H.S. Pub. No. (PHS) 86-1250. Hyattsville, MD: Public Health Service.

Schwartz, J. L., Rider, G. 1978. *Review and evaluation of smoking control methods: the United States and Canada, 1969–1977.* D.H.E.W. Pub. No. (CDC) 79-8369. Washington, D.C.: Department of Health, Education, and Welfare.

Selikoff, I. J., Churg, J., Hammond, E. C. 1964. Asbestos exposure and neoplasia. *Journal of the American Medical Association* 188:22–26.

Selikoff, I. J., Hammond, E. C., Churg, J. 1968. Asbestos exposure, smoking, and neoplasia. *Journal of the American Medical Association* 204:104–110.

Selikoff, I. J., Lee, D. H. K. 1978. *Asbestos and disease.* New York: Academic Press.

Selikoff, I. J., Seidman, H., Hammond, E. C. 1980. Mortality effects of cigarette smoking among amosite asbestos factory workers. *Journal of the National Cancer Institute* 65:507–513.

Steenland, K., Thun, M. 1986. Interaction between tobacco smoking and occupational exposures in the causation of lung cancer. *Journal of Occupational Medicine* 28:110–118.

Thaler, R., Rosen, S. 1976. The value of saving a life: evidence from the labor market. In Terleckyj, N. E., ed. *Household production and consumption.* Studies in income and wealth, no. 40. New York: Columbia University Press for the National Bureau of Economic Research, Inc.

Theil, H. 1971. *Principles of econometrics.* New York: Wiley.

Townsend, P., Davidson, N., eds. 1982 *Inequalities in health: the Black Report.* Harmondsworth, England: Penguin Books.

Trussell, J., Richards, T. 1985. Correcting for unobserved heterogeneity in hazard models: an application of the Heckman-Singer procedure to longitudinal data. In Tuma, N., ed. *Sociological methodology 1985.* San Francisco: Jossey Bass.

Vesey, C. J., Saloojee, Y., Cole, P. V., Russell, M. A. 1982. Blood carboxyhaemoglobin, plasma thiocyanate, and cigarette consumption: implications for epidemiological studies in smokers. *British Medical Journal* 284:1516–1518.

Viscusi, W. K. 1979. *Employment hazards: an investigation of market performance.* Cambridge, MA: Harvard University Press.

Werko, L. 1987. The enigma of coronary heart disease and its prevention. *Acta Medica Scandinavica* 221:323–333.

Whitehead, M. 1987. *The health divide: inequalities in health in the 1980s.* London: The Health Education Council.

Wilkinson, R. G. 1986. Socioeconomic differences in mortality: interpreting the data on their size and trends. In Wilkinson,

R. G., ed. *Class and health: research and longitudinal data.* London: Tavistock.

Willis, R. J. 1973. A new approach to the economic theory of fertility behavior. *Journal of Political Economy* 81:S14–S64.

Yashin, A. I., Manton, K. G., Vaupel, J. W. 1985. Mortality and aging in a heterogeneous population: a stochastic process model with observed and unobserved variables. *Theoretical Population Biology* 27:154–175.

Annotated Bibliography

Recent Publications on Socioeconomic Status and Health

Mary N. Haan, George A. Kaplan,
S. Leonard Syme and Anne O'Neil

Abramson, J. H., Gofin, R., Habib, J., Pridan, H., Gofin, J.
1982. Indicators of social class. A comparative appraisal of
measures for use in epidemiological studies. *Social Science and
Medicine* 16:1739–1746.

Various indicators of social class were compared in a community health survey in Jerusalem to determine their value in de-
tecting associations with health characteristics. Correlation
among the indicators and between them and selected health-
relevant variables were measured. Results suggested that there
were few differences between the occupation scales tested for
use as general indicators of social class, as the correlations between them were very high, and the patterns of their correlations with health variables were very similar. Other indicators
of social class (e.g., education, income, crowding) were not
strongly correlated with occupation, and there were differences in their association with the health variables, indicating
that conclusions about the relationship between health and social class are not insensitive to the measure used. Despite these
discrepancies, the patterns of association with the health measures were broadly similar for occupation scales, education,
and income.

Adelstein, A. M. 1980. Life-style in occupational cancer. *Journal of Toxicology and Environmental Health* 6:953–962.

Data on cancer mortality, for twenty-seven sites, from the Registrar General's Decennial Report based on the census of 1971 were examined in relationship to occupation. For all cancer deaths there was a gradient rising regularly from class I, the highest, to class V, the lowest. Contributions of the separate cancers to the gradient varied; some were high in social class I, such as leukemia and testis, but many of the important sites such as lung, stomach, and rectum show a negative gradient. The expected number of deaths for 25 ordered occupations were calculated after standardizing for 1) age differences, 2) social class, 3) area, and 4) town and county. The results suggested that social class accounted for 88 percent of the variation in cancer mortality.

Antonovsky, A. 1967. Social class, life expectancy, and overall mortality. *Milbank Memorial Fund Quarterly* 45:31–73.

Evidence concerning the association between social class and life expectancy and mortality is reviewed. Studies presented begin in the 13th century and, despite wide variations in methodology, virtually all find a consistent, graded relationship between various socioeconomic measures and mortality.

———, Bernstein, J. 1977. Social class and infant mortality. *Social Science and Medicine* 11:453–470.

The general pattern between social class and infant mortality is described. Historically, infant mortality has declined substantially. A review of the literature and data on neonatal and postneonatal mortality rates demonstrated that the decline in infant mortality was the result of a steep drop in the postneonatal component. The relationship between social class and infant mortality has been narrowing, largely because postneonatal mortality, which has an inverse relationship to SES, has declined. This has not been the case for neonatal mortality. Other studies have indicated that as one gets closer to birth, the smaller the mortality difference between classes becomes. Thus, in these studies, the social class gap for neonatal death reflected late postneonatal deaths. One possible explanation for this was a common exposure (i.e., hospital). For still-births, the loss rate was higher and the social class gap wider than for neonatal mortality. Lower class per se does not cause high infant mortality, as social class subsumes a large set of more directly causative biological and behavioral variables (low birthweight, prematurity, cigarette smoke, and alcohol consumption).

Arnesen, E., Forsdahl, A. 1985. The Tromso heart study: coronary risk factors and their association with living conditions during childhood. *Journal of Epidemiology and Community Health* 39:210–214.

The relationship between risk factors for cardiovascular disease and information about economic conditions during childhood was examined as part of the Tromso Heart Study. Men and women (7,405 men and 7,247 women) age 20 to 49 answered questions concerning living conditions during childhood and concerning cerebrovascular disease risk factors. Significant age-adjusted differences in cholesterol, height, and current smoking were found for those with very difficult vs. very good childhood economic circumstances. When adjustment was made for age, cholesterol, body mass index, leisure time activity, coffee, alcohol consumption, and cigarette smoking, childhood living circumstances were significantly associated for women, but not for men. When the analysis was restricted to subjects born in Tromso, this relationship was seen for men.

Baker, S. P., O'Neill, B., Karpf, R. S. 1984. *The injury fact book.* Lexington, MA: Lexington Books.

Data from the National Center for Health Statistics, the National Highway Traffic Safety Administration, the Bureau of the Census, and other sources are used to present the descriptive epidemiology of mortality from injuries in the United

States for 1977–1979. Topics covered include intent of injury and injury etiology, often presented by age, race, sex, and census tract income. For most injury outcomes, there are substantial variations by socioeconomic status.

Bakketeig, L. S., Hoffman, H. J., Oakley, A. R. T. Oxford University Press 1984. Perinatal mortality. In Bracken, M. B., ed. *Perinatal epidemiology*, pp. 99–151. New York: Oxford University Press.

A review of the factors associated with perinatal mortality, based primarily on analyses of Norwegian births during 1967–1976. Particular attention is given to socioeconomic factors, with information presented on social class, income, occupation, education, and ethnicity. In general, social disadvantage is associated with higher rates of perinatal mortality.

Barker, D. J. P., Osmond, C. 1986. Infant mortality, childhood nutrition, and ischaemic heart disease in England and Wales. *Lancet* I:1077–1081.

Although the rise in ischemic heart disease in England and Wales was associated with increasing prosperity, mortality rates are highest in the least affluent areas. On division of the country into 212 local authority areas, a strong geographical relation was found between ischemic heart disease mortality rates in 1968–1978 and infant mortality in 1921–1925. Of the twenty-four other common causes of death, only bronchitis, stomach cancer, and rheumatic heart disease were similarly related to infant mortality. These diseases are associated with poor living conditions, and mortality from them is declining. Ischemic heart disease is strongly correlated with both neonatal and post neonatal mortality. It is suggested that poor nutrition in early life increases susceptibility to the effects of an affluent diet.

Baughman, B. B., Knutson, C. O., Ahmen, W., Jones, C. E., Polk, H. C. 1976. The surgical treatment of carcinoma of the colon and rectum. *Annals of Surgery* 183:550–555.

Reasons for increased mortality risk following operations for colorectal cancer were examined. Outcomes varied by type of hospital and social class. The authors speculated that because county facilities provided care to the underprivileged and because that care was of lesser quality, patients admitted were less likely to experience favorable results. The higher mortality may be explained by the small numbers of operations for cancer of the bowel, meager facilities, and the fact that patients cannot count on seeing the same physician consistently.

Berg, J. W., Ross, R., Latourette, H. B. 1977. Economic status and survival of cancer patients. *Cancer* 39:467–477.

The relation of economic status to survival was studied for 39 kinds of cancer representing all types for which 60 or more indigent patients were seen in University of Iowa Hospital for primary care during 1940–1969. For every type, the indigent patients had poorer survival than nonindigent patients. These differences were also found when nonindigent ward patients were compared to indigent patients. Age differences and differences in stage of disease accounted for less than half of the survival deficits in the indigents. The two important problems were high mortality from causes other than cancer and excess cancer mortality not accounted for by stage differences, particularly among patients who should have had 5-year survival rates between 40 percent and 72 percent. In these patients, cancer recurred more often and earlier among the indigent. Host differences associated with poverty are postulated to account for these differences.

Bice, T. W., Eichorn, R. L., Fox., P. D. 1972. Socioeconomic status and use of physician services: a reconsideration. *Medical Care* 10:261–271.

National trends in relationships between indicators of socioeconomic status and the use of outpatient physician services were described, and evidence for various explanations examined. The relationship between income and use has diminished considerably over the past four decades. Race and education remain consistently related to use. There is little evidence that social psychological variables account for differences in use among socioeconomic groups. Research shows that use among low income persons is sensitive to the price of services.

Blair, A., Fraumeni, J. F., Mason, T. J. 1980. Geographic patterns of leukemia in the United States. *Journal of Chronic Disease* 33:251–260.

Age-adjusted mortality rates for leukemia during 1950–1969 by race and sex were examined in relation to demographic, industrial, and agricultural data for 3,056 United States counties. Despite relatively uniform mortality across the country, there were high rates among whites in the north and south-central states, and among nonwhites in the northeast and midwest, with corresponding lower rates in the southeast. Mortality increased in proportion to county socioeconomic indices (income and education). The rates for counties in the upper socioeconomic category were about 30 percent higher among males, and 15 percent higher among females, than those in the lowest category, with the excess primarily in the group over 55 years of age. The rising mortality over time was greatest for counties with lower socioeconomic levels. After controlling for demographic and regional influences, leukemia mortality showed a positive correlation with tobacco and primary metal industries among males, but no occupation gradients were seen among females. Agricultural factors were not correlated with leukemia mortality.

Blane, D. 1985. An assessment of the Black Report's "explanations of health inequalities." *Sociology of Health and Illness* 7:423–445.

The Black Report identifies four types of possible explanations for social class differences in health, and judges one of these ("materialist") to be the most important. This paper seeks to support this assessment with additional evidence from the literatures of sociology and medicine. It suggests questions that could usefully be the subject of future research.

Blattner, W. A., Blair, A., Mason, T. 1981. Multiple myeloma in the United States, 1950–1975. *Cancer* 48:2547–2554.

Geographic patterns, recent temporal trends, and racial differences of multiple myeloma in United States counties for 1950–1969 are examined. A total of 68,400 whites and 10,533 nonwhites died during this period. Age-adjusted mortality rates for nonwhites were approximately two times as high as for whites. During the 25 years of this study, there was a two- to three-fold increase in multiple myeloma mortality. Multiple myeloma mortality was somewhat higher in socioeconomic areas with residents of higher median income, but the trend was not statistically significant for either race. There was a positive correlation of multiple myeloma mortality among whites and number of years of schooling (r = .25, p < .001). Income was not statistically significant. Urban areas had the highest rates, and rural areas had the lowest. Mortality rates were higher in areas with high petroleum and paper production and slightly higher for those with furniture manufacturing.

Blaxter, M. 1983. Health services as a defense against the consequences of poverty in industrialized societies. *Social Science and Medicine* 17:1139–1148.

The role of health services as a "defense" against the consequences of poverty is discussed. General questions addressed are: Is it true that industrialized nations have reached a stage of development where health care is irrelevant to health? Is the issue inequality in health, or, more narrowly, the particular problems of a minority, the "poor"? Are the causes of disadvantage in health to be seen as behavioral or structural, and if health systems concern themselves with social-structural issues, is this medical imperialism or the proper exercise of responsibility? The role of health services is considered in relation to primary prevention (or curative medicine) and tertiary prevention (or rehabilitative medicine). It is concluded that (though the impact of any form of universally available health service must not be minimized) health systems in industrialized societies are not in general successful in mitigating or preventing social inequalities in health.

Blot, W. J., Fraumeni, J. F., Jr. 1976. Geographic patterns of lung cancer: industrial correlations. *American Journal of Epidemiology* 103:539–550.

A survey of lung cancer mortality by county in the United States in 1950-1969 revealed an excess mortality for males where industry was present. The industrial correlation was not attributed to SES or to urbanization alone. Multiple regression was used to relate lung cancer to demographic and occupational indices. Rates of lung cancer increased with urbanization in each geographical region and increased as the density increased within each percent urbanization category. SES, independent of geographic and urban influences, was also related to lung cancer. Although statistically insignificant, higher rates of lung cancer tended to occur at the lowest education levels. After adjusting for demographic factors, lung cancer for whites was significantly elevated ($p<0.05$) in counties with four manufacturing industries: paper, chemical, petroleum, and transportation.

Brennan, M. E., Lancashire, R. 1978. Association of childhood mortality with housing status and unemployment. *Journal of Epidemiology and Community Health* 32:28–33.

Childhood mortality rates for two age groups (0–4 and 4–14 years) in each county and metropolitan borough of England in 1971 were examined in relation to type of housing and unemployment. At ages 0–4 years, there was a significant and positive association between mortality and low socioeconomic position, high density housing, inadequate housing amenities, and unemployment rate ($p<.001$). The significant association between housing remained even after controlling for SES and unemployment. Between ages 4–15, there was a statistically significant association (p<.001) between housing density and mortality when SES was held constant. There was no association between mortality and unemployment rates in those ages 4–15.

Brenner, M. H. 1979. Mortality and the national economy. *Lancet* 2:568–573.

The hypothesis that indicators of economic instability and insecurity are associated with higher mortality rates while smooth, long-term exponential trends in economic growth are inversely correlated with mortality was tested. A theoretical model using national economic changes based on United States data is applied to England and Wales for 1936–1976. Secular declines in the mortality rate were associated with long-term trends in economic growth and recessional losses, while rapid economic growth was associated with fluctuating mortality rates. The lag effect of unemployment varied by cause of death: suicides and homicides increased within a year, while coronary heart disease mortality increased two to three years after an increase in unemployment.

Brooks, C. H. 1975. Path analysis of socioeconomic correlates of county infant mortality rates. *International Journal of Health Services* 5:499–514.

The relationship between selected socioeconomic characteristics of counties and infant mortality rates was examined in 2,237 United States counties. Low family income, low education, sound housing, and the percentage of blacks were examined. The percentage of blacks and percentage of persons who had completed fewer than five years of schooling were important determinants of infant mortality. These two factors were responsible, in large part, for the associations between low family income, sound housing, and rates of infant loss. It was estimated that approximately two thirds of the zero-ordered correlation between a given county's measure of SES and infant mortality occurred through the postneonatal component.

Byckling, T., Akerblom, H. K., Viikari, J., Louhivouri, K., Uhari, M., Rasanan, L., Souninen, P., Pietikainen, M., et al. 1985. Atherosclerosis precursors in Finnish children and adolescents. *Acta Paediatrica Scandinavica Supplement* 318:155–167.

Children and adolescents in Finland whose 3rd, 6th, 9th, 12th, 15th, and 18th birthdays occurred in 1980 were examined to determine whether there was a relationship between parental socioeconomic status and coronary heart disease risk factors. SES was assessed using father's occupation or information regarding mother's occupation when there was no father present. An association was observed between parents' occupation and children's dietary polyunsaturated/saturated fat ratio. Farmers' children had, in all age groups, the lowest ratio. There were no other associations between parental social status indicators and children's coronary heart disease risk factor levels.

Cantor, K. P., Fraumeni, J. F., Jr. 1980. Distribution of non-Hodgkin's Lymphoma in the United States between 1950 and 1975. *Cancer Research* 40:2645–2652.

Average annual Non-Hodgkin's Lymphoma (NHL) mortality rates per 100,000 were calculated for each of the United States' 3,056 counties. Age-adjusted rates using the direct method were employed. Multiple regression analysis was used to examine the association of sex and race-specific mortality with several demographic, socioeconomic, and occupation measures. Variables such as median income, median years of school completed, population density, and ethnicity were obtained. Mortality from NHL increased from 1950 to 1975 in most race-sex-regional groups. Median family income and education showed a consistent association with NHL mortality. Among whites, rates in both sexes showed a positive gradient with median county income. Rates in southern counties were consistently lower, which may be related to SES. After adjustment for SES, southern counties made no statistically significant contribution to mortality. Nonwhites experienced lower mortality during 1950–1975 than whites.

Carstairs, V. 1981. Multiple deprivation and health state. *Community Medicine* 3:4–13.

Data from Glasgow and Edinburgh were examined to assess the association between health state and multiple deprivation. Health data were gathered through the census bureau and were standardized to remove the effects of differences in age and sex. A deprivation index was defined by overcrowding, lack of amenities, employment, number of rooms, and inside water closet. A strong association between deprivation and health indicators such as mortality, discharges, and bed days was found. The association was moderately strong for mental hospital admissions and low birthweight. The coefficients were high for parasitic and infectious diseases but only moderate for hospital discharges. The coefficients were low for cancer and circulatory disorders and high for accidents for both deaths and discharges.

Chirikos, T. N., Reiches, N. A., Moeschberger, M. L. 1984. Economic differentials in cancer survival: a multivariate analysis. *Journal of Chronic Diseases* 37:183–193.

Economic differentials in cancer survival were investigated in this study of 1,180 white males. A Cox regression model was employed to estimate the direct and interaction effects of economic status on survivorship, controlling for age at diagnosis, stage, severity of disease, and initial course of treatment. The results did not show a strong relationship between economic status and survival. Estimates of direct or main economic effects rarely reached borderline statistical significance; they were highly sensitive to model specification and the measurement of the economic variable. A weak interaction effect between economic status and stage was detected in several cases, but the parameter estimates were unstable. Measurement and specification error may have exaggerated the importance of economic factors in cancer survival in earlier investigations.

Chirikos, T. N., Horner, R. D. 1985. Economic status and survivorship in digestive system cancers. *Cancer* 56:210–217.

The association between occupation and survivorship was examined using data from the Tumor Registry of the Ohio University hospitals. A group of 1,180 men registered with a first primary malignancy from July 1977 to May 1981 were included. Patients' occupational level influenced survival. Whereas low income patients did not differ significantly from middle income patients, high income patients had substantially better chances of survival over middle. The relationship between income level and survival was especially different for colorectal cancer. All things being equal, high income patients enjoyed a more favorable survival experience.

Cohen, B. B. 1978. *Social class, morbidity, and use of medical services: studies in a prepaid health plan.* Unpublished dissertation, University of California, Berkeley.

This study investigated the relationships between SES, the use of medical services, and morbidity. A random sample of 2,804 enrollees of a prepaid health plan (Kaiser-Permanente) were followed for subsequent hospitalization between 1971–1976. The rate of outpatient physician visits was compared among SES groups taking into account their morbidity status. No statistically significant differences were found between SES groups for the diagnosis-specific rates of physician visits. Adjusting for morbidity, there was no statistically significant SES difference in the rate of physician visits not related to hospital discharge, rate of total physician visits, and the rate of non-physician contact with the medical care system. These findings persisted when alternative measures of SES were considered. There was a gradient in the frequency of morbidity between SES groups. Persons in low SES groups had a greater number of discharge diagnoses than persons of upper SES groups for many diagnostic categories including diseases of the heart, endocrine, digestive, skin, and muscular systems. The risk of hospitalization was higher in the low SES group even after adjustment for age, race, and sex. Persons of low SES have increased utilization and higher morbidity. Once morbidity was controlled, no excess in utility existed in low SES persons.

Comstock, G. W., Tonascia, J. A. 1977. Education and mortality in Washington County, Maryland. *Journal of Health and Social Behavior* 18:54–61.

The association between level of education and mortality over eight years was studied in 47,423 persons who were residents of Washington County, Maryland in 1963. There was an inverse relationship between years of education and risk of death, even after adjustment for important confounders. Residence in housing which lacked complete bathroom facilities for exclusive use of the household was also associated with increased risk. When mortality from specific causes was studied, deaths from diabetes mellitus, suicide, rheumatic heart disease, and arteriosclerotic heart disease were significantly and inversely related to education level.

Cooke, K. R., Skegg, D. C. G., Fraser, J. 1984. Socio-economic status, indoor and outdoor work, and malignant melanoma. *International Journal of Cancer* 34:57–62.

All occupations recorded with malignant melanoma of the skin between 1972–1976 and deaths occurring between 1973–1976 were obtained from the NZ Cancer Registry in order to study the role of SES and exposure to sunlight in malignant melanoma. SES was determined using the Elley-Irving scheme based on occupation. An increased risk with higher SES was evident among all workers and similar trends were evident among indoor and outdoor workers. Specifically, the malignant melanoma incidence rate was highest among professional, administrative, and managerial workers, and lowest among production and transport workers. After adjustment for SES, there was little difference in the risk of dying from malignant melanoma between indoor and outdoor workers.

Cunningham, L. S., Kelsey, J. L. 1984. Epidemiology of musculoskeletal impairments and associated disability. American Journal of Public Health 74:574–579.

Data from the US HANES I study were used to examine the relationship between education, income, and other variables, and the prevalence of musculoskeletal impairments. The prevalence of musculoskeletal impairments tended to be higher among persons of lower education and income.

D'Arcy, C., Siddique, C. M. 1985. Unemployment and health: an analysis of "Canada Health Survey" data. *International Journal of Health Services* 15:609–636.

Analyses of data on over 14,000 persons, who were part of a national probability sample in Canada, examined the relationship between unemployment and self-reported physical and mental health problems and physician-diagnosed problems. The unemployed reported higher levels of distress, greater disability, health problems, and utilization of medical care. The unemployed were diagnosed with higher rates of heart trouble, pain in heart or chest, high blood pressure, and other conditions. The effect of unemployment was more severe for females, the older unemployed, and blue-collar workers.

Davies, J. M. 1981. Mortality trends for stomach cancer in England and Wales. *British Journal of Cancer* 44:879–885.

Stomach cancer has been a major cause of death in England and Wales. Using national death data from 1916 to 1979, sex, age, and social class (manual vs. nonmanual) specific rates were calculated. Male and female rates have declined since 1931; the decline has been unequivocal for women and slight for men until 1941. Men in manual (lower) classes had consistently higher death rates than nonmanual in each age group. Since 1951, the difference between the rates for manual and nonmanual classes has generally been larger for men than for married women, but this was not the case in 1931. Between 1931–1951, rates for nonmanual men and both groups of married women fell sharply, but the rate for manuals fell only slightly.

Davies, J. M. 1981. Testicular cancer in England and Wales: some epidemiological aspects. *Lancet* 1:928–932.

Mortality data and trends for testicular cancer in England and Wales were examined in relation to social class. The 1951 Decennial Supplement was used to determine social class. General trends suggested that the overall increases in testicular cancer incidence and mortality since the beginning of the century were probably due to some feature of modern life that has gradually become more common throughout life, but has always affected men in higher socioeconomic classes more than manual workers. Occupation per se was deemed unlikely to have had a significant role.

Dayal, H. H., Chiu, C. 1982. Factors associated with racial differences in survival for prostatic carcinoma. *Journal of Chronic Diseases* 35:553–560.

The role of race, age, extent of disease at diagnosis, histological grade, and SES in survival for prostatic cancer patients was investigated. Data were abstracted from the Medical College of Virginia tumor registry for the period 1968–1977. SES score was determined for each census tract using six predictors: median school years, median income, percent high school graduates, median rent, median house value, and percent below poverty. White patients had a higher probability of survival compared to black patients. The relationships of SES to survival was not statistically significant, although the survival plots indicated better survival prognosis for higher SES patients. When adjusted for race, the significant association between SES and survival disappeared.

Dayal, H. H., Power, R. N., Chui, C. 1982. Race and socioeconomic status in survival from breast cancer. *Journal of Chronic Diseases* 35:675–683.

Survival data for 388 black and 515 white female breast cancer patients diagnosed at the Medical College of Virginia between 1968 and 1977 were examined with respect to racial and socioeconomic strata. Each of the six SES variables had a significant association with survival. Age and stage did not explain the difference in survival between the two racial groups. Race and SES were highly associated; a higher percent of blacks than whites were at the lower end of the socioeconomic scale. Racial differences became less significant when controlling for SES.

Dayal, H. H., Chui, C. Y. Sharrar, R., Mangan, J., Rosenwaike, I., Shapiro, S., Henley, A., Goldberg-Alberts, R., Kinman, J. 1984. Ecologic correlates of cancer mortality patterns in an industrialized urban population. *Journal of the National Cancer Institute* 73:565–574.

The association between cancer mortality, air pollution, and SES for Philadelphia in 1968–1980 was studied. SES was determined for each census tract and included variables such as median income and education, percent below poverty, and median rent or house value. A significant clustering of all cancers was seen for males but not for females. Lung cancer accounted for 22 percent of all cancer deaths. Male lung cancer rates exhibited a clustering pattern. Neighborhoods with statistically significant mortality due to smoking-related cancers were also the lowest in terms of SES. Air pollution levels were only slightly higher in these areas. Neighborhoods that had either high SES or average air pollution levels did not exhibit higher lung cancer, suggesting that a synergistic effect was operating.

Dayal, H. H., Polissar, L., Dahlberg, S. 1985. Race, socioeconomic status, and other prognostic factors for survival from prostate cancer. *Journal of the National Cancer Institute* 74:1001–1006.

Survival data on prostate cancer patients from 11 Comprehensive Cancer Centers contributing data to the Centralized Cancer Patient Data System were analyzed to examine the contribution of various factors to the probability of survival from prostate carcinoma. Application of a number of exclusion criteria resulted in 2,513 patients (1,032 blacks and 1,481 whites) for whom complete data on variables of interest were available. The stage of disease at diagnosis was a major determinant of survival. The proportion of blacks presenting the disease in advanced stage was substantially higher than that of whites—a difference that was maintained within each socioeconomic status (SES) category. White patients had a better prognosis than black patients for each disease stage. A dose-response relationship between SES and survival prognosis was observed, and this relationship persisted for each stage of the disease. Although both race and SES turned out to be significant in regression models in which one or the other was considered, the model including both race and SES showed only SES to be a significant factor. Hence, it can be hypothesized that the racial difference in the survival prognosis for prostate cancer is, to a large extent, due to the differences in the distribution of SES in the two races.

Dayal, H., Goldberg-Alberts, R., Kinman, J., Ramos, J., Sharrar, R., Shapiro, S. 1986. Patterns of mortality from selected causes in an urban population. *Journal of Chronic Diseases* 39:877–888.

Mortality data for selected noncancer causes for the period 1974–1980 in Philadelphia were analyzed for spatial patterns. Four categories of conditions—ischemic heart disease (including acute myocardial infarction), chronic liver disease and cirrhosis, cerebrovascular disease, and external causes—demonstrated significant variation in death rates by area. Neighborhoods with high levels of mortality for these conditions appeared in significant clusters. With the exception of ischemic heart disease, neighborhoods with high levels of mortality were characterized by below average levels of SES. A group of predominantly black neighborhoods in the central part of the city had extremely high rates for five or more of the nine causes investigated in this paper. In an earlier analysis, all but one of these neighborhoods were found to have the highest level of overall cancer mortality. These findings support the hypothesis that there are social and behavioral factors that are associated with a wide range of disease conditions, and many of these factors are associated with socioeconomic status.

Degoulet, P., Menard, J., Vu, H. A., Golmard, J. L., Devries, C., Chatellier, G., Plouin, P. F. 1983. Factors predictive of attendance at clinic and blood pressure control in hypertensive patients. *British Medical Journal* 287:88–93.

Patients with blood pressure greater than 160/95 mm Hg (N = 1,396) were followed for three years to determine what factors were predictive of poor attendance and inadequate blood pressure control in a hypertension clinical trial. SES was classified by occupation: 1) manual workers, 2) middle executives, and 3) senior executives. Among the 801 patients with regular employment at entry, the dropout rate was higher in the 399 patients belonging to the lowest occupational category (21.9 percent at one year) than in the 136 patients belonging to the highest category (16.2 percent) or the middle category (16.6 percent). Other factors that significantly related to dropout rate were obesity, young age, male sex, cigarette smoking, and type of referral.

Department of Health and Human Services, Great Britain. 1980. *Inequalities in health: report of a research working group (Black Report)*. London: Department of Health and Human Services.

Evidence is reviewed concerning the nature, extent, and trends in the association between social class and mortality from various causes in the United Kingdom and other countries. Various alternative explanations are considered, and the policy implications of the consistent relationship between social class and health discussed.

Devesa, S. S., Diamond, E. L. 1980. Association of breast cancer and cervical cancer incidences with income and education among whites and blacks. *Journal of the National Cancer Institute* 65:515–528.

Data from the Third National Cancer Survey were studied to evaluate the relationship between cancer of the uterus cervix and breast with income and education. In the 19,344 cases of breast cancer diagnosed among white females during the three year survey, there was a strong positive association between income level and breast cancer. The age–area–adjusted relative risk of the highest to the lowest group was 1.37. Cancer of the breast also showed an association with education in white females. Depending on which education group was used as the referent category, the age-specific relative risk of the highest to the lowest group varied from 1.3 to 1.6. Rates estimated by regression method showed a highly significant association with income and education before and after adjusting for other SES variables. Adjustment for socioeconomic variables reduced the black-white difference in breast cancer rate; education had a stronger effect than income. Among 1,570 cases diagnosed in black females, there was a significant association between education but not income. Of the 3,802 cases in white females and 954 in black females, the incidence of cancer of the cervix showed a negative association with education and income. The negative gradient persisted in all areas and decreased with age. After adjusting for socioeconoimc variables, the excess risk among blacks was reduced by two thirds but remained statistically significant.

———. 1983. Socioeconomic and racial differences in lung cancer incidence. *American Journal of Epidemiology* 118:818–831.

Using data from the Third National Cancer Survey, the association between lung cancer incidence and two indicators of SES (income and education) among blacks and whites was examined. The Third National Cancer Survey provided incidence data for approximately 10 percent of the United States population for the years 1967–1971. For white males, cancer of the lung exhibited a strong and significant gradient with decreasing income. Among males, the rate of the lowest income group was 50 percent greater than the highest income group. Among white females, the pattern was U-shaped. A negative trend was also apparent among men when SES was defined by education level. With adjustment for other SES variables, the significance of education and income remained for white males. For black males, there was the same trend as for white males when SES was defined by income and education. There was no significant trend among females. Lung cancer occurred 10 percent more frequently among black than white males.

Diehl, A. K., Rosenthal, M., Hazuda, H. P., Comeaux, P. J., Stern, M. P. 1985. Socioeconomic status and the prevalence of clinical gallbladder disease. *Journal of Chronic Diseases* 38:1019–1026.

Data from the San Antonio Heart Study, a population-based survey, allowed the relationship of SES to the prevalence of diagnosed gallbladder disease to be examined. Between October 1979 and November 1982, subjects age 25–64 were randomly selected from three urban neighborhoods (one low and almost exclusively Mexican American, one middle, and one high SES). Home interviews and examinations were conducted. Measures of SES included occupation, education, family income, and neighborhood. Logistic regression controlling for potential confounders (body mass index, age, and parity) indicated that neighborhood, occupation, and education were separate significant predictors of gallbladder disease in women. Education showed the strongest association, with odds ranging from 1.57 when comparing the second most educated to the least educated and 3.88 when comparing the most and least educated class. Income was not a significant predictor. These findings did not apply to men.

Dobson, A. J., Gibberd, R. W., Leeder, S. R., O'Connell, D. L. 1985. Occupational differences in ischemic heart disease mortality and risk factors in Australia. *American Journal of Epidemiology* 122:283–290.

Occupational differences in mortality data and trends from ischemic heart disease and ischemic heart disease risk factors in Australia were examined. Occupational status was divided into seven categories for men and five for women (Group 1 being the highest). Between 1969–1978, death rates for professionals (Group 1) were relatively low at the beginning of the period and declined by 36 percent. The trades/labor group experienced a less severe decline (25 percent). The highest rate throughout the period was for the service group (Group 5). With respect to risk factors, mean diastolic blood pressure increased with decreasing socioeconomic status for men and women. No statistical differences in mean cholesterol or HDL-cholesterol among occupations for men and women were found. Mean plasma triglycerides values increased with decreasing SES for men and women. Body mass index showed the same pattern. Smoking was less prevalent among professionals (Group 1) and highest in Group 4. Exercise scores followed the typical pattern of other risk factors. This study showed a very significant difference in risk factor levels among occupations, which were consistent with the mortality experience from ischemic heart disease among men.

Duncan, G. J. 1984. *Years of poverty/years of plenty.* Ann Arbor, MI: University of Michigan.

Data from the Panel Study of Income Dynamics, a longitudinal study of 5,000 American families with yearly follow-up, is presented. Chapters include discussions of family economic mobility, dynamics of poverty, dynamics of welfare use, dynamics of work hours, unemployment, and earnings-trends in relative earnings of black males, and differences in earnings of males and females.

Dutton, D. B. 1978. Explaining the low use of health services by the poor: costs, attitudes, or delivery system. *American Sociological Review* 43:348–368.

The poor, especially children, continue to receive fewer health services relative to need than the affluent. Explanations have traditionally focused on cost constraints or on cultural differences. The paper provides empirical evidence that such explanations do not account fully for income trends in preventive and symptomatic use. A third explanation, based on inadequacies in delivery systems used by the poor, is required. Factors representing each explanation are added sequentially to a multivariate model to shed light on their role in the income-user relationships. Particularly instructive are changes in estimates when types of delivery systems are added, since system differences have been ignored in much previous research. The importance of factors promoting use among the poor, e.g., public assistance, is underestimated, while the role of individual characteristics, e.g., attitudes, is overestimated. Results suggest that neither financial access nor health education, without accompanying improvements in delivery systems, will eliminate income differentials in use.

———. 1985. Socioeconomic status and children's health. *Medical Care* 23:142–156.

The relationships between SES and three common children's health problems (ear disease, hearing loss, and visual problems) are examined. Data were from a household survey and independent clinical examination of 1,063 black children in Washington, D.C. All three problems had a U-shaped relationship with income, with significantly higher prevalences among both upper and lower income children than among the middle income group, even controlling statistically for other socioeconomic variables. Except for past illness, income was generally the strongest determinant of children's health, followed by housing, crowding, and neighborhood income level. Some risk faactors varied between upper and lower income children. Doctors' contacts seemed to reduce illness among poor children but not among the more affluent, while the use of "private" rather than "public" settings did not appear to benefit either group.

Edwards, G., Kyle, E., Nicholls, P., Taylor, C. 1978. Alcoholism and correlates of mortality. *Journal of Studies of Alcohol* 39:1607–1617.

The contribution of alcoholism-associated mortality to social class gradients of health was studied in a cohort of alcoholics admitted to four English mental hospitals over five years. Alcoholism had a differential impact on mortality risk according to social group. Alcoholism was likely to increase the risk of death more in classes I and II than in classes IV and V. Persons in class III hold an intermediate position, closer to I and II.

Eisinger, R. A. 1972. Psychosocial predictors of smoking behavior change. *Social Science and Medicine* 6:137–144.

A prospective study was undertaken in an attempt to discover the possible predictors of smoking behavior change. Respondents subjected to a lengthy interview in 1966 were reinterviewed in 1968, at which time their smoking behavior was assessed. Respondents were classified as either "quit," "reduced," "no change," or "increased." Males were found to be more willing to have quit or to have reduced smoking than females. Respondents with children present in the household were more likely to quit or reduce. As the number of cigarettes increased per day, respondents were less likely to quit or reduce. The relationship between smoking pattern change and age and education was not significant.

Elinson, J. 1977. Have we narrowed the gap between the poor and the nonpoor? *Medical Care* 15:675–677.

This paper reviews trends in health status of the poor and nonpoor. Evidence is presented that there is a widening in the existing gap between the poor and the nonpoor. A narrowing of the gap in the utilization of health services has been accompanied by a widening of the gap in health status. The gap in health status between the poor and nonpoor in terms of various disability measures has also been widening.

Ell, K. O., Haywood, L. J. 1985. Sociocultural factors in myocardial infarction recovery: an exploratory study. *International Journal of Psychiatry and Medicine* 15:157–175.

The role of SES and ethnicity in recovery during one year following a first myocardial infarction was studied. The analyses were based on a panel of patients recruited from the coronary care units of two large teaching centers in Los Angeles (N = 70). Medical information was obtained by medical records abstraction and face-to-face interviews. Significant differences in anxiety, functional status, self-reported health status, personal sense of control, belief about recovery, coping response, and social support systems were found. Coping variables were associated with the post-myocardial infarction outcomes that varied among different sociocultural groups. Low SES patients were less likely to seek information in coping with myocardial infarction recovery. A strong religious perspective and sense of personal efficacy was found among Hispanics.

Ericson, A., Eriksson, M., Westerhold, P., Zetterstrom, R. 1984. Pregnancy outcome and social indicators in Sweden. *Acta paediatrica Scandinavica* 73:69–74.

Differences between social classes in the perinatal mortality rate, birthweight, distribution of gestational age, and incidence of congenital malformations were studied in Sweden. All births reported to the Registry of Births during the years 1976–1977 were used (N = 190,024). An SES index was defined, based on income, occupation, and housing standards. There was no difference in perinatal mortality between groups I and III. The incidence of low birthweight preterm and postterm births were statistically different in group III compared to group I. This relationship persisted after adjustment for age and parity of the mother. SES had the greatest impact on low birthweight.

Ericson, A., Eriksson, M., Zetterstrom, R. 1979. Analysis of perinatal mortality rate in the Stockholm area. *Acta Paediatrica Scandinavica Supplement* 275:35–40.

Information obtained from the birth certificate of the National Board of Health and Welfare for the years 1973–1976 was used to study the association between SES measures and perinatal mortality. SES was measured by occupation, income, and number of home owners in each area. During 1973–1976, the perinatal mortality decreased from 14.8/1,000 to 9.8/1,000. In spite of the low perinatal mortality, there was marked variation between different maternal hospitals. With one exception, the five hospitals with the lowest annual number of deliveries had a perinatal mortality above the mean. In the referral areas with hospitals with a perinatal mortality above the mean, there was a higher percentage of low income households, overcrowded dwellings, and fewer professional people.

Ernster, V. L., Selvin, S., Sacks, S. T., Austin, D. F., Brown, S. M., Winkelstein, W., Jr. 1978. Prostatic cancer: mortality and incidence rates by race and social class. *American Journal of Epidemiology* 107:311–320.

The role of SES differences in the higher black mortality rates for cancer of the prostate was examined. Socioeconomic class was based on census tract of residence. Age-specific incidence and mortality rates by SES revealed no gradient for prostate cancer in either whites or blacks.

Ernster, V. L., Winkelstein, W., Jr., Selvin, S., Brown, S. M., Sacks, S. T., Austin, D. F., Mandel, S. A., Bertolli, T. A. 1977. Race, socioeconomic status, and prostatic cancer. *Cancer Treatment Reports* 61:187–191.

Using population-based mortality and incidence data, cases of death from prostatic cancer were assigned to a social class based on census tract of residence, and rates by race and SES were compared. Census tracts were grouped into four economic levels based on education and income. Mortality rates by SES revealed no gradient for prostate cancer in either whites or blacks. The higher risks for blacks held up at almost every SES level.

Feder, J., Hadley, J., Mullner, R. 1984. Falling through the cracks: poverty, insurance coverage, and hospital care for the poor, 1980 and 1982. *Milbank Memorial Fund Quarterly* 62:544–566.

Evidence is reviewed concerning the magnitude, trends, and factors associated with unmet medical needs among the poor. The role of economic recession, declines in private insurance coverage, Medicaid cutbacks, and limits on the growth of government spending are discussed. Policies to sustain care for the poor are considered.

Fisher, S. 1978. Relationship of mortality to socioeconomic status and some other factors in Sydney in 1971. *Journal of Epidemiology and Community Health* 32:41–46.

In Sydney in 1971, low SES was found to be associated with high mortality. This relationship became more marked with increasing age. SES was not statistically significantly related to infant mortality. Mortality was higher among those born in Australia than among immigrants. SES was characterized by an area-type index applied to the results of the 1971 census and calculated for local government areas in the Sydney Statistical Division. Among men, lower SES was linked with higher mortality from all causes except diabetes and, among women, from all causes other than neoplastic diseases. In low SES areas, females were more disadvantaged with respect to cerebrovascular disease and males with respect to respiratory causes.

Forbes, J. F., Boddy, F. A., Pickering, R., Wyllie, M. M. 1982. Perinatal mortality in Scotland: 1970–9. *Journal of Epidemiology and Community Health* 36:282–288.

The impact of demographic factors on the decline in Scottish perinatal mortality, trends in the distribution of birthweight and weight-specific mortality, regional differences in perinatal mortality, and recent changes in the registered causes of perinatal mortality were examined using data on all registered births. Changes in the social class, maternal age, and parity distribution of legitimate births between 1970–1979 account for 7 percent of the improvement in perinatal mortality. Changes in the social class distribution of births accounted for 13 percent and 17 percent of the decline in perinatal mortality among women age 30–34 and 35–39, respectively. Despite the overall improvements in perinatal mortality, the approximately relative risk in social class IV and V, relative to I, changed only slightly from 1.5 to 1.3 in 1979 with most improvement occurring in 1977.

Forsdahl, A. 1977. Are poor living conditions in childhood and adolescence an important risk factor for arteriosclerotic heart disease? *British Journal of Preventive and Social Medicine* 31:91–95.

The hypothesis that poverty during adolescence is positively correlated with the risk of dying from heart disease in later years was studied. The analysis is based on official statistical data. Adjustments have been made for differences in sex and age by direct standardization (population of Norway in 1960 used as the standard). In countries where male infant mortality was high, middle age mortality was also high generations later (r = +.93). This trend is similar for females, but the correlation was weaker (r = +.75). When different causes of death were examined, there was a strong correlation between the coronary heart disease mortality for ages 40 and 69 and infant mortality and not during the early years of that cohort (males: r = +.79, females: r = +.61).

Fortmann, S. P., Williams, P. T., Hulley, S. B., Maccoby, N., Farquhar, J. W. 1982. Does dietary health education reach only the privileged?: the Stanford three community study. *Circulation* 66(1):77–82.

One control and two treatment towns were studied before and after a three-year bilingual, mass-media health education program. An examination of the relationship of SES and cardiovascular risk factors (diet, cholesterol, weight) was obtained by dietary questionnaires. SES was measured by income and education (Hollingshead). SES was related to dietary cholesterol, alcohol, weight, and plasma cholesterol (p = 0.06) when adjusted for age, sex, and language group. When adjusting for SES, language group was related to dietary cholesterol, saturated fats, alcohol, and relative weight, but not to plasma cholesterol. Prospectively, SES and language group were not associated with changes in risk factors after adjustment for age, SES, and other covariates.

Fox, A. J., Adelstein, A. 1978. Occupational mortality: work or way of life? *Journal of Epidemiology and Community Health* 32:73–78.

Assumptions in the traditional method of examining occupational contributions to mortality by comparing the mortality of employed men in a particular occupation with married women with husbands in that occupation are discussed. The validity of these assumptions is questioned, and a new technique based on social class standardization of mortality rates for a particular occupation is presented. Social class variations appear to explain, to a considerable extent, the increased mortality rates in certain occupations.

Fox, A. J., Goldblatt, P. O., Jones, D. R. 1985. Social class mortality differentials: artefact, selection, or life circumstance? *Journal of Epidemiology and Community Health* 39:1–8.

Data from 10 years of follow-up of mortality in the OPCS Longitudinal Study were used to relate deaths of men in 1976–1981 to their social class as recorded by the 1971 census. Explanations of social class mortality differentials are critically reviewed in the light of these new data. The similarity between the class differentials observed for men aged 15–64 years in this study and those reported in the 1970–1972 Decennial Supplement on Occupational Mortality indicated that the published gradients were not grossly distorted by numerator/denominator biases. Distortions to gradients observed in the early years of the longitudinal study and ascribed to selective health-related mobility out of employment from the principal social class to the permanently sick had largely worn off after five years of follow-up. Sharp gradients at ages over 75 years, similar to those at younger ages, suggest that, for men aged over 50 years, selective health-related mobility between social class does not contribute to differentials in mortality.

Frerichs, R. R., Chapman, J. M., Nourjah, P., Maes, E. F. 1984. *Cardiovascular disease in Los Angeles, 1979–1981*. Los Angeles: American Heart Association—Greater Los Angeles Affiliate, Inc.

Mortality data for major cardiovascular diseases in Los Angeles during 1979–1981 are presented by cause, race, sex, and income of census tract of residence. Persons in poor neighborhoods experienced higher rates of death from cardiovascular causes among both blacks and whites and males and females. Deaths among the poor were more likely to occur out of hospital than deaths among wealthier residents.

Gee, S. C., Lee, E. S., Forthofer, R. N. 1976. Ethnic differentials in neonatal and postneonatal mortality: a birth cohort analysis by a binary variable multiple regression method. *Social Biology* 23:317–325.

Ethnic differences in neonatal and postneonatal mortality among three ethnic groups (Spanish surnames, white, and nonwhite) were examined in birth and matched infant death certificates for 1958–1960 in Houston, Texas. There were 46,320 single live births during this time. Spanish surname and white infants exhibited a 13 percent below average risk of neonatal mortality factors adjusted for all. The risk for non-whites was 30 percent above average. Of the four sociodemographic factors, birthweight and legitimacy status were responsible for most of the changing differentials when statistical adjustments were made. There were greater ethnic differences in postneonatal mortality than neonatal mortality, suggesting that environmental factors intervened after 27 days of an infant's life. Despite the Spanish surnames' much less favorable SES condition, their experience in this study resembled that of Anglos. This may be attributed to favorable weight distribution and full-term gestation period.

Gillum, R. F. 1982. Coronary heart disease in black populations: I. Mortality and morbidity. *American Heart Journal* 104:839–851.

Coronary heart disease is the leading cause of death among black Americans (57,999 deaths in 1977) despite the widely held belief that CHD is not common in blacks. CHD death rates were lower in black men than in white men in the United States in the 1940s, but rose rapidly until they exceeded those of whites in 1968. Since 1968, CHD death rates in blacks have fallen by about 30 percent, to levels similar to whites, but still higher than 1940 rates. Black women have higher CHD mortality than white women. The few population studies of myocardial infarction in the 1970s suggest similar or lower age-specific incidence in black than white men but higher case fatality and more out-of-hospital deaths.

————, Paffenbarger, R. S., Jr. 1978. Chronic disease in former college students. *American Journal of Epidemiology* 108:289–298.

Former Harvard University students, age 15–29 at physical examination upon college entrance in 1930–1950, answered mailed questionnaires concerning their health. Information regarding the presence of medically diagnosed angina pectoris, high blood pressure, myocardial infarction, and other diseases was ascertained. There were 98 cases of coronary heart disease, 78 cases of myocardial infarction, and 48 cases of angina pectoris. For each of these cases, four controls were randomly selected. SES data were collected during entrance examination and mobility status gained by subsequent questionnaires. When fatal coronary heart disease and myocardial infarction categories were combined, a univariate analysis showed an inverse relationship between father's occupation and coronary heart disease risk. This association persisted when stratifying on individual confounders and a multivariate confounder-summarizing score. Intergenerational mobility (as indicated by low occupation status of father) was associated with a 1.5 times greater risk of myocardial infarction and fatal coronary heart disease.

Gortmaker, S. L. 1979. The effects of prenatal care upon the health of the newborn. *American Journal of Public Health* 69:653–660.

The data from all birth and infant death records in New York in 1968 were analyzed. Educational status of the mother and father, age of mother, birth order of the child, and wedlock status were all significant predictors of adequacy of prenatal care received by mother and infant. Mothers with 0–8 years of education with similarly educated husbands and who were less than 20 years of age experienced a 7.5 times greater chance of receiving inadequate care compared to those who were older with more education. These analyses also found that white mothers who delivered on a general service, as well as black mothers, tended to experience a substantially increased risk of low birthweight when receiving inadequate as opposed to adequate care.

Greenlick, M. R., Shekelle, R., Syme, S. L. 1986. Social-demographic factors in coronary heart disease: the Multiple Risk Factor Intervention Trial (MRFIT) experience. Presented at the Annual Meeting of the Society for Epidemiologic Research, Pittsburgh, PA, June 19.

The associations between level of education, income, marital status, occupation, occupation-education incongruity, race, and incongruity with wife's education and fatal and total (fatal plus nonfatal) myocardial infarction were studied in the 12,000 men who participated in the MRFIT study. Education, occupation, incongruity with wife's education, and race were related to outcomes in age-adjusted analyses. However, most of these associations were due to risk factor profiles that differed between sociodemographic groups. There was no evidence for an interaction between sociodemographic factors and treatment.

Grossman, M., Jacobowitz, S. 1981. Variations in infant mortality rates among counties of the United States: the roles of public policies and programs. *Demography* 18:695–713.

The role of birth control and family planning services in infant mortality is examined for United States counties between 1964–1977. After a period of relative stability, the neonatal mortality rate began to decline in 1964, possibly as a lagged response to the extremely rapid increase in the percentage of women who used the pill and the IUD in 1961 and 1964. The decline was further fueled by an increase in the percent of low income women who used subsidized family planning services between 1965–1971 and the dramatic rise in the legal abortion rate between 1969–1971. The acceleration in the rate of the decline in the mortality rate between 1971–1977 was due primarily to the increase in the abortion rate in that period.

Guggenheim, K., Kark, S. L., Abramson, J. H. 1964. Diet, social class, and neighborhood in Jerusalem, Israel. *Journal of the American Dietetic Association* 45:429–432.

The food consumption of 148 pregnant women living in three regions of Jerusalem was studied. The neighborhoods were selected because of contrasts in the prevalence of anemia and in social status. Considerable differences in food consumption were found between these three neighborhoods with the differences being reflected in differences in nutritive value of the diets. The diet eaten in the area of the highest social class was significantly superior with respect to animal protein, calcium, vitamin A, riboflavin, and ascorbic acid. There was evidence suggesting that the nutrient differences were primarily related to social class rather than to the differences in countries of origin between the neighborhoods. In all three neighborhoods, iron intake was well below that recommended for women in the second half of pregnancy.

Haan, M. N. 1985. *Organizations and ischemic heart disease: an epidemiologic study of employees in a Finnish metal fabrication company.* Unpublished doctoral dissertation. University of California.

This research examines the association between job strain and incident and fatal ischemic heart disease in a cohort of 902 Finnish metal workers followed between 1973–1983. The Job strain measure included subscales assessing job variety, job control, and physical-ergonomic demands on the job. After adjustment for age, sex, systolic blood pressure, total serum cholesterol, years of smoking, relative weight, alcohol consumption, and physical exercise, the analyses showed that persons exposed to high job strain had a 4.5-fold higher risk of ischemic heart disease than persons exposed to low job strain. The research concluded that job strain appeared to be a risk factor for ischemic heart disease which is not modified or accounted for by differences in more traditional cardiovascular risk factors.

————, Kaplan, G. A. 1985. The contribution of socioeconomic position to minority health. In Heckler, M., ed. *Report of the Secretary's task force on black and minority health: crosscutting issues in minority health.* Washington, D.C.: Department of Health and Human Services.

Evidence is reviewed that tests the contribution of differences in socioeconomic position to the disparities in health status between minorities and whites in the U.S. In analyses of all-cause mortality, survival differences in cancer of the breast and prostate, male lung cancer incidence, and mortality from coronary heart disease, minority white differentials in health decrease significantly when socioeconomic position is taken into consideration. For many other outcomes, the evidence suggests a diminution of these differentials with adjustment for socioeconomic level. The evidence is, in general, consistent with the hypothesis that the poorer health of some minorities, particularly blacks, represents the impact of their lower socioeconomic position.

————, Camacho, T. 1987. Poverty and health: prospective evidence from the Alameda County Study. *American Journal of Epidemiology* 125:989–998.

To explore the reasons for the association between socioeconomic status and poor health, the nine-year mortality experience of a random sample of residents in Oakland, California, was examined. Residents of a federally designated poverty area experienced higher age-, race-, and sex-adjusted mortality over the follow-up period compared to residents of non-poverty areas (odds ratio = 1.71, 95 percent confidence interval: 1.20–2.44). This increased risk of death persisted when there was multivariate adjustment for baseline health status, race, income, employment status, access to medical care, health insurance coverage, smoking, alcohol consumption, physical activity, relative weight, sleep pattern, social isolation, marital status, depression, and personal uncertainty. These results support the hypothesis that properties of the sociophysical environment may be important contributors to the association between low socioeconomic status and excess mortality, and that this contribution is independent of individual behaviors.

Haberman, P. W., Baden, M. M. 1974. Alcoholism and violent death. *Quarterly Journal of Studies of Alcohol* 35:221–231.

The association between alcohol and alcohol ingestion prior to death and violent causes of death in New York City was studied. The demographic characteristics of and the postmortality findings for 1,000 decedents age 18 or older were examined. The sample had a disproportionately large number of males, blacks, younger persons, those in blue-collar occupations, and persons with less education. Among the alcoholics, there were more persons age 30–59, blacks, more separated and divorced, and blue-collar workers. Among nonalcoholics there were more persons younger than 30 and older than 59, and more married and with some college education.

Hadley, J., Osei, A. 1982. Does income affect mortality? An analysis of the effects of different types of income on age-sex-race-specific mortality rates in the United States. *Medical Care* 20:901–914.

The effects of total family income on mortality rates were examined in eight adult and four infant age-sex-race-specific population cohorts. Income was a significant factor that could explain the geographic variations in adult mortality rates, displaying a generally negative relationship, although the relationship was not always statistically significant. Earned income had a negative impact on the middle age cohort but a positive impact on the elderly cohort. The reverse was true for unearned income.

Haenszel, W., Kurihara, M., Locke, F. B., Shimuzu, K., Segi, M. 1976. Stomach cancer in Japan. *Journal of the National Cancer Institute* 56:265–274.

A case control study of two Japanese prefectures was undertaken to provide information on the importance of environmental factors and stomach cancer. Seven hundred eighty-three patients with stomach cancer and 1,588 hospital controls participated in the study. Questionnaires covering dietary habits, residency history, occupation, tobacco use, customs, previous illness, and reproductive history were completed. There was an increased risk associated with being a farmer. This was not explained by place of residence since the increased risk for farmers persisted in data for rural and urban residences. Although education could be regarded as a good index of social status in Japan, the findings in the two prefectures diverged sharply. In one, non-farmers with middle school or better education had a lower risk of stomach cancer, while the opposite was true in the other prefecture.

Haglund, B. J. A. 1985. Geographical and socioeconomic distribution of high blood pressure and borderline high blood pressure in a Swedish rural county. *Scandinavian Journal of Social Medicine* 13:53–66.

The association between socioeconomic factors and hyperten-

sion was studied in a stratified random sample of 7,986 individuals ages 25 to 75 in Skararborg County, Sweden. There
were differences in systolic blood pressure and diastolic blood
pressure between individuals with different levels of education, including an inverse relationship between education and
high blood pressure. This association persisted after controlling for age, sex, weight, smoking, and treatment for blood
pressure. These differences were more prominent in women.
There was also a difference in blood pressure between socioeconomic groups based on occupation; these differences were
greater among women than men. Stepwise regression indicated that, for men, occupation was the explanatory variable
with the highest correlation to borderline high blood pressure, and marital status the strongest for systolic blood pressure. This pattern was repeated for women, with less formal
education being the strongest predictive variable.

Hakama, M., Hakulinen, T., Pukkala, E., Saxen, E., Teppo, L.
1982. Risk indicators of breast and cervical cancer on ecologic
and individual levels. *American Journal of Epidemiology*
116:990–1000.

The role of environmental and individual factors in the cancers of the breast and cervix uteri was studied using all new
cases of breast and cervical cancer diagnosed between 1954
and 1974 in Finland. The risk of both types of cancer increased with increasing urbanization. Women living in towns
had 1.5 times the risk as those living in rural areas. Eight variables were used to define the standard of living for a munici-
pality: income, social class, education, number of television
sets, crowdedness, availability of running water, central heat
and electricity. Both cancers increased with an increase in living standards; relative risk ranged from 1.5 to 2.0 when the
highest living standards were compared to the lowest. Individual analysis demonstrated that those in high occupation
positions had a higher risk of breast cancer and lower risk of
cervical cancer (relative risk for breast 1.7 and .3 for cervical
cancer). When SES was defined by education, the magnitude

of the difference was the same. Among farmers, the risk of both types of cancer was low.

Halliday, M. L., Anderson, T. W. 1979. The sex differential in ischaemic heart disease: trends by social class 1931 to 1971. *Journal of Epidemiology and Community Health* 33:74–77.

Trends in the sex differential for ischemic heart disease were studied using data on death rates in social classes I and V, for persons age 45–64, between 1931–1971 in England and Wales. Death rates were calculated from death certificates, and population data was taken from the Decennial Supplement. In 1931, the recorded death rate from angina pectoris and other ischemic heart disease-specific terms was almost four times greater in men of social class I than V. The authors hypothesize that this may be due to the misclassification of certificates. To estimate this number, they classified nonspecific diagnoses as ischemic heart disease. When this was done, social class I and V had approximately the same total ischemic heart disease death rate in 1931. By 1961, class I had decreased while the mortality rate for V had increased. For married women in 1931, the death rate was higher in I than V, but the nonspecific ischemic heart disease term reversed this order, so that V had almost double the rate of I. Between 1931 and 1971, the rate went down for class I and stayed the same for class V.

Harburg, E., Erfurt, J. C., Chape, C., Hauenstein, L. S., Schull, W. J., Schork, M. A. 1973. Socioecological stressor areas and black-white blood pressure: Detroit. *Journal of Chronic Diseases* 26:595–611.

Socioenvironmental differences in blood pressure between black and white urban populations were studied. All census tracts in Detroit were ranked by SES (income, education, occupation, and home ownership) and by instability factors (adult and juvenile crime rate, marital instability, and percent of residents over five years of age). Blood pressure did not vary by sex, race, and residence. Black males of high stress tracts had higher adjusted blood pressure levels than blacks of low stress areas; this was also true for whites. Black high stress males had a significantly higher percent of borderline and hypertensive blood pressure than other male groups. White low stress females had the lowest of all groups.

Hathcock, A. L., Greenberg, R. A., Dakan, W. A. 1982. An analysis of lung cancer on a microgeographical level. *Social Science and Medicine* 16:1235–1238.

Variations in lung cancer mortality by small geographic areas, internally homogeneous, but externally heterogeneous, were related to SES. Standard mortality ratios were calculated by age-sex-race groupings within each area using death certificates from the Commonwealth of Kentucky for 1968–1977 and SES data from the 1960 and 1970 censuses. Areas were described by income, education, and crowding indexes, and a summary index was generated. Area 1 was the lowest and Area 5 the highest on this index. After adjustment for covariates, lung cancer in Areas 1 and 3 showed consistently higher standard mortality ratios (p<.05) in both five-year age periods and Area 1 was significantly higher for the entire study period. Areas 2 and 5 had consistently lower standard mortality ratios. Males had a significantly higher standard mortality ratio in Areas 1 and 3, but females showed an insignificantly higher standard mortality ratio.

Haynes, S. G., Cohen, B., Harvey, C., Murphy, R. 1983–84. *Cigarette smoking patterns among Mexican-Americans: HHANES, Southwest United States, 1982–84.* Presented at the 113th Annual Meeting of the American Public Health Association, November 19, 1985.

Cigarette smoking and trends in smoking were compared in Mexican American and non-Hispanic whites in the Southwest United States. Mexican American men were twice as likely as Mexican American women to smoke. There were no secular trends in smoking. White rates of cigarette smoking were higher among Mexican American than non-Hispanic whites. Among groups that smoked, usage was one half for Mexican

American compared to non-Hispanic whites. Mexican American women were less likely to smoke and smoked fewer cigarettes than non-Hispanic whites and blacks. Smoking status among Mexican American men varied by education level and smoking status varied by acculturation for women.

Hazuda, H. P., Stern, M. P., Haffner, S. M. 1985. *Acculturation, socioeconomic status, and coronary heart disease (CHD) prevention in Mexican Americans: San Antonio heart study.* Presentation at the 58th Scientific Sessions of the American Heart Association, November 13, 1985.

The relationships between acculturation, SES, and preventive knowledge and behavior were studied in participants in the San Antonio Heart Study. Acculturation and SES make independent contributions to preventive knowledge and behavior in Mexican Americans. At all levels, more highly acculturated Mexican Americans have a higher level of preventive knowledge and behavior than do the less acculturated. Mexican Americans at the highest acculturation level closely resemble non-Hispanic whites in their preventive knowledge and behavior. However, even in the highest acculturation and SES subgroups, Mexican Americans score low on preventive knowledge and behavior.

Hazuda, H. P., Haffner, S. M., Stern, M. P., Knapp, J. A., Eifler, C. W., Rosenthal, M. 1986. Employment status and women's protection against coronary heart disease. *American Journal of Epidemiology* 123:623–640.

Data were collected between October 1979 and November 1982 as part of the San Antonio Heart Study, a community-based investigation of diabetes and coronary heart disease risk factors in Mexican Americans and non-Hispanic whites. Women were classified as employed or full-time homemakers according to their response to an open-ended questionnaire. Major demographic characteristics were sampled, and SES was measured by the Duncan socioeconomic index. Differences in the profile of cardiovascular risk factors between currently employed women and homemakers were examined. There were no significant differences between employed women and homemakers in terms of cholesterol, low density lipoproteins, obesity, systolic and diastolic blood pressure, or cigarette smoking. There was a significant statistical difference in high density lipoproteins, favoring employed women over homemakers. The magnitude of the difference in mean high density lipoprotein levels was in a range associated with protection against coronary heart disease in women and men. The protective effect of employment was more pronounced for women in professional and managerial occupations and sales and clerical occupations than for those in blue-collar occupations.

Heller, R. F., Williams, H., Sittampalam, Y. 1984. Social class and ischemic heart disease: use of the male/female ratio to identify possible occupational hazards. *Journal of Epidemiology and Community Health* 38:198–202.

The male/female ratio for ischemic heart disease for social class, socioeconomic group, and occupation was explored to identify particular occupations that might be important in the etiology of ischemic heart disease. Data from the Occupational Mortality Decennial Supplement for England and Wales for 1931, 1951, 1961, and 1971 were used. From 1931 to 1971, the excess ischemic heart disease mortality ratio in groups VI and V was considerably higher at younger ages for males and females. During this time, there was never an excess of ischemic heart disease in classes I and II for all age groups. Men of social class I and II had a relative excess of ischemic heart disease compared to women of the same class, even though they had a low standard mortality ratio compared with other men. The magnitude of this difference was not seen for other diseases. Individual socioeconomic groups were examined: self-employed professionals appeared at the greatest risk compared with their spouses, whereas agricultural workers were at the lowest risk when compared to their spouses.

Herold, J., Waldron, I. 1985. Part-time employment and women's health. *Journal of Occupational Medicine* 27:405–412.

Data from a national probability sample of noninstitutionalized women age 30–44 in 1967 were used to examine the health differences between part-time and full-time workers and between part-time workers and housewives. The relationship between part-time employment and health varied depending on race and marital status. Part-time workers reported poorer health than full-time workers for married black women and for unmarried women, but for married white women health differences between part- and full-time workers were small and generally not significant. Longitudinal data provided evidence that part-time employment, or characteristics that were associated with part-time employment, may contribute to the poorer health of married black and part-time workers.

Holme, I., Helgeland, A., Hjermann, I., Leren, P., Lund-Larsen, P. G. 1981. Physical activity at work and at leisure in relation to coronary risk factors and social class. *Acta Medica Scandinavica* 209:277–283.

The association between physical activity at work and during leisure time, other coronary risk factors, social class, and mortality over four years was studied in 15,000 men as part of the Oslo Study. Those with low education and income are at increased risk of death, even with adjustment for both types of physical activity, total serum cholesterol, systolic blood pressure, and smoking.

Holme, I., Hjermann, I., Helgeland, A., Lund-Larsen, P. G., Leren, P. 1976. Coronary risk factors and socioeconomic status. *Lancet* II:1396–1398.

Coronary heart-disease (CHD) has been reviewed as a "manager's disease." However, deaths from CHD are now said to be more common in groups from the lower social classes than in those of higher socioeconomic status. The authors examined whether these differences in CHD mortality can be explained by differences in the conventional risk factors for CHD.

Holme, I., Helgeland, A., Hjermann, I., Leren, P. 1980. Four-year mortality by some social indicators: the Oslo Study. *Journal of Epidemiology and Community Health* 34:48–52.

Risk factors for mortality from several causes were studied. Approximately 25,000 men were invited to participate in age group 40–49, and 16,202 men agreed to participate in the Oslo Study. Lower social classes exhibited higher cancer mortality rates. After adjusting for cigarette smoking, 75 percent of the gradient persisted. There was a gradient for coronary heart disease as well, and after adjusting for coronary heart disease risk factors, 60 percent of the gradient remained. Accidents and homicides also showed a strong gradient; after adjusting for risk factors, 70 percent of the gradient remained. Because social class and coronary heart disease risk factors are intercorrelated, the authors concluded that 20 to 40 percent of the social class mortality gradient can be explained by these risk factors. Additionally, if one considers possible measurement error, then 50 percent of the social class gradient can be explained by these risk factors and 50 percent by other factors.

Illsley, R. 1955. Social class selection and class differences in relation to stillbirths and infant deaths. *British Medical Journal* II:1520–1524.

Selective movement between classes and its effect on the rates of prematurity and obstetric death was examined in an analysis of all married primiparae who were residents and delivered in the city of Aberdeen between July 1950 and December 1954. Social class was based on husband's and father's occupation. Father's occupation was defined by his main occupation during the patient's school years. Women who raised their social status at marriage tended to be better educated, of superior intelligence, and had greater occupational skills. They also tended to be in good health. Conversely, women whose social status fell at marriage tended to have the opposite characteristics.

Institute of Medicine. 1985. *The prevention of low birth weight.* Washington, D.C.: National Academy Press.

A comprehensive review of the demographic, behavioral, biologic, and social factors associated with low birthweight. Consistent relationships between socioeconomic status and low birthweight are demonstrated. The prospects for the prevention of low birthweight are discussed.

Jenkins, C. D. 1983. Social environment and cancer mortality in men. *New England Journal of Medicine* 308:395–398.

Characteristics of the social environment associated with cancer mortality were examined using data from death certificates from the Massachusetts Division of Health Statistics. Age-, sex-, and cause-specific mortality rates were calculated for the Commonwealth to determine the expected number of deaths due to all cancers for men and women. Male cancer mortality was higher than expected in areas where a high proportion of families and children lived in poverty. Cancer rates were higher in men where a high proportion of underemployed and unemployed men were present. The type of housing was also associated with excess cancer mortality.

————, Tuthill, R. W., Tannenbaum, S. I., Kirby, C. R. 1977. Zones of excess mortality in Massachusetts. *New England Journal of Medicine* 296:1354–1356.

Social and demographic correlates of excess mortality by select causes were studied in 39 areas of Massachusetts in the 1970s. One area ranked the highest in excess mortality for 17 of 34 specific causes of death. Overall, 28 percent of the total excess mortality in 1972–1973 would not have occurred had the rates for the Commonwealth prevailed. High mortality areas were ones with severe economic deprivation, poor housing, overcrowding, loneliness, family breakdown, personal disability, social instability, and minority status. Ranked correlation coefficient calculations between the 39 areas for total mortality and sociodemographic indicators showed 76 of 131 correlations that were statistically significant.

Johnston, J. M., Grufferman, S., Bourguet, C. C., Delzell, E., Delong, E. R., Cohen, H. J. 1985. Socioeconomic status and risk of multiple myeloma. *Journal of Epidemiology and Community Health* 39:175–178.

This study tested the hypothesis that individuals of higher SES are at increased risk of developing multiple myeloma. A hospital-based case-control study of 153 patients with multiple myeloma and 459 matched controls seen at Duke University Medical Center between June 1976 and May 1982 was carried out. Cases were matched on age, sex, race, hospital, date of admission, and in/out patient status. SES was defined by family income, education, occupation, home ownership, and number of rooms per number of occupants. No meaningful difference between cases and controls on years of education, number of rooms, or crowding index were found using bivariate and multivariate analysis. Home ownership was the only SES indicator that showed a positive association with multiple myeloma (relative risk of 1.6). There was a dose response relationship of increased multiple myeloma with increased occupational rank; the relationship was statistically significant only for outpatients.

Kaplan, G. A. 1985. Psychosocial aspects of chronic illness; direct and indirect associations with ischemic heart disease mortality. In Kaplan, R. M., Criqui, M., eds. *Behavioral epidemiology and disease prevention*. New York: Plenum Press.

The association between socioeconomic, behavior, social, and psychological factors and nine-year mortality risk for ischemic heart disease was studied in 2,352 persons, aged 50 years or more, who were participants in the 1965 Alameda County Study. Analyses of the patterns of mutual confounding between these factors indicated that those with low education and income had 40 percent higher risk of death, and this increased risk was independent of all other covariables. In addition, socioeconomic status was responsible for some of the increased risk associated with low levels of perceived health and with high levels of depressive symptoms.

————, Haan, M. N., Sept. 1986. *Socioeconomic position and health: prospective evidence from the Alameda County Study*. Presented at 114th Annual Meeting of the American Public Health Association, Las Vegas, Nevada.

The association between education and income and mortality from all causes, the role of other risk factors in explaining these associations, and the contribution of education and income to black/white mortality differentials is examined in the Alameda County Study 1965 Cohort. The analyses are based on 18 years of mortality experience. The association between income level and risk of death is influenced very little by adjustment for age, sex, smoking, physical activity, relative weight, sleep habits, alcohol consumption, social network participation, and depression. The association between level of education and mortality risk is lowered somewhat by adjustment for these factors, but it remains significant. Black/white differences in mortality risk are reduced substantially by adjustment for level of income, and there is no longer a significant association between race and mortality risk. Adjustment for education has a relatively small effect on the black/white difference.

Kaplan, G. A., Haan, M. N., Syme, S. L., Minkler, M., Winkleby, M. 1987. Socioeconomic status and health. In Amler, R. W., Dull, H. B., eds. *Closing the gap: the burden of unnecessary illness*. New York: Oxford University Press.

As part of the Carter Center "Closing the Gap" Conference, evidence is reviewed concerning the relationship between socioeconomic status and a wide variety of health outcomes. The evidence supports the position that socioeconomic status is a generic risk factor worthy of consideration in prevention efforts.

Karasek, R., Baker, D., Marxer, F., Ahlbom, A., Theorell, T. 1981. Job decision latitude, job demands, and cardiovascular disease: a prospective study of Swedish men. *American Journal of Public Health* 71:694–705.

The association between specific job characteristics and subsequent cardiovascular disease was tested using a large random sample of the male working Swedish population. The prospective development of coronary heart disease (CHD) symptoms and signs was analyzed. Additionally, a case-controlled study was used to analyze all cardiovascular-cerebrovascular (CHD-CVD) deaths during a six-year follow-up. A hectic and psychologically demanding job increases the risk of developing CHD symptoms and signs (standardized odds ratio 1.29) and premature CHD-CVD death (relative risk 4.0). Low decision latitude—expressed as low intellectual discretion and low personal schedule freedom—is also associated with increased risk of cardiovascular disease. Low intellectual discretion predicts the development of CHD symptoms and signs, while low personal schedule freedom, among the majority of workers with the minimum statutory education, increases the risk of CHD-CVD death (relative risk 6.6, p<.0002). The associations exist after controlling for age, education, smoking, and overweight.

Keirn, W., Metter, G. 1985. Survival of cancer patients by economic status in a free care setting. *Cancer* 55:1552–1555.

All patients with a diagnosis of lung, breast, and colorectal cancer treated at the City of Hope Medical Center between 1976–1981 were included in a study of SES and survival. Patients were defined as indigent and nonindigent based on public assistance criteria. Comparisons were made between indigent and nonindigent subjects by tumor site for age, sex, and stage of diagnosis. For each tumor site the only variable that was statistically associated with survival after adjustment for other variables was the stage at which the disease was diagnosed. There was no independent association of SES with survival.

Kitagawa, E. M., Hauser, P. M. 1973. *Differential mortality in the United States: a study in socioeconomic epidemiology.* Cambridge, MA: Harvard University Press.

The results of three major studies of the relationship between socioeconomic indicators and mortality are presented. The first study matched death certificates for 340,000 persons who died in the U.S. in May through August of 1960 with the 1960 Population Census. The second studied variations in mortality in the Chicago area from 1930 to 1960 as a function of socioeconomic characteristics of census tracts. The third study involved a detailed analysis of mortality gradients as a function of education for all deaths in the U.S. in 1959–1961. Considerable information is presented on the association between education, income, and occupation and mortality.

Knox, E. G., Marshall, T., Kane, S., Green, A. 1980. Social and health care determinants of area variation in perinatal mortality. *Community Medicine* 2:282–290.

Data on perinatal mortality for 90 English areas for 1974–1976 were related to a series of social indicators obtained from census and other sources, and a set of statistics describing the facilities, staffing, and throughputs of perinatal and other health care services. Birthweight standardization accounts for more than half the initial variation in perinatal mortality rates. Social descriptors also accounted for a lot of the variation of the weight-standardized expectations. The social descriptors also account for a large fraction of the mortality variance that remained following the standardization by birthweight. Variations in health care descriptors showed little evidence of an effect upon either component. In particular, the effect of the social variables on the stillbirth rates did not operate to any discernible extent through associated underinvestment in health care services.

Koskenvuo, M., Sarna, S., Kaprio, J. 1978. Mortality by marital status and social class in Finland during 1969–1971. *Scandinavian Journal of Social Medicine* 6:137–143.

The distribution of mortality rates by social class and marital status for men and women in three age groups (25–44, 45–64 and 65–84) in Finland is presented in these analyses. Natural and violent causes of death were analyzed separately. The death certificates of 137,780 Finnish citizens for the years 1969, 1970, and 1971 were analyzed and mortality rates standardized using as reference population the data from the 1970 census. Social class and marital status were significant risk factors for mortality, from both natural and violent causes.

————, Lonnqvist, J. 1979. Cause-specific mortality by marital status and social class in Finland during 1969–1971. *Social Science and Medicine* 13a:691–697.

The mortality experience of 25- to 64-year-olds in Finland was examined by marital status and social class. Social class was based on the occupational data found on the death certificates. Nonemployed and retired individuals were identified by their former occupations or the occupations of their supporters. The referent population was taken from the 1970 census. Mortality data were evaluated for 44,548 death certificates for the years 1969, 1970, and 1971. For mental disorders, respiratory illnesses, nervous disorders, infections, homicides, fires, and poisonings, men in social class 4 (unskilled workers) had the highest mortality rate. No clearcut pattern could be seen for women. This may be explained by the fact that nongainfully employed women were classified by their husbands' occupations. If the mortality rates in other classes were the same as class 1, there would have been 21 percent lower rate from natural causes and 40 percent lower rate for violent causes in men. Cancer and coronary heart disease showed the least variation with a 1.8-fold risk for cancer and 1.7-fold risk for coronary heart disease.

Koskenvuo, M., Kaprio, J., Kesaniemi, A., Sarna, S. 1980. Differences in mortality from ischemic heart disease by marital status and social class. *Journal of Chronic Diseases* 33:95–106.

This paper presented mortality data from ischemic heart disease in a Finnish population by marital status and social class. The death certificates for all persons aged 25–84 dying from ischemic heart disease between 1969–71 were studied. Social class was based on occupation status. The referent population was based on 1970 census returns. In different marital status–social class combinations, the proportion of deaths from ischemic heart disease was highest when total disease mortality was lowest. The variation with marital status or social class, separately, was less than when both variables were analyzed simultaneously. The highest ischemic heart disease mortality was concentrated among widowed and divorced unskilled workers, the differences between marital status and social class being most marked (3.3-fold) for men age 25–54. Divorced and widowed persons had a higher risk of sudden death than married persons. Other than divorced persons, less educated persons in either blue-collar or white-collar occupations had higher risks of dying from ischemic heart disease than their more educated counterparts.

Koskenvuo, M., Kaprio, J., Romo, M., Langinvainio, H. 1981. Incidence and prognosis of ischaemic heart disease with respect to marital status and social class: a national record linkage study. *Journal of Epidemiology and Community Health* 35:192–196.

The relationship between social class and marital status and ischemic heart disease in men age 40–64 during 1972 in Finland were analyzed by linking death certificates and hospital records (7,499 cases and 3,136 deaths). Age-adjusted incidence, mortality, and survival rates for the first and third year were calculated by marital status and social class. The highest mortality rate was found among unskilled workers; the highest incidence was among widowers and those in lower professional classes, and the lowest survival rate was among divor-

cees, single persons, and unskilled workers. The ratio of
mortality by marital status (1.77) was in part due to survival
(ratio 1.44) and in part due to incidence (ratio 1.32). The ratio
of mortality by social class (1.44) seemed to be due more to
differences in incidence (ratio 1.36) than to differences in survival (ratio 1.18). The distribution of conventional risk factors
of ischemic heart disease by marital status and social class
seemed to explain only part of the mortality differences.

Kraus, J., Redford, R. J. 1975. Some ecological correlates of
perinatal mortality in a metropolis. *Medical Journal of Australia*
2:16–18.

Geographical differences in perinatal mortality and select
population characteristics were studied in the metropolitan
areas of Sydney. The sample included 39 municipalities and
shires. Perinatal mortality was higher in areas of high juvenile
delinquency, low socioeducational status, high unemployment, and low home ownership. High birth rates were found
in areas that tended to coincide with low socioeducational status, adult and juvenile crime, child neglect, crowding, and
unemployment.

Kraus, J. F., Fife, D., Ramstein, K., Conroy, C., Cox, P. 1986.
The relationship of family income to the incidence, external
causes and outcomes of serious brain injury, San Diego
County, California. *American Journal of Public Health* 76:1345–
1347.

The relationship of SES to the incidence, external causes, and
outcome of serious brain injury in a defined U.S. population
was studied. Identification of subjects was made by examining records in acute-care hospitals, all coroner's records, all
death certificates, nursing homes, and extended care facilities
in San Diego and the major hospitals in adjoining cities. U.S.
census data for 1980 were used to estimate the population size
of San Diego, enumerate subgroups, and identify census
tracts by median family income. Incidence rates of serious
brain injury in 1981 was 44 per 100,000. Rates for persons in

low, middle, and high income tracts were 58, 40, and 37, respectively. Adjustment for age did not significantly change these rates. Overall, for all racial/ethnic groups except Hispanic, the rates declined with increased family income. Brain injuries from firearms and assaults were highest in the lowest income groups. There was no significant difference in the injury rate to motor vehicle occupants, but rates were higher for pedestrian and motorcycles in low compared to high. Type of emergency transport, time from injury to first contact, and probability of death were not related to income.

Kraus, J. F., Borhani, N. O., Franti, C. E. 1980. Socioeconomic status, ethnicity, and risk of coronary heart disease. *American Journal of Epidemiology* 111:407–414.

The authors undertook this study to determine whether the risk of coronary heart disease was related to SES for five major self-reported race/ethnic groups. SES was defined using occupation and education, a modified version of the Hollingshead Index. The prevalence of coronary heart disease event was 2.3 percent for men in the highest SES categories and 3.2 percent for men in the lowest categories. The proportion of men in the upper quartile of coronary heart disease risk increased with decreasing SES for all race/ethnic groups, except blacks for whom this proportion varied only slightly by SES. Blacks had the highest prevalence of hypertension, Hispanics the highest cholesterol levels, and the proportion of heavy smokers was highest among whites.

Kristiansen, C. M. 1985. Seat belt legislation and seat belt use: effects on differences related to sex, social class and smoking. *Accident Analysis and Prevention* 17:75–78.

The present study examined the association between general preventive health behavior and reported seat belt use, and the impact of legislation upon sex and social class differences in seat belt use. Respondents (n = 177) were categorized as High SES (nonmanual) or Low SES (manual) on the basis of information about occupation. Both SES groups reported significant increases in frequency of seat belt use after legislation was enacted, suggesting that the legislation had been effective. Regression analysis showed that while SES, gender, and general preventive behavior were significant predictors of prelegislation seat belt use (p<.001), only SES was a significant predictor of postlegislation seat belt use (p<.05).

Kronenfeld, J. 1979. Access to dental care: a comparison of medicine/dentistry and the role of a regular source. *Medical Care* 17:1000–1011.

The purpose of this paper was to determine the relative importance of income and education as the explanatory variables in access to dental care as compared to access to medical care using a random sample of Rhode Island residents. SES was important in determining whether someone had a regular source of dental care. The gap between low and high income and education was 24 percent and 41 percent, respectively. As education and income increased, those who reported a regular source of dental care increased. Only 50 percent of the people in the poorest families had a regular source of dental care compared to 91.5 percent of the wealthiest. Of those with low education, 58.6 percent had a regular source compared to 82.9 percent in the highest education groups. The primary role of income was confirmed in a discriminant function analysis, which also found education, sex, race, and age to be significant predictors of dental care use. These five variables predicted 71 percent of those with a regular source and 61.5 percent without a regular source.

Kuller, L., Seltser, R. 1967. Cerebrovascular disease mortality in Maryland. *American Journal of Epidemiology* 86:442–450.

A multiple-cause tabulation of death certificates for 1960–1962 was conducted in Baltimore and several counties of Maryland to study cerebrovascular disease mortality. All death certificates of residents age 20 and over were reviewed. As expected, the proportion of cerebrovascular disease deaths increased with age. This percent was greater in blacks than in whites and in females than males. Rates were higher for blacks than whites in both urban and rural areas. An attempt was made to analyze SES computed from census tract information. SES was defined by median rental value and adjustments were made for owner-occupied homes. Death rates were higher in low socioeconomic areas for all four race-sex groups, although differences were small compared to racial differences.

Lambert, C. A., Netherton, D. R., Finison, L. J., Hyde, J. N., Spaight, S. J. 1982. Risk factors and life style: a statewide health-interview survey. *New England Journal of Medicine* 306:1048–1051.

In 1980, the Division of Preventive Medicine of the Massachusetts Department of Public Health surveyed the health-related behaviors of 1,091 adults. Persons with higher educational attainment, and to a lesser extent those with higher incomes, reported less smoking and alcohol consumption, less overweight, and more exercise.

Lapidus, L., Bengtsson, C. 1986. Socioeconomic factors and physical activity in relationship to cardiovascular disease and death: a 12-year follow-up of participants in a population study of women in Gothenburg, Sweden. *British Heart Journal* 55:295–301.

A prospective cross-sectional study of 1,462 women aged 38, 46, 50, 54, and 60 was undertaken. Information about education, marital status, number of children, and SES was obtained by questionnaire. The women were divided into five SES groups according to Carlsson. Group I consisted of large-scale employers or officials of high or intermediate rank. Group II included groups two and three and was made up of small-scale employers and officials of low and intermediate rank. Group III (groups 4 and 5) was made up of skilled and semiskilled workers. After controlling for six risk factors and (SES, education level, smoking, blood pressure, obesity, cholesterol), physical activity was found to be independently correlated with stroke in women. A significant negative correlation between physical activity at work and physical activity was shown (p<.05). Myocardial infarction was associated with SES when classified by husband's occupation. Multivariate analysis showed that low education levels among women were significantly associated with angina pectoris, after adjustment for confounding variables.

Leaf, P. J., Livingston, M. M., Tischler, G. L., Weissman, M. M., Holzer, C. E., Myers, J. K. 1985. Contact with health professionals for the treatment of psychiatric and emotional problems. *Medical Care* 23:1322–1337.

This study focuses on the predisposing, enabling, and need factors affecting contact with health professionals for the treatment of psychiatric and emotional problems during a six-month period. Data are from 5,034 community interviews from a 13-town area of New Haven. Race emerges as a significant factor in utilization once level of symptomatology is taken into account. Whites are more likely to report some mental health–related contacts than nonwhites. Income is only associated with the use of services before controlling for other factors in the analysis not related to the number of contacts. Education emerges as a significant factor in utilization only after controlling for clinical and other factors. The authors believe that these results indicate that lack of awareness concerning the nature of psychiatric disorders as well as low receptivity to mental health professionals exert a greater barrier to obtaining treatment than does income.

Lebowitz, M. D. 1982. Multivariate analysis of smoking and other risk factors for obstructive lung diseases and related symptoms. *Journal of Chronic Disease* 35:751–758.

A longitudinal study in a community population sample of approximately 3,600 white, non-Mexican American adults, stratified on SES and age were selected. The relationship of risk factors and respiratory symptoms were studied. Information regarding education and income were obtained by questionnaire. In a linear discriminant analysis, among males age 18 and older, income and education, alcohol consumption, and occupation exposure all contributed to the classification of diagnosis, symptoms, and lung function.

Leren, P., Helgeland, A., Hjermann, I., Holme, I. 1983. The Oslo Study: CHD risk factors, socioeconomic influences, and intervention. *American Heart Journal* 106:1200–1206.

Social class was defined by gross income and years of education (1 being the highest and 5 the lowest). Coronary heart disease risk was approximately 2.5 times greater in class 5 than in class 1. Total mortality increased sharply with decreasing social status, even for those subjects who were initially healthy. Mortality from cancer, accidents, and homicides followed the same pattern. Men employed in industrial jobs were at higher risk for coronary heart disease, compared to those in occupations requiring more education. Those with lower education levels also smoked more cigarettes and had higher cholesterol levels.

Lerner, M. 1986. Cancer mortality differentials by income, Baltimore, 1949–51 to 1979–81. In *Cancer in the economically disadvantaged*. New York: American Cancer Society.

The association between income and cancer mortality and secular trends in this association were compared in Baltimore for the period 1949–1951 to 1979–1981. There was a relative narrowing of the mortality differentials for low and high income over this time period for most major sites except female breast cancer. Greatest differentials in the last time period were seen for cancer of the cervix uteri, stomach, ovary and Fallopian tube, respiratory system, and corpus uteri. The overall income gradient was seen, separately, for whites and nonwhites. Race exerted an effect independent of income only among the low income population.

———, Stutz, R. N. 1978. Mortality by socioeconomic status 1959–62 and 1969–71. *Maryland State Medical Journal* 27(12):35–43.

This paper presents mortality data for Maryland for 1959–1961 and 1969–1971 from the Maryland Center for Health Statistics. Counties and State Economic areas are the units of analysis. The analysis examines whether socioeconomic differentials in total and cause-specific mortality changed during the decade of the 1960s. The authors concluded that some evidence exists to indicate that SES differentials in mortality are narrowing. Between 1959 and 1964, service programs narrowed existing socioeconomic differentials in mortality as well as in other aspects of health status.

Levin, D. L., Connelly, R. R., Devesa, S. S. 1981. Demographic characteristics of cancer of the pancreas: mortality, incidence and survival. *Cancer* 47:1456–1468.

Information on 9,668 patients with pancreatic cancer diagnosed during 1973–77 was obtained from a population-based cancer registry in five states and five metropolitan areas covered by SEER. Sex and age-specific incidence rates for pancreatic cancer were calculated. No significant association with either income or education was found among men of either race or among black females. Nonsignificant trends were suggested in the lower income groups of each race among men. Incidence rates among white females were significantly associated with both socioeconomic variables. Age and area adjusted rates were about 30 percent higher among blacks compared with whites of each sex. Blacks continued to have an excess risk for pancreatic cancer within comparable levels of income and education, although in some instances these differences were not statistically significant. Adjustment for income reduced the difference somewhat in men. Only small, not statistically significant, differences in pancreatic cancer incidence rates among urban and rural residents were found in the data analysis.

Lilienfeld, A. M. 1971. Variation in mortality from heart disease. Race, sex, and socioeconomic status. *Public Health Reports* 1956:545–552.

Using information on certified deaths in Baltimore during the period 1949–1951, mortality from various types of heart disease was analyzed by race, sex, and socioeconomic status. No significant differences in arteriosclerotic heart disease were noted in the rates for five socioeconomic groups. For both sexes and both races, the highest rates were noted in the lowest socioeconomic group, with a gradual decrease in rates as socioeconomic status increased. This risk distribution is similar to that observed in England and Wales. The lowest socioeconomic group had the highest rates of hypertensive disease, and there tended to be a decrease in rates with an increase in socioeconomic status, although the pattern was not regular. The female rates were higher than the male rates in the lower socioeconomic groups, whereas the reverse was true in the upper groups. This was observed for both races. The use of death certificate information for analysis of mortality and the use of census tracts for socioeconomic classification both impose certain limitations on the data derived. Nonetheless, the apparent existence of differences in the social distribution of coronary disease deaths in two geographic areas indicates a need for further study of the subject.

Lines, D. R. 1977. An Auckland high school health survey. *Australia and New Zealand Journal of Medicine* 7:143–147.

To assess the relevance of racial and socioeconomic factors on teenager health, clinical examinations were performed on students in a New Zealand school. Social class was determined on the basis of parental occupation as defined by the Elley-Irving Socio-Economic Index. Only one third of the children were considered completely healthy, and even when the cases of scabies, impetigo, and visual defects were ignored, only 50 percent were considered healthy. The four racial groups (Europeans, Maori, Pacific Islanders, and Asians) were predominantly from SES classes 4 and 5. Health patterns were not significantly different between racial groups with the exception of a high rate of skin infections among Maori and Pacific Islanders. Dental caries were more common in Maori. The author concluded that socioeconomic conditions, not differences in susceptibility to disease, were responsible for the poor health conditions.

Lipworth, L., Abelin, T., Connelly, R. R. 1970. Socioeconomic factors in the prognosis of cancer patients. *Journal of Chronic Diseases* 23:105–116.

The role of socioeconomic factors in observed differences in the cancer survival of patients from Connecticut and Massachusetts was examined utilizing data from the state cancer registries. The differences observed were consistent with the greater concentration of low income patients in the Massachusetts registry. To examine the issue in more detail, survival data was examined for patients from low and high income census tracts in Boston. There was evidence of a trend toward better survival associated with higher income.

Lloyd, O. L., Smith, G., Lloyd, M. M., Holland, Y., Gailey, F. 1985. Raised mortality from lung cancer and high sex ratios of birth associated with industrial pollution. *British Journal of Industrial Medicine* 42:475–480.

Geographical and temporal associations were shown between high mortality from lung cancer and a high sex ratio of births both in the town of Bathgate (Scotland) and in the area of that town that was most exposed to polluted air from a local steel foundry. These findings constituted a replication of a similar association in an adjacent town.

Lynge, E., Jeune, B. 1983. Excess mortality among male unskilled and semi-skilled workers. *Scandinavian Journal of Social Medicine*, 11:37–40.

All-cause mortality and its relationship with age for skilled and unskilled workers in Denmark, Norway, England, and Wales was examined. Compared to all employed men, there was a 40–50 percent higher risk of total mortality between ages 30 to 40 for unemployed men. The rise decreased with age. Deaths due to accidents and violence were higher among lower SES men at younger ages. The same effect was seen for natural causes of death as well. The age-related decline in excess mortality among lower SES workers was due partly to the fact that sick and disabled unskilled and semiskilled workers leave the market earlier than similarly disadvantaged persons from other social groups.

Mack, T. M., Paganini-Hill, A. 1981. Epidemiology of pancreas cancer in Los Angeles. *Cancer* 47:1474–1483.

Information describing the characteristics of diagnosed cases of carcinoma of the pancreas for 1972–1977 was obtained using the Cancer Surveillance Program data. Medical records were abstracted for demographic data. Social class was not determined individually but on the basis of a geographic index determined by census tract of residence. An index from 1 (high) to 5 was assigned based on average education level and family income level (Hollingshead Index). Overall, an inverse association between social class and pancreatic cancer was present in men and women. There was a high rate in the lowest social class category for both sexes. This association was strongest in men, at older ages, and for confirmed cases. The high risk among both whites and blacks of low social class suggested that some attribute of poverty contributes to mortality.

MacMahon, B., Johnson, S., Pugh, T. F. 1963. Relation of suicide rates to social conditions: evidence from U.S. Vital Statistics. *Public Health Reports* (Washington) 78:285–293.

This article reviews evidence from United States vital statistics on factors associated with suicide rates during 1948–1952. Differences by sex, age, race and employment status are examined as are secular trends during the depression of the 1930s. Suicide rates were higher during the 1930s, and higher rates are also reported among unemployed people compared to employed people for the years 1930–1960. In contrast, nonwhites have lower suicide rates than whites at almost all ages and for both sexes.

Marcus, A. C., Reeder, L. G., Jordan, L. A., Seeman, T. E. 1980. Monitoring health status, access to health care, and compliance behavior in a large urban community. *Medical Care* 18:253–265.

This article summarized the results from two health surveys conducted in Los Angeles County in 1974 and 1977. The original objective of this analysis was to identify aggregate changes in the health status of this population, in access as measured by the use/disability ratio, and in self-reported compliance with medical regimens. The investigators found evidence of improved access relative to disability, and a corresponding reduction in the traditional income differential. Analysis of self-reported compliance showed little change over time, with Anglos and the middle and upper socioeconomic groups reporting less compliance with their doctors' recommendations.

Mare, R. D. 1982. Socioeconomic effects on child mortality in the United States. *American Journal of Public Health* 72:539–547.

This paper reported the analysis of socioeconomic differentials in mortality among persons under age 20 in the United States. Data from the Current Population Survey (CPS) were used. CPS contained mothers' accounts of the survival of their children. Child mortality estimates specific to education attainment of mothers and income of the family were compared to those observed for adults in the 1960 Matched Records Study. For most age-race-sex groups, the percent of children dead differed substantially by mother's education. Among white boys of dropout mothers, 3.36 percent had died by age 10–14, in contrast to 1.94 percent of mothers with more education. Advantages to children of mothers with better education occurred at every age for white and black boys, but the difference was minimal for black girls. Mortality differences by family income were similar to those for maternal schooling. An inverse association between accidental death and SES accounted for a large proportion of the SES differences in total mortality among children.

Markides, K. S., Barnes, D. 1977. A methodological note on the relationship between infant mortality and socioeconomic status with evidence from San Antonio, Texas. *Social Biology* 24(1):38–44.

Total, neonatal, and postneonatal infant mortality rates were calculated for four SES groups (High, Med-high, Med-low, and Low) in 115 census tracts for San Antonio, Texas, for the years 1970–74. Indices used to define SES were income, education, and occupation. Infant death rates for groups of census tracts delineated by each of these indices separately demonstrated that all three rates were most sensitive to income differentials. The data indicated a strong relationship between SES and total infant mortality and an even stronger one between SES and postneonatal mortality. The postneonatal rate went from 2.3 to 6.3 as SES decreased (combined scores). Because of the large number of Mexican Americans, the proportion of persons with Spanish surnames or language for the four SES groups was calculated. This proportion rose from 16.9 percent in high SES to 92.6 percent in low SES. However, when Non-Anglo and Anglo rates were compared, the differences were small.

Markowe, H. L. J., Marmot, M. G., Shipley, M. J., Bulpitt, C. J., Meade, T. W., Stirling, Y., Vickers, M. V., Semmence, A. 1985. Fibrinogen: a possible link between social class and coronary heart disease. *British Medicine* 291:1312–1314.

Mortality in England and Wales for civil servants in lowest grade of employment was found to be three times higher than for men in the highest grade. Seventy-five of 1,274 civil servants age 34–54 were stratified by grade of employment and whether they smoked. Questionnaires and physical exams were completed. There was a statistically significant difference in plasma fibrinogen concentrations between men in lower grades (n = 29) and those in higher grades (n = 45). The

means were 3.39 and 2.95, respectively (p<0.01). There was
an independent association for fibrinogen concentration and
cigarette smoke (p<0.05) and grade of employment (p<0.05).
A summary measure of job stress was significantly related to
fibrinogen concentration (p<0.01). Physical activity and behavior type was not related to fibrinogen concentration.

Marmot, M. G. 1986. Social inequalities in mortality: the social environment. In Wilkinson, R. G., ed. *Class and health—
research and longitudinal data*, pp. 21–33. London: Tavistock
Publications.

This paper addressed two questions: (1) Are the general social
class differences in mortality more likely to have a general explanation or to be the results of the combined effect of a number of specific factors? (2) What role might psychosocial factors play in causing social differences in mortality?

Data from the British Civil Servants study (see reference below, Marmot 1978) is presented along with other data examining childhood and adult differences in physical stature,
health, and behavioral risk factors. The author concludes that
there is urgent need to take action on social class differences in
established risk factors, such as smoking.

————, Adelstein, A. M., Robinson, N., Rose, G. A. 1978.
Changing social-class distribution of heart disease. *British
Medical Journal* 2:1109–1112.

The purpose of this study was to describe whether and why
there had been a change in the social-class distribution of heart
disease in England and Wales. The most recent data (1970–
1972) on mortality for the different classes showed people in
the higher social classes had lower mortality than the working
classes. Death rates were taken from the Registrar General's
Decennial Supplement which reported SES by occupational
status. Mortality from heart disease in 1931 was higher for
classes I and II than for IV and V in age groups 55–65 and 45–
54. In each age group, mortality increased over time, and this

increase was most rapid in groups IV and V. By 1961, in each age group, male mortality was higher in IV and V than I and II; this was not the case for women. From 1931–1971, women in IV and V had the highest mortality. The authors thought that changes in diet, smoking, or intake of refined carbohydrates or cereal fiber contributed to the changing SES-CHD association.

Marmot, M. G., Rose, G., Shipley, M., Hamilton, P. J. S. 1978. Employment grade and coronary heart disease in British civil servants. *Journal of Epidemiology and Community Health* 32:244–249.

This paper reported the coronary heart disease mortality in 7½ years of follow-up for employed men in different grades. Analysis of the association between employment grade and coronary heart disease was confined to 17,530 men from England and Wales. Data were collected by questionnaires. Within each age group, there was an inverse association between grade of employment and risk of coronary heart disease. Overall, men in the lowest grade had 3.6 times the coronary heart disease mortality rate of the men in the highest grade. To understand this association, the age-adjusted risk factor distribution was studied. Systolic blood pressure showed a negative association with grade, while the association with plasma cholesterol was positive. The proportion of smokers was two times greater in the low grade. There was a positive association between grade and height, while those in the lower grades were heavier.

Marmot, M. G., Shipley, M. J., Rose, G. 1984. Inequalities in death-specific explanations of a general pattern? *Lancet* I:1003–1006.

The relationship between employment grade and 10-year mortality was studied in 17,500 civil servants as part of the Whitehall Study. There was a steep inverse relation between grade and risk of death from coronary heart disease, from a number of other causes, and from all causes combined. Although smoking and other coronary risk factors are more common in the lower grades, these differences accounted for only a part of the increased risk associated with lower employment grade.

Marmot, M. G., McDowall, M. E. 1986. Mortality decline and widening social inequalities. *Lancet* II:274–276.

Mortality from coronary heart disease (CHD) is higher in manual than in nonmanual occupational classes. Trends in these inequalities were examined in the light of the decline in CHD mortality in Great Britain. Mortality from all causes, coronary heart disease, cerebrovascular disease, and lung cancer were compared. A standardized mortality ratio was used, referenced to the 1979 population. Despite the general fall in mortality, the relative disadvantage of manual compared with nonmanual classes has increased between 1970–1979 for each of these causes. Among men, in every region of Great Britain, CHD mortality has declined in nonmanual classes. Among women, lung cancer and CHD mortality has fallen in nonmanual classes but has increased in manual classes. Differences in smoking between social classes are likely to be important, but the effect of unemployment and increased income differentials should also be explored.

Mathews, J. D. 1976. Alcohol usage as a possible explanation for socio-economic and occupational differentials in mortality from hypertension and coronary heart disease in England and Wales. *Alcohol, Hypertension and Coronary Disease* 6:393–397.

Using 1951 occupational mortality data for men aged 20–64 from England and Wales, standard mortality ratios for hypertension, vascular lesions of the nervous system, coronary heart disease, and cirrhosis were analyzed. SES was defined by the Registrar General's Classification. Socioeconomic groups with high standard mortality ratios for cirrhosis tended to have high standard mortality ratios for hypertension, vascular lesions, and coronary heart disease. As a single predictor variable, the standard mortality ratio for cirrhosis accounted for 65–69 percent of the variance in the standard mortality ratio for hypertension, stroke, and coronary heart disease. Lung cancer accounted for 17–22 percent of the variance. The occupations that had the greatest risk for cirrhosis represented individuals from all social classes.

McCarthy, P., Byrne, D., Harrisson, S., Keithley, J. 1985. Respiratory conditions: effect of housing and other factors. *Journal of Epidemiology and Community Health* 39:15–19.

This survey examined the hypothesis that poor health is related to poor housing. Occupants of the local authority accommodations in a metropolitan district of England were interviewed. Information regarding several facets of health and illness were ascertained. The present summary involved 533 adults below retirement age. Analyses indicated that housing area, smoking, and an unhealthy environment were predictors of poor health. When age, housing type, cigarette smoke, and work experience were held constant, people who lived in areas where poor housing predominated reported more respiratory conditions than those who lived in "good" areas.

McCormick, M. C. 1985. The contribution of low birth weight to infant mortality and childhood morbidity. *New England Journal of Medicine* 312:82–90.

Evidence was reviewed on the contribution of low birthweight to infant mortality and childhood morbidity. In the neonatal period, the proportion of low birthweight infants, particularly very low weight, was a strong predictor of mortality rates. Differential prevalence of low birthweight infants may account for the higher rates of infant mortality observed in economically disadvantaged groups.

McMichael, A. J., Hartshorne, J. M. 1982. 1982. Mortality risks in Australian men by occupational groups, 1968–1978: variations associated with differences in drinking and smoking habits. *Medical Journal of Australia* 1:253–256.

Analysis of patterns of male mortality in Australia during 1968–78 showed elevated death rates from liver cirrhosis, alcoholism, and alcoholic psychosis in various occupations. The risks of mortality from lung cancer and cancers of the upper alimentary tract and larynx were raised in service and blue-collar groups. In contrast, the risk of mortality from cancer of the colon, thought to be influenced by dietary "affluence," were higher in professional and white collar groups. As reported in other populations, stomach cancer mortality risk was higher for service and blue-collar groups. The risks of mortality from coronary heart disease and cerebrovascular disease were also higher for these two groups.

McWhirter, W. R., Smith, H., McWhirter, K. M. 1983. Social class as a prognostic variable in acute lymphoblastic leukaemia. *Medical Journal of Australia* 2:319–321.

This study presented some of the characteristics thought to affect the prognosis of childhood acute lymphoblastic leukemia. Seventy children under the age of 15 and residents of Queensland who were diagnosed with the disease between 1975–1979 were enrolled in the study. Follow-up ranged from 31 to 88 months. There were differences in survival between the two groups. Children from upper class families (Group 1) did significantly better than those from lower class families (Group 2) ($p = 0.039$). Group 1 children had a 5-year survival rate that was twice that of Group 2. Median duration of disease remission was 48 months for Group 1 and 17 months for Group 2 ($p = 0.048$). There was no detectable difference between treatment given the two groups. Although differences in white cell count, platelet count, and spleen size were not statistically significant, differences in each of these parameters indicate that the disease was more advanced in children of low SES.

Metropolitan Life Insurance Company. Socioeconomic mortality differentials by leading causes of death. 1977. *Metropolitan Life Insurance Company Statistical Bulletin* 58(Jan):5–8.

Mortality by specific causes of death was related to socioeconomic variables such as occupation, education, and income. An examination of the ratios of death rates in each occupation class to the death rates for all classes combined indicated an inverse relationship between socioeconomic status. The ratios at the lowest level (Class V) were 1.5 to 2 times greater than they were at the highest level for all ages and all causes of death combined. The ratio of mortality in the lowest salaried group to mortality for the middle and highest groups ranges from 1.1 for heart disease to 1.8 for suicide. For both males and females, those with eight years of education or less had a higher mortality than those with more education for every cause except diabetes, coronary heart disease, and cirrhosis of the liver for men, and breast cancer, cirrhosis of the liver, and accidents for women.

Mettlin, C., Cummings, M. K., Walsh, D. 1985. Risk factors and behavioral correlates of willingness to participate in cancer prevention trials. *Nutrition and Cancer* 7:189–198.

This paper assessed the interest of individuals in participating in cancer prevention research that would involve making changes in diet or regularly taking medications, such as vitamin supplements. The eligible population consisted of a 33 percent random sample of persons seen at the Prevention-Detection Center at Roswell Park Memorial Institute between May 1979 and December 1982 (N = 556). Respondents who expressed the greatest interest in participating in research involving changes in eating habits or taking vitamin supplements to prevent cancer were younger, more likely to have at least a high school education, and to have come from a family that had an average annual income above $16,000.

Milio, N. 1985. Health policy and the emerging tobacco reality. *Social Science and Medicine* 21:603–613.

This paper outlined the changing reality of tobacco use and production, emphasizing the economic picture. Policy implications were suggested. Economic data revealed that the tobacco sector of affluent nations has been declining at an accelerated rate. At the same time, the tobacco economy has been growing in less industrialized nations. Economic strategy was suggested for dealing with these changes.

Millar, W. J., Wigle, D. T. 1986. Socioeconomic disparities in risk factors for cardiovascular disease. *Canadian Medical Association Journal* 134:127–132.

This paper examined the prevalence of risk factors (smoke, blood pressure, obesity, alcohol consumption, diabetes, cholesterol, physical activity) associated with coronary heart disease by SES in Canadian adults to determine preventive health promotion programs. Among men age 20–69, the largest differences in risk factor prevalence between education groups were found for smoking, obesity, physical inactivity, and excessive alcohol consumption. For women in the same age group, the largest differences were found for smoking, overweight, obesity, increased blood pressure, and physical inactivity. The prevalence of risk factors in the lowest education group tended to be higher than those in the highest education groups. Women with elementary education were least likely to use oral contraceptives. The decline in smoking prevalence among women was greatest for university educated.

Millard, A. V. 1985. Child mortality and economic variation among rural Mexican households. *Social Science and Medicine* 20:589–599.

Two rural Mexican communities were compared and child mortality rates were examined. Although the two communities differ with respect to ethnicity, ecology, history, family economic strategy, and agricultural systems, two economic measures emerged as important correlates of child mortality rates in both communities: a woman's marital status at the time of the interview and housing quality. The correlation of the rate of child mortality per woman with economic factors ranged from -.25 to -.54 and accounted for up to 30 percent of the variation in children's mortality. A high rate of child mortality could impoverish a household by diminishing the family agricultural work force. Other studies have not found a similar relationship because they have not used culturally appropriate research designs and field techniques.

Miller, A. B. 1982. Risk factors from geographical epidemiology for gastrointestinal cancer. *Cancer* 50:2533–2540.

This article reviews the associations between various cancer sites and race, nationality, migration, and socioeconomic status (SES). The latter association is summarized here. SES is inversely associated with colon and rectal cancer in several studies in the United States. Finnish studies have reported similar associations between SES and a number of cancer sites, while Norwegian records suggest higher cancer incidence and mortality among urban compared to rural residents for most sites. United States urban-rural comparisons were similar for colon and rectal cancer. Migrants from urban to rural areas show a reversal in this latter association.

Miller, D. R. 1982. Editor's column: prognostic factors in childhood leukemia. *Journal of Pediatrics* 87:672–676.

This editorial contained no original contributions with respect to the factors affecting the prognosis of leukemia in children. It did make the following comments with regard to other studies on this subject: "The incidence of acute lymphoblastic leukemia in white and nonwhite children is similar, and the differences in mortality are likely to be related to SES and the availability of medical care rather than ethnic or racial factors. The remission rate and median duration of remission and survival are much lower in black children than in white children, and it has been suggested that black children be studied separately."

Miller, W. J., Jr., Cooper, R. 1982. Rising lung cancer death rates among black men: the importance of occupation and social class. *Journal of the National Medical Association* 74:253–258.

Thirty years ago the age-adjusted cancer mortality rate for black men was about 20 percent lower than for whites in the United States. This difference was thought to be due to underreporting and to poorer medical care. In the last three decades, death rates among black men have risen sharply. Most of the increase was due to an increase in lung cancer among blacks. From 1950–1977, nonwhite males experienced a 320 percent increase, compared to a 161 percent for whites. This may be explained by increased smoking patterns, occupational exposure, or migration patterns.

Monson, R. R. 1980. Cause of death in Boston. *Journal of Chronic Diseases* 33:21–28.

The purpose of this paper was to report an evaluation of the relationship between cause of death and ethnicity, occupation, and residence. Death certificates for Boston residents who died in 1970 were reviewed. There were deficits of deaths from motor vehicle accidents and suicide. Slight to moderate excesses of specific causes of death were seen for specific ethnic, occupation, and residence groups. An analysis of observed to expected deaths by occupation showed little variation within each sex for the major categories of deaths. Cancer of the buccal cavity and pharynx and esophagus was lowest among male workers in professional/managerial and clerical/sales groups. In contrast, pancreatic cancer was higher in service machining and bench-pressing groups and structural/miscellaneous groups. Suicide was markedly higher in the professional/managerial group.

Morgan, M., Chinn, S. 1983. ACORN group, social class, and child health. *Journal of Epidemiology and Community Health* 37:196–203.

This study compared the extent to which ACORN and social class groups identify differences in rates of morbidity and service use based on data collected in a longitudinal study based on children age 5–11 attending designated primary school in England and Scotland. Occupation of the father was recorded on a sample of 5,500 children. ACORN differentiated at least as well as social class on selected measures of children's health. It was also found to be valuable in identifying small areas with particularly high rates of morbidity. Two questions remained: Can ACORN identify variation in health outcomes that are independent of regional variation? Does it produce consistent ranking of health outcomes among different age groups, sexes, and regions of the country?

Morgenstern, H. 1980. The changing association between social status and coronary heart disease in a rural population. *Social Science and Medicine* 14a:191–201.

This analysis of the Evans County Heart Study was designed to test the hypothesis that changing social status was related to health outcomes. Mortality comparisons were made for 1960–67 and 1967–74, correcting for length of follow-up. The data indicated that high social class males were more likely to develop coronary heart disease before 1960 and low social class males were more likely to develop the disease after the mid-1960s.

Morris, J. N. 1979. Social inequalities undiminished. *Lancet* 1:87–90.

Information regarding social inequality from Registrar General's "social class" and "socioeconomic group" were based on occupation. Social class (skills and status in the community) and "socioeconomic group" (SEG) encompassed lifestyles. Postneonatal mortality rates increased uniformly between class I and IV and rose by as much again in V. Neonatal mortality in England and Wales for 1975–1976 ranged from 7.4 to 14.4 with gradient effect. Post neonatal mortality had an inverse relationship to SEG (range: 2.8 to 8.6). Using the highest qualification attained by SEG showed a gradient effect. Those in low SEG consumed more refined carbohydrates and sugar and less brown bread and fruit. Men of lower SEG smoked more cigarettes, 29, 42, 47, 49, 55 percent respectively. The amount of active participation in leisure-time sports was greater for professional (37 percent) than unskilled (8 percent), and a gradient effect was present. The all-cause standard mortality ratio for working men in 1970–1972 was 77, 81, 99, 106, 114, and 137. Coronary heart disease standard mortality ratio for the same period ranged from 88 to 111. Mortality rates for bronchitis, pneumonia, lung and stomach cancer, cerebrovascular disease, peptic ulcers, and motor vehicle accidents showed a I–V gradient, but the gradient was reversed for leukemias and malignancies of lymphoma.

———, Heady, J. A. 1955. Social and biological factors in infant mortality. V. Mortality in relation to father's occupation, 1911–1950. *Lancet* 1:554–560.

This paper is a historical study of the mortality of children of men in different occupations. Reports of the General Register Office relating to the censuses of 1911, 1921, and 1931 are used, together with data for 1939 collected for the project census of 1941. Infant mortality rates are shown to vary significantly with the occupation of the father. The postneonatal rate is more sensitive to the father's occupation than the neonatal rate. There is reported a continuous decline in infant mortality for all occupational classifications. However, the differences remain fairly constant, such that mortality among children of miners and textile workers remains highest compared to mortality among children of professional workers and teachers. There has been no narrowing of the social gap in infant mortality; if anything, it may have widened slightly.

Moser, K. A., Fox, A. J., Jones, D. R. 1984. Unemployment and mortality in the OPCS longitudinal study. *Lancet* 2:1324–1329.

This paper examined the relationship between SES and unemployment using mortality data for 1971–1981. Controlling for the distribution of unemployed men and looking at the mortality for women married to unemployed men, this relationship was studied. Social class was defined by the man's most recent job. Men "seeking work" in 1971 had a standard mortality ratio of 136 over the next 10 years. Some of the excess can be explained by more unemployment in classes IV and V, but a 20 to 30 percent excess remained after controlling for SES. Cancer and suicide had significantly raised levels of mortality. Among women of unemployed husbands, the standard mortality ratio was 120, which remained unchanged after controlling for the tenured distribution. Some of the excess mortality may be explained by SES and some may be explained by possible ill health that leads to unemployment.

Murrells, T. J., Catford, J. C., Smith, T. M. F., Machin, D. 1985. The use of logit models to investigate social and biological factors in infant mortality. II. Stillbirths. *Statistics in Medicine* 4:189–200.

This paper examined the stillbirth data for 1945–1950 and 1975 by formally incorporating the year of data collection into a statistical model enabling changes in the age, parity, and social class effect and time to be investigated. The mother's social class was determined by her husband's occupation. In both time periods, there was a high stillbirth rate among the less privileged social classes (IV and V). Maternal age and parity explained more of this variation in 1949 than 1975, but SES explained more in 1975 (Chi Squared increased from 8 to 33). The odds ratio for class times time effect showed that the odds of stillbirth in social class I against V have increased by a factor of 1.32 between 1950 and 1975. The combined effect of age, parity, and social class was also important in explaining the variation. In sum, the social class gradient has widened for stillbirths.

Nagi, M. H., Stockwell, E. G. 1973. Socioeconomic differentials in mortality by cause of death. *Health Services Reports* 88:449–456.

This study described the relationship between SES and mortality for nine leading causes of death. The approach examined variations that had been differentiated according to an index of SES. Using official 1960 census statistics, the following scores were used to define each census tract: the number of employed persons who were working at blue-collar occupations, the number of persons age 25 and over who had completed less than eight years of school, and the number of families with annual incomes less than $3,000. In the areas with the highest SES, observed deaths were generally fewer than the expected, but for cancer and respiratory diseases, the differences were not large. In the lowest SES areas, the observed deaths from several causes (with the single exception of the genito-urinary diseases) were much higher than the expected. Areas 2 and 3 fell in between these two extremes with area 2 (being more affluent) showing fewer differences than 3. Thus, the general pattern revealed a pronounced inverse relationship between SES and mortality from nine causes of death. The strongest association was for infectious and parasitic diseases.

Nandakumar, A., Armstrong, B. K., de Klerk, N. H. 1986. Multiple myeloma in western Australia: a case-control study in relation to occupation, father's occupation, socioeconomic status and country of birth. *International Journal of Cancer* 37:223–226.

This study investigated multiple myelomas in relationship to father's occupation by means of a death certificate–based case-control study. Cases were identified through a cancer registry and controls were selected from death registrations. There was an increased mortality among those where fathers were woodworkers (crude odds ratio was 1.5, CI=0.87–2.87). The odds ratio did not change when adjustments for SES or place of birth were made. There was no increase in the odds ratio with increasing SES (from Group III to Group I). An elevated odds ratio in rural residents was independent of the association of multiple myeloma and farming and suggested that bias created by matching on death certificate may be operating.

National Center of Health Statistics. 1986. Current estimates from the National Health Interview Survey, United States, 1983. *Vital and Health Statistics*. Series 10, No. 154. D.H.H.S.

1983. Pub. N. (PHS) 86–1582. Public Health Service. Washington, D.C.: G.P.O.

———. 1985. Health characteristics according to family and personal income, United States. *Vital and Health Statistics.* Series 10, No. 147. D.H.H.S. Pub. N. (PHS) 85–1575. Public Health Service. Washington, D.C.: G.P.O.

———. 1986. Types of injuries and impairments due to injuries, United States. *Vital and Health Statistics.* Series 10, No. 159. D.H.H.S. Pub. No. (PHS) 87–1587. Public Health Service. Washington, D.C.: G.P.O.

———. 1986. Disability days, United States, 1983. *Vital and Health Statistics.* Series 10, No. 158. D.H.H.S. Pub. No. (PHS) 87–1586. Public Health Service. Washington, D.C.: G.P.O.

Nayha, S. 1977. Social group and mortality in Finland. *British Journal of Preventive Social Medicine* 31:231–237.

Social class was based on occupation of respondents at the time of census. Those no longer working were classified by their former occupation or by supporter's occupation. Mortality rates for the various social groups for the population of Finland were compared using 179,919 death certificates for 1969–72. Age adjustment by sex and cause of death revealed that mortality rates from all causes are generally lowest in the high social group (I) and increase up to the IV and fall again for the V. Farmers were generally on the better side of average. Difference between groups IV and I was greatest for men with respect to pulmonary tuberculosis, respiratory disease, drowning, and suicide. For women these differences were small. Cancer of the breast and intestine and suicide are lowest for women. Lifetable analysis showed that the difference in life expectancy at birth between IV and I is 7.2 and at age 55 the difference is 2.1. These findings are similar to those of other researchers.

Newton, R. W., Hunt, L. P. 1984. Psychosocial stress in pregnancy and its relation to low birthweight. *British Medical Journal* 288:1191–1194.

A prospective study designed to examine the relationship of low birthweight to psychosocial stress was undertaken in Great Britain. The number, nature, and subjective effect of any life event was recorded, the pregnancy outcome defined, and the contribution of cigarette smoking and social class was considered for 224 women. Social class was defined by the Registrar General's Classification. No significant difference was found in the social class distribution between the study group and a random selection of 300 women delivering at the hospital over the same period. There were significantly more smokers among single women in class IV and V than those in class I and II. Seventy percent of the women who gave birth to babies that were small for gestational age had experienced an objective major life event during pregnancy, but this was not statistically significant ($p \leqslant .08$).

Notkola, V., Punsar, S., Karvonen, M. J., Haapakoski, J. 1985. Socio-economic conditions in childhood and mortality and morbidity caused by coronary heart disease in adulthood in rural Finland. *Social Science and Medicine* 21:517–523.

The aim of this study was to determine whether there was a relationship between living conditions in childhood and subsequent development of coronary heart disease morbidity and mortality in adulthood. Additionally, the influence of risk factors such as smoke and cholesterol on this process was assessed. From 1959–1974, 823 men in Eastern Finland and 888 men in Western Finland were followed and their risk factors studied. SES in childhood was measured by father's occupation and by farm size. The relative risk of coronary death, myocardial infarction, and ischemic heart disease increased with decreasing social class. A partial explanation for this finding was an increase in body weight and smoking habits among individuals in lower classes. On the other hand, the effects of cholesterol were negligible. Findings that relative risk of coronary heart disease events were increased for those of small height suggested that nutritional deficiency in childhood or some unknown hereditary or other factor was connected to coronary heart disease.

Nowotny, M., Stretton, P. J. 1979. The health of the preschool child. *Medical Journal of Australia* 7:289–291.

To assess the effectiveness of a standardized medical examination of 4- and 5-year-olds in Victoria, a random sample of 512 children from inner urban and disadvantaged outer urban preschools was compared with a group of 500 children from preschools in more advantaged areas. SES was composed of a cluster of variables that included occupation, type of housing, number of persons per household, education, religion, and shared accommodations. Children from disadvantaged areas had a higher incidence of previously unrecognized disabilities. Thirty-four percent of the disadvantaged group as compared to 17.6 percent of the advantaged group were referred for intervention. The prevalence of visual problems was almost identical in the two groups.

Oken, B., Hartz, A., Giefer, E., Rimm, A. A. 1977. Relation between socioeconomic status and obesity changes in 9,046 women. *Preventive Medicine* 6:447–453.

This was a study of weight reduction in 9,046 members of TOPS. A structured questionnaire was used to identify SES and obesity history. SES was measured by the educational level of the woman, husband's income, and family's total income. Unmarried students, retired women, and those with missing data were omitted. The obesity index used was height/weight. Initial analysis showed that as income or education increased, there was a decrease in the amount of weight gained. The association between obesity and SES could not be explained by the effect of income or education alone, since each was statistically significant ($p<0.0001$) after adjustment for the other. This relationship was examined using analysis of covariance (ANCOVA); covariates included age and maximum teenage obesity. Estimate from ANCOVA for excess weight at the lowest education and income groups relative to the highest was 17.5 lbs., but when age was the only covariate in the model, this difference increased by 75 percent. Less than 2 percent of the variation in adult weight change during childbearing years was explained by SES. The authors concluded that SES was related to obesity primarily because of its effect on weight changes during childbearing years.

Ostfeld, A. M. 1973. Heart disease and stroke in an elderly welfare population. *Bulletin of the New York Academy of Medicine* 49:458–466.

The primary aim of this prospective study was to identify factors associated with the risk of stroke among elderly patients in Illinois. A stratified probability sample of 4,800 persons was selected from a population between 65 and 74 receiving old-age assistance. The prevalence of cerebrovascular disease and coronary heart disease per 1,000 was substantially different between the sexes and between blacks and whites. Of those invited to participate in the study, two thirds agreed. Interviewers found that many of the participants starved themselves before getting onto the welfare rolls. Additionally, good care was not being given to those with diabetes and/or hypertension. These are important risk factors in the development of stroke, and they need to be addressed in this population. The substantially higher incidence rate of stroke among blacks than whites may in part be due to the fact that blood pressure in blacks was higher than in whites.

Pamuck, E. R. 1985. Social class inequality in mortality from 1921 to 1972 in England and Wales. *Population Studies* 39:17–31.

Secular trends between 1921–1972 in the social class gradient for mortality in England and Wales were examined, and a number of methodological problems in the interpretation of these trends were addressed. The evidence suggests that the gradient declined during the 1920s. These trends do not seem to be the result of numerator/denominator errors, changes in classification of occupations, or other factors.

Papiernik, E., Maine, D., Rush, D., Richard, A. 1985. Prenatal care and the prevention of preterm delivery. *International Journal of Gynaecology and Obstetrics* 23:427–433.

An innovative program of prenatal care at the Hospital Antoine Beclere in Clamart, France, was studied. The study population consisted of 11,000 women. At the first prenatal visit, all patients completed a questionnaire regarding education, SES, ethnicity, health, living conditions, and OB/GYN history. The group of women were stratified into two groups: one had early care, and less than one half had late care. The early care group had significantly lower rates of both early and preterm delivery. There were also significantly fewer low birthweight babies in this group and the relative risk was 3.6 ($p<.0001$). Youth primigravidity, low SES, and history of preterm delivery were all associated with current preterm delivery. Women who came early for prenatal care were more advantaged. The low frequency of preexisting risk factors in the early care group did not account for the low rates of current preterm delivery. The advantage of early care persisted within strata by preexisting risk factors.

Pearce, N. E., Davis, P. B., Smith, A. H., Foster, F. H. 1983. Mortality and social class in New Zealand I: overall male mortality. *New Zealand Medical Journal* 96:281–285.

This paper concentrated on New Zealand males age 15–64 and documented social class differences in overall mortality using two different systems of social class classification (the British Registrar General's Classification and the Elley-Irving Classification). A 10 percent sample of the 1976 Census data was taken. Direct age-standardized mortality rates per 100,000 person-years were calculated for each social class. All data were classified into five-year age groups, and Segi's world population was used as the standard. Tests for trend were performed using the Mantel-Hanzsel extension. Whichever classification scheme was used, New Zealand data showed a genuinely higher mortality rate for low socioeconomic classs as compared with the higher classes ($p<0.001$). The New Zealand experience parallels that of England and Wales, although the gradient was significantly nonlinear ($p<0.001$)

―――. 1983. Mortality and social class in New Zealand II: male mortality by major disease groupings. *New Zealand Medical Journal* 96:711–716.

This paper investigated social class patterns of mortality among New Zealand males age 15–64 for each major disease. SES was defined using the British Registrar General's Classification and Elley-Irving Classification. Denominator data were produced from a 10 percent sample of the 1976 New Zealand census population and dwellings, and numerator data from the National Health Statistic Centre. Coronary heart disease, neoplasms, accidents, poisonings, and violence together accounted for 74 percent of the overall mortality. All categories had at least some tendency for the lower social class to experience higher mortality rates than the upper social classes and the test for trend was statistically significant for each of the disease groupings except congenital anomalies. In general, disease groups with the strongest social class gradient contained the highest percent of excess deaths (i.e., 55 percent for accidents, poisonings and violence). Neoplasms and coronary heart disease had weaker (but still significant) social class gradients than diseases of respiratory, genito-urinary, digestive, metabolic, or mental disorders.

―――. 1984. Mortality and social class in New Zealand III: male mortality by ethnic group. *New Zealand Medical Journal* 97:31–35.

Social class differences in male mortality in New Zealand

were investigated separately for Maori, Pacific-Island, and other New Zealand males age 15–64. All three groups displayed strong social class mortality gradient but, for each class, the Maori mortality rates were approximately 50 percent higher than the rates for the other category, while the Pacific-Island rates generally occupied an intermediate position. The Maori mortality rates were particularly high for respiratory, infectious, genito-urinary, endocrine, nutritional and metabolic disorders, and circulatory and other coronary heart and cardiovascular diseases—even after adjustment for age and social class factors. Overall, there were substantial social class and ethnic differences in mortality. About 20 percent of the Maori mortality excess was attributable to social class factors.

————. 1985. Social class, ethnic group, and male mortality in New Zealand, 1974–1978. *Journal of Epidemiology and Community Health* 39:9–14.

This paper examined social class differences in male mortality in New Zealand. Denominator data were produced from a 10 percent sample of 1976 New Zealand census statistics and the numerator from the National Health Centre records of deaths for 1974–1978. Direct age-standardized mortality rates per 100,000 person-years at risk were calculated for each social class and ethnic group. Smoking data were also included. SES was defined by the Registrar General's Classification. A test for trend confirmed that mortality was higher in lower social classes ($p<.001$). The New Zealand gradient was nonlinear; high mortality for V but higher rate for I than II. Maori and non-Maori experienced a statistically significant social class gradient ($p<.001$). Overall, there were 74 percent more Maori deaths than non-Maori (53 percent more than there would have been if the Maori had experienced the same mortality rate as non-Maori in each class and age group). Crude calculations suggest that smoking patterns explained much of the increased risk for classes III–IV but not the very high mortality for class V.

Phillips, R. A., Garfinkel, L., Kuzma, J. W., Beeson, W. L., Lotz, T., Brin, B. 1980. Mortality among California Seventh-Day Adventists for select cancer sites. *Journal of the National Cancer Institute* 65:1097–1107.

This study reported the differences of cancer risk among California Seventh-Day Adventists (SDA) compared with a demographically similar segment of the general population. The study consisted of 17 years of follow-up on 22,940 white SDA and 13 years of follow-up on 112,725 white non-SDA (NSDA). Both groups responded to the same four-page self-admission questionnaire in 1960. Mantel-Haenszel chi-squared produced age-adjusted, sex-specific mortality ratios for SDA vs. NSDA vs. U.S. population. Deaths were ascertained by periodic follow-up. SDA are more comparable to NSDA than to the general population in terms of education achievement and marital status. The SDA: NSDA mortality ratio remained significantly below 1.0 for smoke-related cancer and male and female colorectal cancer ($p<.01$) and male leukemia ($p<.05$) were below 1.0. When SDA were compared to a more socioeconomically similar population (NSDA), the risk difference of fatal cancer was reduced (except for those mentioned).

Pincus, T., Callahan, L. F. 1985. Formal education as a marker for increased mortality and morbidity in rheumatoid arthritis. *Journal of Chronic Diseases* 38:973–984.

Eighty-nine patients who had been referred to the Department of Orthopedic Surgery at Vanderbilt University between 1964–1973 were evaluated during 1973. In 1982, a retrospective analysis of 75 of the 89 was undertaken to study adult-onset rheumatoid arthritis. Higher mortality was associated with lower formal education. The mean formal education level of patients who died was 9.0 vs. 11.5 for those surviving nine years ($p<.002$). Baseline measures were different in the survivors and nonsurvivors. Potential confounding variables were stratified in the analysis, but the association persisted. Mortality experience for the three education groups was as follows: 79 percent of grade school, 43 percent of high school, and 20 percent of college educated subjects either died or decreased in functional capacity more than 50 percent over the nine-year period.

Pirkle, J. L., Schwartz, J., Landis, J. R., Harlan, W. R. 1985. The relationship between blood lead levels and blood pressure and its cardiovascular risk implications. *American Journal of Epidemiology* 121:246–258.

The relationship between blood pressure and blood lead levels in the second National Health and Nutrition Examination Survey (1976–1980) was examined for white males age 40–59 years. After adjustment for age, body mass index, nutritional factors, and blood biochemistries in a multiple linear regression model, the relationship of systolic and diastolic blood pressures to blood lead levels was statistically significant ($p<0.01$). There was no evidence of a threshold blood level for this relationship. Although these data alone do not prove a causal relationship between low blood lead levels and blood pressure, the findings are consistent with current epidemiologic and animal studies, indicating that a causal relationship is probable. To examine the potential risks, the multiple logistic risk factor coefficients from the Pooling Project and Framingham studies were used to predict the impact of the 37 percent decrease in mean blood lead levels that occurred in adult white males between 1976–1980. As a result of this blood lead level decrease, the calculations predicted a 4.7 percent decrease in the incidence of fatal and nonfatal myocardial infarction over 10 years, a 6.7 percent decrease in the incidence of death from all causes over 11.5 years. In addition, as a result of this blood lead decrease, the predicted number of white males in this age group with hypertension (diastolic blood pressure> 90 mmHg) decreased by 17.5 percent.

Powles, J. 1978. The effects of health services on adult male mortality in relation to the effects of social and economic factors. *Ethics in Science and Medicine* 5:1–13.

This article described the general problem of declining cost-effectiveness in health services by referring to disease control measures in the health care industry. The author also assessed the effect of these control measures on male mortality rates. Powles reminded the reader that higher mortality rates were found among the less privileged. High income, well-educated groups had lower mortality experiences. When age-standardized mortality ratios were calculated, an SES gradient was observed. The standard mortality ratio for those with high family income ($10,000) was 84, and for those with low incomes ($2,000) in 1960, the standard mortality ratio was 100. The authors concluded that without a substantial social re-ordering to secure greater social stability and better employment conditions, improvements in adult male mortality could not be achieved.

Rantakallio, P. 1979. Social background of mothers who smoke during pregnancy and influence of these factors on offspring. *Social Science and Medicine* 13a:423–429.

This was an analysis of 1,819 Finnish mothers who smoked after their second month of pregnancy. Data were collected at the sixth or seventh month of pregnancy from 157 antenatal clinics during 1966. Controls were chosen from among nonsmokers and matched on the number of children born, marital status, age +/– 2 years, parity, and place of residence. Perinatal mortality was higher among mothers with less schooling, ranging from 19.2 among poor women with less education, to 55.6 per 1,000 among women with highest education births. Additionally, postneonatal mortality was greater for social class IV than for social classes I to III when mother's education was the marker for SES. These differences were not explained by differences in smoking patterns between the cases and the controls.

Roberts, R. W., Mack, J., Woodhead, D. 1976. Health survey—disadvantaged schools. *Australian Paediatric Journal* 12:31–36.

In July 1974, a study was mounted to compare a variety of

health measures in disadvantaged and nondisadvantaged government schools. Census information was collected, and an index based on school characteristics was designed to describe the quality of education. Variables included in this index were migrant population, mobility, family structure, occupation, employment, and ethnic origin. Questionnaires and physical exams were completed for 167 children from disadvantaged schools and 154 from nondisadvantaged schools. No differences in physical measure (height), haemoglobin level, nutritional status, or social condition were found. In the disadvantaged schools many more children threw tantrums, or were bullies, attention seekers, noncompatible, disruptive, distressed, and had poorer concentration spans.

Rodin, J. 1986. Aging and health: effects of the sense of control. *Science* 233:1271–1276.

The relation between health and a sense of control may grow stronger in old age. This could occur through three types of processes: Experiences particularly revelant to control may increase markedly in old age; the association between control and some aspect of health may be altered by age; and age may influence the association between control and health-related behaviors or the seeking of medical care. Studies show that there are detrimental effects on the health of older people when their control of their activities is restricted. In contrast, interventions that enhance options for control by nursing home patients promote health. With increasing age, however, variability in preferred amounts of control also increases, and sometimes greater control over activities, circumstances, or health has negative consequences including stress, worry, and self-blame. Mechanisms mediating the control-health relation include feelings of stress, symptom labeling, changes in the neuroendocrine and immune systems, and behavior relevant to health maintenance.

Rogot, E., Murray, J. 1980. Cancer mortality among nonsmokers in an insured group of U.S. veterans. *Journal of the National Cancer Institute* 65:1163–1168.

This study examined the cancer mortality in a group of veterans at low risk of developing cancer (nonsmokers). Policy holders were mostly white, and from upper and middle socioeconomic classes. Information was available for those who served in the U.S. armed forces between 1917–1940. Death certificates were abstracted and 97.6 percent of them were complete. The standard mortality ratio for nonsmokers was calculated with age-specific probabilities of death in the period of all respondents used as the standard. About 66 percent of the population was 55- to 65-years-old at the start of the study. More nonsmoking veterans lived in urban areas than those in the general population (80 percent vs. 63 percent). The veterans occupied more professional and managerial positions than those of the general population. Standard mortality ratios for selected occupations follow: 42 for dentists, 48 for carpenters, 56 for lawyers, 79 for auto mechanics, 80 for mail carriers, and 82 for doctors.

Roos, N. P., Roos, L. L., Jr. 1982. Surgical rate variations: do they reflect the health or socioeconomic characteristics of the population? *Medical Care* 20:945–958.

This paper attempted to assess the unexplained variations in surgical rates across geographic areas. The focus was the relationship between elderly surgical rates and population characteristics of 56 hospitals in a rural area of Canada. In 1971, extensive interviews of a five-percent probability sample were conducted. Three measures of SES were studied: education, income, and poverty. Although 76 percent of the respondents replied that their incomes were satisfactory, only 16 percent were found to be above the poverty line. Neither income variable was significantly associated with surgical measures. Education and ethnicity were strongly and consistently associated with overall surgical rates but not with rates of elective or cataract surgery.

Rose, G., Marmot, M. G. 1981. Social class and coronary heart disease. *British Heart Journal* 45:13–19.

The Whitehall Study examined 7,530 civil servants age 40–64 for signs, symptoms, and risk factors for coronary heart disease, then categorized them by employment status: administrator, executive, clerical, and others. "Others" were the lowest grade and were comprised mostly of unskilled laborers. Age adjustment was done by the direct method using the total population as the standard. In the lowest grade, the rate of EKG abnormality was 177 percent of that for the top grade. The lower the grade, the more likely that angina accompanied an abnormal EKG. Age adjusted 7½ year mortality rates were 3.6 times higher in the lower group than the higher one. Age-adjusted all-cause mortality was also calculated, and the results demonstrated the same trend as for coronary heart disease mortality. Men in the lowest class smoked more than those in the higher classes. Physically active leisure time was less common in lower grades. Additionally, systolic blood pressure was an average of 4.2 mm Hg less among those in higher classes. Blood sugar levels tended to be higher in the lower classes. Because of these class differences, multiple variable analysis was done. After controlling for these factors, the relative risks were 1.0, 1.8, 2.3, and 2.6 for high and low grades respectively.

Rundall, T. G., Wheeler, J. R. C. 1979. The effect of income on use of preventive care: an evaluation of alternative explanations. *Journal of Health and Social Behavior* 20:397–406.

Three alternative explanations for the effect of income on use of physician services for preventive care were evaluated. Path analysis was used to estimate the direct effect of income on use (the financial constraint explanation), the indirect effect of income through health beliefs (the culture of poverty explanation), and the indirect effect through the availability of a usual source of care (the system barrier explanation). Data for the analyses came from household interviews with 781 adult residents of Washtenaw County, Michigan. The data reveal a negligible direct effect of income on preventive use, a positive indirect effect through perceived susceptibility to illness (one operationalization of the culture of poverty explanation), and a positive indirect effect through usual source of care.

Rush, D., Cassano, P. 1983. Relationship of cigarette smoking and social class to birth weight and perinatal mortality among all births in Britain, 5–11 April 1970. *Journal of Epidemiology and Community Health* 37:249–255.

Perinatal mortality, cigarette smoking, and social class were examined in all singleton births for whom there was valid data on birthweight, perinatal mortality, social class, and smoking (N = 16,688). Of all the women delivering singletons, 41.3 percent reported smoking at term. Rates differed tremendously by class. In social class I, 15.4 percent of women were light smokers, whereas 46.0 percent of women in social class V smoked at term. More upper than lower class women stopped smoking before and during pregnancy. There was a difference of 215 g between mean birthweight of infants of nonsmokers and those who smoked more than 15 cigarettes per day. This varied little across social class. After controlling for maternal age, height, and gravidity, being single was associated with 136 g depression in birthweight ($p<.001$), and there was a 23 g decrement in birthweight associated with one lower class category ($p<.001$). Thirty-seven percent of the association of birthweight with social class can be attributed to the difference in smoking habits across class.

Salonen, J. T. 1982. Socioeconomic status and risk of cancer, cerebral stroke, and death due to coronary heart disease and any disease: a longitudinal study in eastern Finland. *Journal of Epidemiology and Community Health* 36:294–297.

The relationship between socioeconomic indicators and disease risk was examined in a mainly rural area in Finland. A random sample of men 30–59 with no prior history of coronary heart disease, cancer, or risk factor history for the two diseases were recruited into the study. SES was defined by years of education, gross family income, place of residence, number of episodes, and marital status. The analyses showed an association between death due to ischemic heart disease and unmarried status, less education, and low income, and, similarly, death due to any disease. Cerebrovascular disease was associated with urban/rural markers and cancer with low education. The relationship between SES and coronary heart disease could not be explained by the three primary coronary heart disease risk factors (smoking, blood pressure, and cholesterol). Education had an independent impact on cancer risk even after controlling for age and smoking in a multivariate model.

Savage, D., Lindenbaum, J., Van Ryzin, J., Struening, E., Garrett, T. J. 1984. Race, poverty, and survival in multiple myeloma. *Cancer* 54:3085–3094.

The relationship between race, clinical findings, poverty and survival was examined in patients with multiple myeloma. Fifty-two black patients with diagnosis of multiple myeloma during 1965–1980 at a community hospital in Harlem and age-sex matched black and white patients at a university-affiliated hospital were studied. Patients at the community hospital had poorer survival than those from university-affiliated. Survival was shorter among patients from blocks that were overcrowded, had more families below poverty, and had higher unemployment. Patients from blocks with low educational backgrounds had a shorter median survival (14 months) vs. those with more education (27 months). Those with low family income had a mean survival of 18 months vs. 28 months for high. In a stepwise multiple regression analysis of community-hospital based patients, the most important variable related to survival was overcrowding. The same trend was true for university-affiliated, but the results were not statistically significant.

Schwartz, J. 1985. *The relationship between blood lead levels and blood pressure.* Unpublished report for EPA. Washington, D.C.:Environmental Protection Agency.

This research paper examines the association between blood

lead and blood pressure. Data is derived from the NHANES II and reports an association between blood lead and blood pressure such that for a 10ug/deciliter rise in blood lead, there is a 15 percent rise in blood pressure. Other research is also cited describing interference with calcium metabolism as the potential biological pathway by which blood lead may influence blood pressure.

Shapiro, S., McCormick, M. C., Starfield, B. H., Krischer, J. P., Bross, D. 1980. Relevance of correlates of infant deaths for significant morbidity at 1 year of age. *American Journal of Obstetrics & Gynecology* 136:363–373.

Morbidity data for infants surviving to one year were obtained through a household survey of a random sample of infants born during a six month period in 1976. There were 4,989 infant visits, 3,179 were <2500 gm and 1,777 were >2500 gm. There were more low birthweight infants and a higher neonatal mortality among nonwhites. Factors heavily influenced by environmental conditions (young maternal age, low maternal education, and race) were associated with high postneonatal mortality and also with increased rates of significant postneonatal illness.

Simpson, S. P. 1984. Causal analysis of infant deaths in Hawaii. *American Journal of Epidemiology* 116:1024–1029.

The association between measures of SES and infant deaths was studied in 34,220 live births registered in Hawaii in 1978–1979. Infant death records were linked to birth records. Using information on the birth certificate, a group of high risk infants could be identified. Apgar score was the single most important predictor of infant mortality. Birth certificates in Hawaii used measures of maternal and paternal education as a measure of SES. By path analysis, these were poor indicators of infant mortality. The census tract of residence appeared to be a better predictor. Low risk tracts had higher SES, and high risk tracts had lower SES.

Starfield, B. 1982. Family income, ill health and medical care of U.S. children. *Journal of Public Health Policy* 3:244–259.

Evidence was summarized concerning the link between poverty and ill health in childhood, the relationship between poverty and receipt of medical care, evidence that increased access to medical care reduced the disparity in health status among poor and nonpoor, and the effects of reduced funds for care of the poor. Poor children compared to nonpoor were more frequently and more seriously ill. Although they received care more often than was previously the case, the kind of care they received was different. Data also indicated that near poor were also at a severe disadvantage with regard to their health and with respect to access to and use of services, even more so than the poor.

———, Budetti, P. P. 1985. Child health status and risk factors. *Health Services Research* 19:817–886.

Evidence was reviewed concerning the determinants of children's health. A powerful correlate of ill health in childhood is family income. Illness is more common among the poor, and when it occurs it is more severe. Poor children are two times as likely to be low birthweight and to contract meningitis, three times as likely to lack immunization, two to three times as likely to have rheumatic fever, iron deficiency anemia, and hearing problems, fifty times as likely to have uncorrected vision, nine times as likely to have elevated levels of lead in blood, and 75 percent more likely to die of injuries and leukemia. Poor children have greater deficits in IQ. Average length of stay in hospital is twice as long. Factors such as parents' education level may modify the relationship between income and ill health. Some measures of ill health are more susceptible to the effects of income than to the effects of education. The poorer the family, the more likely that the child has no regular source of medical care, partly because of poor insurance coverage. Low income children are also more likely to wait longer between visits, and the sort of care they receive is often of a different type.

Steinhorn, S. C., Myers, M. H., Hankey, B. F., Pelham, V. F. 1986. Factors associated with survival differences between black women and white women with cancer of the uterine corpus. *American Journal of Epidemiology* 124:85–93.

To investigate the poorer survival among blacks, the authors analyzed a series of patients with cancer of the uterine corpus, diagnosed between 1973–1977. Racial differences were examined in detail with respect to stage of disease, age at diagnosis, histological type, geographic area, and SES. SES was defined by mean family income and mean highest education received. Major racial differences in patient survival were noted among women with adeno cancer, and, although adjustment for prognostic factors reduced the gap, statistically significant differences in survival remained. Median family income and mean education were also found to be significant predictors with relative risk of 1.33 and 1.18, respectively. Inability to close the gap between black and white survival rates after adjusting for these factors suggest that other factors may be involved. Multivariate analysis determined that income and stage of disease were the strongest explanatory variables affecting survival by race.

Stern, J. 1983. Social mobility and the interpretation of social class mortality differentials. *Journal of Social Policy* 12:27–49.

Problems in the assessment of social class mortality differentials were discussed. In particular, emphasis was given to biases associated with differential social class mortality that may yield overestimates of mortality differentials by social class.

Stern, E., Misczynski, M., Greenland, S., Damus, K., Coulson, A. 1977. "Pap" testing and hysterectomy prevalance: a survey of communities with high and low cervical cancer rates. *American Journal of Epidemiology* 106:296–305.

The authors surveyed areas within Los Angeles County with known high and low rates of cervical cancer in order to relate the level of pap screening and prevalence of hysterectomy to differential cancer rates. Highest rates were found in low income, inner-city areas where there were large concentrations of black and Spanish-surname women and small numbers of whites; the rates were high for everyone in these areas. The risk was low in middle and upper income areas even for blacks and Spanish-surname women. The age-adjusted mortality rate was 2.6 to 5.3 in high income areas and 8.4 to 14.3 in the low income areas. Income and health-related information was obtained by surveying 2,063 households. After controlling for age and ethnicity, the authors found that the prevalence of pap testing was lower in low income areas than middle income areas.

Stewart, P. J., Dunkley, G. C. 1985. Smoking and health care patterns among pregnant women. *Canadian Medical Association Journal* 133:989–994.

A population-based study was undertaken to determine the current rate of smoking before and during pregnancy. Between May and October 1983, all women who had delivered a baby at one of the major hospitals with an obstetrics facility in Ottawa were surveyed. Women who agreed to participate completed a self-administered questionnaire. A poverty index was defined on the basis of the number of people supported on a yearly income. Overall, 59.1 percent changed their habit, with 31 percent stopping and 28.1 percent reducing. Logistic regression analysis identified factors associated with cessation. Among smokers, fewer numbers of cigarettes before pregnancy, higher level of education, less use of alcohol, multiparity, and less marijuana use were associated with cessation. Among multiparous women, the first two factors were significant, and among primiparous women, the first three factors were significant. For common-law and single women, lower education and occupation were associated with increased prevalence of smoking. Women below poverty were more likely to smoke after the third month of pregnancy.

Sunderland, R. 1984. Dying young in traffic. *Archives of Disease in Childhood* 59:754–757.

Sheffield, a stable urban community, was studied to determine whether information on the pattern of fatal childhood traffic accidents might aid in the planning of preventive programs. An index of relative prosperity was defined by the number of persons per room per dwelling and the availability of toilet facilities. A disproportionate number of accidents and deaths occurred among children living in crowded dwellings and dwellings situated near a main road. When geographic regions were grouped crudely by prosperity, the most prosperous had lower death rates, while the least prosperous had higher rates.

Syme, S. L. 1985. Socioeconomic factors: content discussion. In Ostfeld, A. M., Eaker, E. D., eds. *Measuring psychosocial variables in epidemiologic studies of cardiovascular disease: proceedings of a workshop*. NIH Publication No. 85–2270. Washington, D.C.: Department of Health and Human Services, Public Health Service.

The role of SES in cardiovascular disease was discussed, including the fact that SES is often ignored by researchers. The author says that poverty contributes to SES and health effects, but that it cannot explain the social class gradient. The changes over time in the SES-CHD association that have been observed by other researchers were discussed.

———, Berkman, L. F. 1976. Social class, susceptibility and sickness. *American Journal of Epidemiology* 104:1–8.

Evidence on the relationship between social class and sickness was reviewed. Previous research found that persons in lower class groups had higher mortality and morbidity from almost every disease or illness and that these differences had not diminished over time. The differences could not be explained by differences in medical care. There has been a reduction in mortality, but a gap between the highest and the lowest social class groups remains significant. Social and cultural mobility, as well as other coping behaviors such as smoking, obesity, and Type A behaviors are also associated with the disease process in man. Future research should include the precise identification and description of subgroups in lower SES classes. Disentanglement of socioenvironmental variables should take place. The clarification of causes and effects and the "downward drift" should be put forth. Lastly, a more comprehensive description of those psychosocial variables that compromise the defenses must be made.

Szklo, M., Gordis, L., Tonascia, J., Kaplan, E. 1978. The changing survivorship of white and black children with leukemia. *Cancer* 42:59–66.

Time trends of survival of white and black children with acute leukemia in a defined metropolitan area were examined. The study population included all cases of acute leukemia diagnosed in children less than 20 years of age. SES was based on median rental value of the census tracts in which the patient was living at the time of diagnosis. Sex, SES, time interval from onset of symptoms to diagnosis, clinical severity at time of diagnosis, and type of therapy were not statistically different between white and black children. For the entire 1960–1075 period, the survival of white children was significantly better than that of black children ($p<.05$). Among the 23 white children in the low SES category the two-year survival rate was lower (28 percent) than that of the 22 (51 percent) children in the highest SES category ($p<.005$).

Taylor, E. M., Emery, J. L. 1983. Family and community factors associated with infant deaths that might be preventable. *British Medical Journal* 287:871–874.

All postperinatal deaths in Sheffield over two years were examined to assess the importance of different pathological, family, community, and health care factors. During the study period, 65 babies between the ages of eight days and two years died. Controls (102) were matched for age. Each child was assessed for 13 potentially adverse social and family factors. Deaths were classified into causal groups. Families of children who died during potentially treatable illnesses had significantly greater numbers of adverse social conditions than children who died from conditions of poor prognosis. Adverse conditions included low intelligence, family crisis, low competence, and domestic and financial problems. Adverse social conditions were independent of social class.

Todson, D. R. 1980. Spatial perspective of infant health care: the distribution of infant health care delivery in Hillsborough County, Florida. *Social Science and Medicine* 14D:379–385.

Infant and postneonatal mortality were examined as a function of SES in a Florida county. The 15 census tracts that recorded 100 or more births for each year between 1971–1973 were ranked according to SES. Infant death rates decreased as socioeconomic level increased. The lowest tract had rates 29 percent above average, while the highest recorded an infant mortality rate 36.8 percent below average. SES had a greater impact on postneonatal mortality than overall mortality.

Tuomilehto, J., Puska, P., Virtamo, J., Neittaanmaki, L., Koskela, K. 1978. Coronary risk factors and socioeconomic status in Eastern Finland. *Preventive Medicine* 7:539–549.

The relationship between coronary heart disease risk factors and socioeconomic factors was examined in 10,951 men and women age 25–59 in Eastern Finland. Men with lower education levels smoked more often than those with higher education levels, with the exception of the lower age group. Women of lower education levels smoked significantly more in age group 25–29, while this association was inverse after age 45. Men with lower income were more often smokers with the exception of the lower age group. Among women the percent of smokers was higher in those with high incomes. Higher cholesterol values were observed more often among those living in rural areas, having low education levels, lower family income, and more physical activity. Among women higher blood pressure was more prevalent in rural areas, with a lower education level, lower family income, and higher level of physical activity at work. The prevalence of a high risk score among men was usually more common among those living in rural areas, with lower education levels, lower family income and higher level of physical activity at work.

Van den Berg, B. J., Oechsli, F. W. 1984. Prematurity. In Bracken, M. B., ed. *Perinatal epidemiology*, pp. 69–85. New York: Oxford University Press.

Using international data and data from the Child Health and Disability Study (CHDS), factors are reviewed that contribute to prematurity. Socioeconomic factors, including education and income, are consistently associated with prematurity. In the CHDS, the mother's educational level was significantly associated with risk of prematurity after adjustment for father's occupation, mother's smoking, length of gestation of previous and current pregnancy, weight gain, first trimester bleeding, and sex of infant.

Wadsworth, M. E. J., Cripps, H. A., Midwinter, R. E., Colley, J. R. T. 1985. Blood pressure in a national birth cohort at the age of 36 related to social and familial factors, smoking and body mass. *British Medical Journal* 291:1534–1538.

The association between blood pressure and SES was followed in a national birth cohort study of men and women age 39. Social class was determined by father's education. Men who had grown up in families in the lowest socioeconomic group had significantly higher mean systolic blood pressure (123.43 mm Hg) than those of non-manual and well educated parents (119.33 mm Hg). Mean diastolic blood pressure was also significantly higher for men of the lower classes compared to the highest (78.87 vs. 76.26). Mean systolic blood pressure of men decreased significantly as their own education qualifications increased. Women who came from families in the lowest socioeconomic group had significantly higher mean systolic blood pressure than families of the highest group (118.00 and 114.60 mm Hg). They also had significantly higher diastolic blood pressure (75.63 vs. 73.64 mm Hg). There were no significant differences in blood pressure associated with women's employment or educational achievement.

Wadsworth, M. E. J. 1986. Serious illness in childhood and its association with later-life achievement. In Wilkinson, R. G., ed. *Class and health—research and longitudinal data.* London: Tavistock Publications.

The relationship between serious illness in childhood, social achievement and mobility, and health as an adult was studied in a sample of children born in one week of March 1946 in England, Wales, and Scotland, who have been followed up periodically through 1982. Analyses indicate that, to some extent, early serious illness is associated with both decreased social mobility in later life, and poorer health.

Waldron, I., Eyer, J. 1975. Socioeconomic causes of the recent rise in death rates for 15–24-year-olds. *Social Science and Medicine* 9:383–396.

The total death rate for 15- to 24-year-olds in the U.S. rose by 20 percent during the 1960s. The rise was due in part to a doubling of suicide and homicide and increases of 33 percent in fatal motor vehicle and other accidents. A major cause of the rise in suicide was an increase in potentially overwhelming life problems, including increased divorce among parents, increased alcohol consumption and attendant family problems, increased illegitimate pregnancy, and a relative decline in income for young people compared to their parents. To study the stress on young people in greater depth, the investigators obtained diaries from college students. The most commonly reported source of tension was related to academic work. Much of the tension associated with academic work was due to the students' fear of failure in the increasing competition for the most desirable jobs.

Watkins, L. O., Neaton, J. D., Kuller, L. H. 1986. Racial differences in high-density lipoprotein cholesterol and coronary heart disease incidence in the usual-care group of the multiple risk factor intervention trial. *American Journal of Cardiology* 57:538–545.

Using MRFIT data, the relationship between high-density lipoprotein-C levels and the risk of first major coronary heart disease event was examined in black and white men randomly assigned to the usual-care group. At baseline, mean SES scores of black men were significantly lower than those of white men. Blacks had fewer years of education and lower incomes than whites and were less likely to be employed in professional, technical, or managerial jobs. Reported daily intake of saturated fatty acids was lower in blacks. The black-white differences in high-density lipoprotein-C levels was largest among those of the lowest SES, education, and income and were smallest at the highest levels. The black-white difference in the extent of change in risk factors was statistically significant for high-density lipoprotein-C and cigarette cessation. The black-white crude risk ratio for a coronary heart disease event was .49 (PV = .005).

Wegner, E. L., Kolonel, L. N., Nomura, A. M. Y., Lee, J. 1982. Racial and socioeconomic status differences in survival of colorectal cancer patients in Hawaii. *Cancer* 49:2208–2216.

The role of SES in racial differences in survival from colorectal cancer was examined in Hawaii. There were 1,446 cases of colon cancer and 881 cases of rectal cancer diagnosed between 1960–1974 eligible for inclusion in the study. SES was based on characteristics of the census tract in which the patient resided. Adjusting for age, sex, stage, and SES resulted in a convergence of survival curves for patients from the five major racial groups. For both colon and rectal cancer the only significant relationship that remained was a higher cancer rate among Japanese Hawaiians. Stage of disease was the single most important factor, and it was independently associated with survival. SES did not have a statistically significant independent association with survival. SES did account for some of the racial difference beyond that which could be explained by age, sex, and stage, but its importance was modest.

West, R. R. 1977. Geographical variation in mortality from ischaemic heart disease in England and Wales. *British Journal of Preventive and Social Medicine* 31:245–250.

An analysis of the proportional mortality attributed to ischemic heart disease, adjusted for age, demonstrated a significant association with socioeconomic indexes for men in England and Wales. This association was not present for women.

Whitman, S., Coonley-Hoganson, R., Desai, B. T. 1984. Comparative head trauma experiences in two socioeconomically different Chicago-area communities: a population study. *American Journal of Epidemiology* 119:570–580.

Incidence and mortality rates from head trauma were studied in an inner-city area of Chicago and a suburb. Rates varied by location and by race, with suburban whites having the lowest rates, suburban blacks intermediate rates, and inner-city residents the highest rates. Examination of demographic information suggested that the black/white differential in the suburb reflected a disparity in socioeconomic levels.

Wilcox, N. S., Prochaska, J. O., Velicer, W. F., DiClemente, C. C. 1985. Subject characteristics as predictors of self-change in smoking. *Addictive Behaviors* 10:407–412.

The current investigation examined the usefulness of subject characteristics such as demographics, smoking history, health history, and life experiences as predictors of self-change in smoking status. There were 961 subjects who volunteered to participate in the study. Individuals with higher income and educational levels were more likely, following a relapse, to try again to abstain from cigarette smoking. In contrast, persons with lower incomes and fewer years of education often moved into a nonaction stage after having relapsed in their abstention efforts. Thus, despite their failed attempts, people in higher socioeconomic groups were more persistent in their self-change efforts.

Wilkinson, R. G. 1986. Socio-economic differences in mortality: interpreting the data on their size and trends. In Wilkinson, R. G., ed. *Class and health—research and longitudinal data*. London: Tavistock Publications.

Methodologic and interpretive issues in understanding the size and trends in social class differences in health in the United Kingdom were discussed, including numerator/denominator problems, heterogeneity and changing classification of occupations, and selective social mobility. None of these were found to compromise seriously the observed mortality differentials or trends in the differentials.

Williams, R. R., Horm, J. W. 1977. Association of cancer sites with tobacco and alcohol consumption and socioeconomic status of patients: interview study from the Third National Cancer Survey. *Journal of the National Cancer Institute* 58:525–547.

From personal interviews obtained for 7,518 incident cases of invasive cancer from the population-based Third National Cancer Survey, the quantitative lifetime use of cigarettes, cigars, pipes, unsmoked tobacco, wine, beer, hard liquor, and combined alcohol were recorded, as well as education and family income level. College education and high income both showed positive associations with cancers of the breast, thyroid gland, uterine corpus, and melanomas in males. These same indicators of high SES showed inverse associations with invasive neoplasms of the uterine cervix, lung, lip-tongue, and colon in females. College attendance (but not income) showed an inverse association with stomach cancer and positive association with pancreatic cancer in males.

Yeracaris, C. A., Kim, J. H. 1978. Socioeconomic differentials in selected causes of death. *American Journal of Public Health* 68:342–351.

The association between SES and mortality was analyzed for three select causes of death in three metropolitan areas: Birmingham, Buffalo, and Indianapolis. In all three cities, white mortality rates from heart disease, the leading cause of death, were inversely associated with socioeconomic group but to varying degrees. The male rate was higher than the female rate in all socioeconomic groups. Following the national trend, mortality from heart disease declined between 1960–1970. Reduction varied by socioeconomic group, generally favoring females over males.